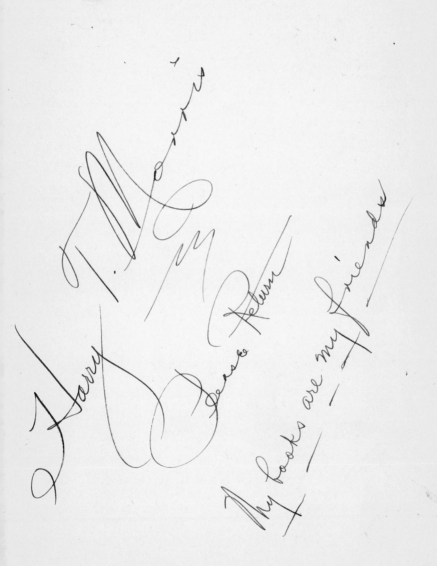

Harry T. Morris

Please Return

My books are my friends

DISCOVERY

THE MACMILLAN COMPANY
NEW YORK · BOSTON · CHICAGO · DALLAS
ATLANTA · SAN FRANCISCO

MACMILLAN & CO., Limited
LONDON · BOMBAY · CALCUTTA
MELBOURNE

THE MACMILLAN CO. OF CANADA, Ltd.
TORONTO

I. WISDOM, OR THE SPIRIT OF SCIENCE.

Mural painting by Edwin Austin Abbey, R.A., (1852-1911), in the Harrisburg Capitol, Pennsylvania. The inscription reads: "I am what is, what shall be, what hath been. My veil hath been disclosed by none. The fruit which I have brought forth is this—the sun is born."

DISCOVERY

Or The Spirit and Service of Science

BY

SIR RICHARD GREGORY

347p

New York

THE MACMILLAN COMPANY

1928

PRINTED IN U. S. A.

PREFACE

THE attention recently given to the position of science in the State, its relation to industry, and its relative neglect in education, suggests that the present is an appropriate time for putting into final shape a project contemplated for many years and practically completed before the outbreak of existing hostilities. This book represents the result; and its main purposes are to promote a more sympathetic attitude towards those who are engaged in the pursuit of scientific truth and to remove the widespread misconception which prevails as to the meaning and influence of science.

To the popular mind, a man of science is a callous necromancer who has cut himself off from communion with his fellows, and has thereby lost the throbbing and compassionate heart of a full life: he is a Faust who has not yet made a bargain with Mephistopheles, and is therefore without human interest. Scientific and humanistic studies are, indeed, supposed to be antipathetic, and to represent opposing qualities; so that it has become common to associate science with all that is cold and mechanistic in our being, and to believe that the development of the more spiritual parts of man's nature belongs essentially to other departments of intellectual activity.

When scientific work is instituted solely with the object of securing commercial gain, its correlative is

selfishness; when it is confined to the path of narrow
specialisation, it leads to arrogance; and when its purpose is materialistic domination, without regard for
the spiritual needs of humanity, it is a social danger
and may become an excuse for learned barbarity. But
scientific research is rarely inspired by these motives,
and devotion to it does not necessarily inhibit response
to other notes with which a well-balanced mind should
be in symphony. Moreover, direct contact with Nature
and inquiry into her laws produce a habit of mind which
cannot be acquired in literary fields, and they are associated with a wide outlook on life more often than is
usually supposed.

The relative influence of different studies on the formation of character need not be discussed here; yet
the following pages will perhaps show that the spirit
of scientific research has inspired the highest ethical
thought and action, as well as increased the comforts of
life, and added greatly to material welfare. We seek to
justify the claim of science to be an ennobling influence
as well as a creator of riches; and therefore as much
importance is attached to motive and method as to
discovery and industrial development, however marvellous or valuable these may be.

Wherever the purposeful inquiry is carried on in the
field of Nature, there the spirit of science is manifest,
and we learn that worthy intention defines its shape
as much as brilliant achievement. For science is not
to be measured by practical service alone, though it
may contribute to material prosperity: it is an intellectual outlook, a standard of truth and a gospel
of light.

Scientific investigation is not usually undertaken
with personal profit in view, and the discoveries to

which it leads are not jealously kept within the precincts of the temple, but are offered freely to the world: self-help thus giving place to the higher attribute of help for others. This virtue, with the qualities of self-sacrifice, persistence, courage, duty, accuracy, humility, and hope may all be abundantly exemplified from the careers of men of science; yet such instances are rarely mentioned. From many countries and many times we have gathered incidents and allusions which display the nobility of scientific aims, and have accentuated them with words of wisdom from the biographies and writings of men who have devoted their lives to the extension of natural knowledge. In substance the book thus largely consists of selected testimony, while in intention it is a stimulus to high endeavour.

No attempt has been made to provide a complete record, in chronological or any other order, of natural philosophers and their triumphs, yet it is hoped that not many points of outstanding human interest have been overlooked. The aim has been eclectic rather than exhaustive; wherefore many scientific pioneers are not mentioned, while others find a place not so much on account of their distinguished eminence as because events in their careers, or results of their work, create a spirit of emulation in those who regard them. The whole is presented with a deep sense of humility before the extent and intricacy of scientific knowledge, and of dissatisfaction at the gap which persists between design and execution.

It remains only to be said that though none of the chapters have been published hitherto in their present form, a few parts have appeared in contributions to the *Cornhill, Fortnightly, Nature, School World, Sunday at Home,* and other magazines during a period extending over nearly a quarter of a century. The book as a whole owes little to these articles; nevertheless, grateful acknowledgment is offered for the further use now made of suitable material extracted from them.

R. A. GREGORY.

CONTENTS

ILLUSTRATIONS

CHAPTER I

OUTLOOK AND ENDEAVOUR

No good work is ever lost. Max-Müller.

There is no darkness but Ignorance. Shakespeare.

All wish to know, but few the price will pay. Juvenal.

All science has one aim, namely, to find a theory of Nature. R. W. Emerson.

Tongues in trees, books in the running brooks. Sermons in stones, and good in everything. Shakespeare.

Nature alone is always true to herself; she alone through the ages never lies, never changes, never hesitates, ever presses onwards. Eden Phillpotts.

There are three voices of Nature. She joins hands with us and says Struggle, Endeavour. She comes close to us, we can hear her heart beating, she says Wonder, Enjoy, Revere. She whispers secrets to us, we cannot always catch her words, she says Search, Inquire. These, then, are the three voices of Nature, appealing to Hand, and Heart, and Head, to the Trinity of our Being. Prof. J. Arthur Thomson.

Since dawn the man had been seated on a stone at the bottom of a ravine. Three peasant women on their way to the vineyards exchanged "Good day" with him as they passed to their work. At sunset when they returned the watcher was still there, seated on the same stone, his eyes fixed on the same spot. "A poor innocent," one whispered to the others, *"pe'caïre!* a poor innocent," and all three made the sign of the cross. Fabre, the incomparable naturalist, patiently waiting to discover what is instinct and what is reason in insect-life is, to these vintagers, an object of supreme com-

1

miseration, an imbecile in God's keeping, wherefore they crossed themselves.

Members of the University of Pisa, and other on-lookers, are assembled in the space at the foot of the wonderful leaning tower of white marble in that city one morning in the year 1591. A young professor climbs the spiral staircase until he reaches the gallery surmounting the seventh tier of arches. The people below watch him as he balances two balls on the edge of the gallery, one weighing a hundred times more than the other. The balls are released at the same instant and are seen to keep together as they fall through the air until they are heard to strike the ground at the same moment. Nature has spoken with no uncertain sound, and has given an immediate answer to a question debated for two thousand years.

"This meddlesome man Galileo must be suppressed," murmured the University fathers as they left the square. "Does he think that by showing us that a heavy and a light ball fall to the ground together he can shake our belief in the philosophy which teaches that a ball weighing one hundred pounds would fall one hundred times faster than one weighing a single pound? Such disregard of authority is dangerous, and we will see that it goes no further." So they returned to their books to explain away the evidence of their senses; and they hated the man who had disturbed their philosophic serenity. For putting belief to the test of experiment, and founding conclusions upon observation, Galileo's reward in his old age was imprisonment by the Inquisition, and a broken heart. That is how a new scientific method is regarded by guardians of traditional doctrine.

The most original experimenter the world has ever seen is lecturing before a distinguished audience at the

Royal Institution in London. He shows that when a magnet is brought suddenly near a coil of wire a slight current of electricity is produced in the wire. The experiment is not very impressive; and a lady probably voiced the feelings of most of the audience when she asked afterwards, "But, Professor Faraday, even if the effect you explained is obtained, what is the use of it?" The memorable reply was, "Madam, will you tell me the use of a new-born child?"

Lecky, in the Introduction to his *Democracy and Liberty*, says that the whole great field of modern scientific discovery seemed out of the range of even such a scholar and statesman as Mr. Gladstone, and that when Faraday was endeavouring to explain to Gladstone and several others an important new discovery in science, Gladstone's only commentary was, "But, after all, what use is it?" "Why, sir," replied Faraday, "there is every probability that you will soon be able to tax it!"

To cultured people, Faraday's discovery of a means of producing electricity by mechanical movement seemed trivial; to the schoolmen of the Middle Ages, Galileo's appeal to the court of Nature against the judgment of authority was impertinent; and to the peasant, Fabre's patient study of insects suggested imbecility.

Three typical scientific workers are here represented; and we see the attitude of three different classes of people towards them. There is first of all the naturalist who seeks knowledge purely for its own sake, and considers no vigil too long if at the end a corner of the veil behind which the mysteries of Nature are hidden has been lifted. He continually sees new beauties in the features of his mistress and new wonders in all her ways. Sufficient for him is the satisfaction he feels at each discovery, and he cares not whether his studies have any value beyond that which he derives from them. In a world of hustle, such lovers of Nature are regarded as creatures to be pitied, if not held up to ridicule, by people who cannot understand why anyone should devote himself to a subject without expecting personal or public profit from it.

Of a different type is the iconoclast — the breaker of images—rebelling against authority, impetuous to prove that the old idols are false, impatient with the world because of its indifference to the new gospel he has to teach. This man is not content to see things for himself; he desires to convince others of the truth revealed to him, and single-handed he is prepared to storm the citadel of traditional belief. In all ages he is a disturber of the peace, and is as unwelcome in scientific circles to-day as he was to the contemplative philosophers of the Middle Ages or before. But be assured of this: you may crucify the body of such an apostle or you may visit him with the despair that follows upon neglect, but if his torch has been lighted from the divine flame of truth and righteousness it cannot be extinguished.

Most men of science are neither suppliants at the feet of Nature nor fiery advocates of truths wrested from her, but by critical inquiry into the origin of her strength and weakness they hope to discover the means of subduing her. She is cross-examined, tested, analysed, and every artifice or weapon which seems likely to induce her to reveal the secrets which she holds is brought into requisition. She is a Katharine to be tamed by the Petruchio of Science rather than a Juliet to be worshipped by a love-sick Romeo. Only those who consider her worthy of battle have the patience or the power to effect a conquest. From whatever side she is approached obstacles arise which prevent a clear vision of her; and infinite labour as well as strong desire are necessary for every step of advance.

Pasteur carried on an unrelenting warfare against the forces of Nature hostile to man; it took him five years to discover the remedy for rabies. Above all, he was an indefatigable worker. He called the interval of night "hours of waiting," which always seemed to him slow to pass. C. G. J. Jacobi (1804-1851), the greatest mathematical teacher of his generation, likewise made the best use of time. "It must not be supposed," he said, "that it is to a gift of Nature that I owe such mathematical power as I possess. No, it has come by hard work, hard work. Not mere industry, but brain-splitting thinking—hard work; hard work that has often endangered my health."

Several years ago the leading astronomers in the United States were asked to set down in order of preference the names of living Americans who had contributed most to the progress of astronomy. The name which headed all the lists was that of Simon Newcomb, yet he made no discovery in astronomy to which the periodical press would give prominence. Far greater, however, than the observation of a new star, planet, or comet, was the exceedingly laborious computations made and directed by Newcomb to enable the positions of the sun, moon, planets and some of the fixed stars to be predicted with greater accuracy than had hitherto been the case. This was the work which gave him the first place in the esteem of men who were best able to judge its value to astronomical science.

When the French astronomer and mathematician, Lalande, was computing with Clairaut the disturbing influences to which Halley's comet had been subjected, he worked at the calculations during six months from morning to night, and often at meal times; and by his devotion to this self-imposed task, contracted an illness which changed his constitution for the rest of his life. It was necessary to calculate the distance of each of the two planets Jupiter and Saturn from the comet separately for every degree over a period of one hundred and fifty years. There was no mercenary motive under this tremendous labour, but only the desire to define the movements of an object which at intervals of about seventy-six years had filled mankind with terror by its appearance in the sky.

Reward—as the world understands it—for work done or results obtained, is the last thought of a student of science. "I have no time to make money," was the reply of the naturalist, Louis Agassiz, to an offer to lend himself to a legitimate and tempting financial scheme. Napoleon the Third once expressed surprise to Pasteur that the great investigator did not endeavour to make his discoveries and their applications a source of profit. "In science," Pasteur replied, "men of science would consider that they lowered themselves by doing so." In a conversation with Lady Priestley, Pasteur remarked, "I could never work for money, but I would always work for science." If he had chosen to keep his discoveries to himself, he could have been one of the most wealthy men in the world, but he gave them to the human race, and was content to end his career as a professor of chemistry in receipt of a modest salary from the Government of his country.

Faraday on one occasion said to Tyndall that, at a certain stage of his career, he was forced definitely to ask himself, and finally to decide whether he would make wealth or science the pursuit of his life. He could not serve two masters, and he chose science. After the discovery of magneto-electricity, his fame was so well recognised that the commercial world would not have considered any fees too high for the aid of abilities like his. Tyndall says he might with ease have realized an income of £10,000 a year during the last thirty years of his life, yet he earned almost nothing by professional services.

Taking the duration of his life into account, this son of a blacksmith, and apprentice to a bookbinder, had to decide between a fortune of £150,000 on one side, and his undowered science on the other. He chose the latter and died a poor man. But his was the glory of holding aloft among the nations the scientific name of England for a period of forty years. *Tyndall.*

The invention of the miner's safety-lamp by Sir Humphry Davy was based upon scientific researches described by him to the Royal Society between 1815 and 1817. The investigations were undertaken at the request of a "Society for Preventing Accidents in Mines," formed in 1813 in consequence of the increase of colliery explosions as pits of greater depth were worked. The Society looked to scientific men to provide "a cheap and effectual" remedy for these calamities, and Davy's assistance was secured in 1815, after a number of impracticable suggestions had been considered.

As the result of experiments, Davy discovered the principle upon which safety-lamps are constructed, namely, "that explosive mixtures of mine-damp will not pass through small apertures or tubes; and that if a lamp or lanthorn be made air-tight on the sides, and furnished with apertures to admit the air, it will not communicate flame to the outward atmosphere."

Davy might have made a fortune by his discovery, by taking out a patent for the invention of the safety-lamp, but he refused to do so. One of his friends, Mr. John Buddle, who urged him on one occasion to secure this recompense for his investigations and their result, said: "I felt that he did not contemplate any pecuniary reward; and in a private conversation I remonstrated with him on the subject. I said 'You might as well have secured this invention by a patent, and received your five or ten thousand a year from it.' Davy's reply was, 'No, my good friend, I never thought of such a thing: my sole object was to serve the cause of humanity, and if I have succeeded, I am amply rewarded in the gratifying reflection of having done so.'"

When Dr. Roux, Director of the Pasteur Institute in Paris, was awarded the Osiris Prize of £4000 for the discovery of the "anti-diphtheria serum," which has been the means of saving the lives of many thousands of children, he made over the whole of the money to the institute of which he is the head, although he is relatively a poor man. The founder of the prize, M. Osiris, one day asked him why he had given the money to the institute. "All that I am," replied Dr. Roux, "I owe to the Pasteur Institute, for all my experiments and discoveries have been made there. Besides, the Institute is very poor, for we have no income except what we make by the sale of serums, and though that brings in enough to keep the establishment going, some fresh remedy may any day be discovered, in which case I fear the Institute would have to close its doors for want of funds." The millionaire said nothing at the time, but at his death, it was found that he had left the bulk of his wealth, amounting to nearly one and a quarter million pounds, to the Pasteur Institute, as a token of admiration for the scientific attainments and self-abnegation of its director.

A correspondent asked Newton's permission to publish in the *Philosophical Transactions of the Royal*

Society, the solutions, which Newton had sent him, of
some mathematical problems. Newton was at a time
of life—his age was about twenty-seven—when most
men wish to obtain credit for their work, but he particularly asked that no mention should be made of his
name in connection with this and like matters. "For
I see not," he added, "what there is desirable in public esteem were I able to acquire and maintain it. It
would perhaps increase my acquaintance, the things
which I chiefly study to decline."

Newton was, indeed, never hasty in announcing his
discoveries, and had little of the spirit of rushing into
print to claim priority to which some investigators
attach so much importance. After he had invented
the reflecting telescope in 1668, he allowed the instrument to lie by him for several years before its existence became known to some of the fellows of the Royal
Society who induced him to send it to the Society,
where it is now carefully preserved. His important
observations of the compound nature of sunlight, a
beam of which he decomposed by passing it through
a glass prism, were not communicated to the Society
until 1672, though they were made before the invention of the reflecting telescope; and his discovery of
the law of gravitation was completed several years
before Halley knew of it and was able to make it
known to the world.

What, then, are the motives of scientific work, if
the praise and rewards of the world have no meaning?
Chiefly love of knowledge and the joy of discovery;
and possessing these things the man of science faces
boldly all difficulties and is undaunted by danger.
During an epidemic of cholera in Paris in 1865, Pasteur for a time undertook the study of the disease
above the cholera ward of a hospital. Henri Saint

Claire Deville once said to him, "Studies of that sort require much courage." "What about duty?" said Pasteur simply. Danger is disregarded by the man of science as by the soldier when duty calls; and the spirit of both is reflected in the words of the battle-hymn:

Grant that with zeal and skill this day I do
What me to do behoves, what thou command'st me to;
Grant that I do it sharp at moment fit,
And, when I do it, grant me good success in it.

Huxley was a warrior of science throughout his life. When he was thirty-one years of age, while awaiting the birth of his first child, on December 31, 1856, he entered in his journal his ambitions for the future.

To smite all humbugs, however big; to give a nobler tone to science; to set an example to abstinence from petty personal controversies, and of toleration for everything but lying; to be indifferent as to whether the work is recognised as mine or not, so long as it is done:—are these my aims? 1860 will show

Wilt shape a noble life? Then cast
No backward glances to the past.
And what if something still be lost?
Act as new-born in all thou dost.
What each day wills, that shalt thou ask;
Each day will tell its proper task;
What others do, that shalt thou prize,
In thine own work thy guerdon lies.
This above all: hate none. The rest—
Leave it to God. He knoweth best.

That such a prayer as this should be offered up at the most anxious moment of his life, by one who was thought to be the apostle of materialistic knowledge, shows how mistaken is the common impression that close devotion to science weakens the spiritual side of a man. The life consecrated to the study of Nature must by this purpose alone have aims and ideals as

high as any which stimulate human endeavour. No
great work—whether in the natural or in the spiritual
world—can be accomplished without noble aspiration.
"Blessed is he," said Pasteur, "who carries with him
a God, an ideal, and obeys it; ideal of art, ideal of
science, ideal of the gospel virtues; therein lie the
springs of great thoughts and great actions; they all
reflect light from the Infinite."

All who labour to extend knowledge and establish
truth are making for righteousness; though they sail
in different seas they have the same guiding star, and
it is set so far away in infinity that compared with its
distance their paths are one. Let, then, the captain
of each ship shape his own course and not concern
himself with the tracks of other navigators; the new
lands encountered may present very diverse characters, but each explorer is expected to describe only
what comes within his own range of observation. He
can know nothing of what pioneers in other directions
have seen, but with hope at the helm and truth at the
prow he strikes the course for which his ship was
chartered, even when it seems to be crossing the tracks
of other vessels or landing him upon the rocks. This
is the spirit in which the scientific investigator sets
out for unknown lands. "When I am in my laboratory," said Pasteur, "I begin by shutting the door on
materialism and on spiritualism; I observe facts alone;
I seek but the scientific conditions under which life
manifests itself."

Facts which appear to be opposed to prevailing belief or theory are often reached in science, but if they
stand unaltered after being subjected to rigorous and
critical examination they must be adhered to and the
belief or theory abandoned. In the world of natural
knowledge, no authority is great enough to support a

theory when a crucial observation has shown it to be untenable. Scientific work must thus be carried on with an open mind, uninfluenced by preconceived ideas, critical of its own observations, cautious in arriving at conclusions from them, and ready to revise any statement which has not stood the test of further experiment or reasoning.

The philosopher should be a man willing to listen to every suggestion, but determined to judge for himself. He should not be biased by appearances; have no favourite hypothesis; be of no school; and in doctrine have no master. He should not be a respecter of persons, but of things. Truth should be his primary object. If to these qualities be added industry, he may indeed hope to walk within the veil of the temple of Nature. *Faraday.*

Scientific truth is not won by prayer and fasting, but by patient observation and persistent inquiry. Nature, like the rich man of the parable, requires importunate pleading before she will bestow any of her riches upon a suppliant at her temple. Every mite of knowledge has almost to be wrested from her; and it takes many such contributions to form a principle or theory which will constitute the stimulus by which further endeavour is sustained.

The world little knows how many of the thoughts and theories which have passed through the mind of a scientific investigator have been crushed in silence and secrecy by his own severe criticism and adverse examinations; that in the most successful instances not a tenth of the suggestions, the hopes, the wishes, the preliminary conclusions have been realised. *Faraday.*

It is necessary to believe in the holiness of scientific work in order to persevere to the end; for without the encouragement which such belief gives, many investigators would fall by the wayside. But no man of

science who has put his hand to the plough of research
ever turns back. He knows that he is at work in a
broad field and that not only will he be judged by the
straightness of his furrows, but also that he is preparing a tilth for a seedtime and harvest of knowledge
of which the chief benefit will be to others. He does
not measure his task by his wage, but performs it
faithfully because of its worthiness and his interest
in it.

If I may speak of the objects I have had more or less def-
inately in view, they are briefly these: To promote the increase
of natural knowledge and to forward the application of scientific methods to all the problems of life, to the best of my
ability, in the conviction, which has grown up with my growth,
and strengthened with my strength, that there is no allevia-
tion of the sufferings of mankind except veracity of thought
and action, and the resolute facing of the world as it is when
the garment of make-believe with which pious hands have
hidden its uglier features has been stripped off. *Huxley.*

A subject which will promote the development of
such noble ambitions as these should be included in
the education of every civilised being; yet science is
still the Cinderella in the house of education.

I do think that the study of natural science is so glorious a
school for the mind that, with the laws impressed on all created
things by the Creator, and the wonderful unity and stability
of matter and the forces of matter, there cannot be a better
school for the education of the mind. *Faraday.*

The study of Nature is elevating, and its material
value is of the highest, yet it is deplorably neglected,
with the result that only very rarely is the simplest
scientific subject referred to accurately in the works
of literary men. Our guides and counsellors, not only
in the periodical press, but also in less ephemeral publications, are, in the great majority of cases, unaware

of the most obvious facts and phenomena of Nature, and have no acquaintance with the most elementary vocabulary of science. In everything that relates to the material universe around them, they are blind leaders of the blind; and they call their darkness light. They are indifferent to the wonderful growth and extent of scientific knowledge, and live in a paradise in which rounded phrases and curious fancies are of more importance than actual facts. In such a world a one-eyed man can be king. A more enlightened view will only be obtained when it is realised that an educated man must know something of science as well as of literature.

The supercilious manner in which science is often treated by men nourished in a purely literary atmosphere is illustrated by an incident related in Lord Morley's *Life of Gladstone*. In 1877 Lord Morley, with Mr. Gladstone, Huxley and Lord Playfair, were staying with Lord Avebury (Sir John Lubbock), at High Elms, in Kent, and on the Sunday afternoon the party went up to the neighbouring village of Downe to visit Darwin.

The illustrious pair, born in the same year, had never met before. Mr. Gladstone as soon as seated took Darwin's interest in lessons of massacre for granted, and launched forth his thunderbolts [against Turkish atrocities] with unexhausted zest. His great, wise, simple, and truth-loving listener, then, I think, busy on digestive powers of the Drosera in his greenhouse, was intensely delighted. When we broke up, watching Mr. Gladstone's erect figure as he walked away, Darwin, shading his eyes with his hand against the evening rays, said to me in unaffected satisfaction, "What an honour that such a great man should come to visit me!" Too absorbed in his own overwhelming conflict with the powers of evil, Mr. Gladstone makes no mention of his afternoon call, and only says of the two days that "he found a notable party, and much interesting conversation," and that he "could not help liking" one of the company, then a stranger to him. *Lord Morley.*

Like many other statesmen and men of letters, Mr. Gladstone was unaware of the greatness of his scientific contemporaries. "Who is Cuvier?" asked Louis Philippe, King of the French, when told that this illustrious naturalist, founder of comparative anatomy and palaeontology, and the most celebrated man of science in France at the time, was dead. "Monsieur Cuvier? I believe he was one of the gentlemen employed at the Jardin des Plantes," was the courtier's response. A similar story is told of the last emperor of the French, Napoleon III., who was asked by a German guest to be introduced to the eminent physiologist, Claude Bernard. "Claude Bernard? Who is Claude Bernard?" the Emperor asked. "He is the most distinguished savant in your Majesty's dominions," was the reply. Truly a man of science is not without honour except in his own country and among his own people.

It is time to understand that no man can now be considered to have received a liberal education unless he has some acquaintance with the principles of science; and that the works of Darwin and Faraday are as worthy of national honour as those of Tennyson and Scott. The training which ends in literary culture without science is just as incomplete as one which promotes scientific knowledge without the power of clear expression.

That man, I think, has had a liberal education, who has been so trained in youth that his body is the ready servant of his will, and does with ease and pleasure all the work that, as a mechanism, it is capable of; whose intellect is a clear, cold, logic engine with all its parts of equal strength, and in smooth working order; ready, like a steam engine, to be turned to any kind of work, and spin the gossamers as well as forge the anchors of the mind; whose mind is stored with a knowledge of the great and fundamental truths of Nature and of the laws of her operations; and who, no stunted ascetic, is full of life and fire, but whose passions are trained to come to heel by a vigorous will, the servant of a tender conscience; who has learned to love all beauty, whether of Nature or of art, to hate all vileness, and to respect others as himself. *Huxley.*

Do you wish education to cultivate supreme regard for truth? Then let it include the study of Nature, for in dealings with her every false coin is inexorably nailed to the counter. Do you wish to create a sense of moral responsibility? Then learn from Nature that every act has a consequence, and every sin a penalty. Is a habit of mind required which will not be deceived by the noisy huckster of sensational statements? Then give attention to training in scientific method, by which a critical faculty is developed that enables fact to be distinguished from fable and is cautious in arriving at conclusions. Do you believe in the dignity of work and the duty of self-sacrifice? Then turn to science, which demands devoted labour for the benefit of others. Are satisfaction with the superficial, and a desire for continuous excitement to be the characteristics of the new generation? If not, see that interest is aroused in the nobler views of life opened by scientific knowledge. Regard for veracity, patience, logical thought, responsibility, discipline and original work, are all taught by the study of science; and these attributes are as desirable in every one of us as in the investigator whose life is an exemplar of them.

My success as a man of science, whatever this may have amounted to, has been determined, as far as I can judge, by complex and diversified mental qualities and conditions. Of these, the most important have been—the love of science, unbounded patience in long reflecting over any subject, industry in observing and collecting facts, and a fair share of invention as well as of common sense. With such moderate abilities as

I possess, it is truly surprising that I should have influenced to a considerable extent the belief of scientific men on some important points. *Darwin.*

The pleasure derived from the discovery of some secret of Nature unknown before except to the architect of the universe surpasses all the rewards the world can give. It is a compensation which takes the place of worldly riches and enables unselfish work to be done from which others often make commercial gain. While men engaged in other pursuits lose their interest in later life, in the man of science the love of Nature and the desire for new knowledge is eternal. Dr. Weir Mitchell relates that once, at his table, some one asked that ever-happy naturalist, Joseph Leidy, if he were never tired of life. "Tired!" he said; "Not so long as there is an undescribed intestinal worm, or the riddle of a fossil bone, or a rhizopod new to me." These subjects may seem uninspiring, but the words reveal the spirit of the ardent lover of a mistress of unfading charm. Of this great student and teacher, the following lines were spoken on the occasion of the inauguration of a memorial lectureship in his honour:

> The wisest man could ask no more of fate
>   Than to be simple, modest, manly, true,
>   Safe from the many, honoured by the few;
> Nothing to count in world, or church, or State,
> But inwardly in secret to be great;
>   To feel mysterious Nature ever new,
>   To touch, if not to grasp, her endless clue,
> And learn by each discovery how to wait,
> To widen knowledge and escape the praise;
>   Wisely to teach because more wise to learn;
>   To toil for science, not to draw men's gaze,
> But for her love of self denial stern;
> That such a man could spring from our decays
>   Fans the soul's nobler faith until it burn.
>
>   *Prof. E. F. Smith.*

Testimony to the complete satisfaction and perennial interest derived from the study of Nature has been given by many men of science. "In my laboratory," said Robert Boyle, "I find that water of Lethe which causes that I forget everything but the joy of making experiments." This great natural philosopher is said to have remarked that he feared death only because after it he would know all things, and no longer have the delight of making discoveries. Dumas, the renowned French chemist, was a man of affairs as well as a man of science, yet he said:

The recollections of an already long life have permitted me to become acquainted with a great variety of personages. And if I call on memory to picture to me how the type of true happiness is realised on earth I do not see it under the form of the powerful man clothed in high authority, nor under that of the rich man to whom the splendours of luxury and the delicacies of well-being are granted, but under that of the man of science, who consecrates his life to penetrating the secrets of Nature and to the discovery of new truths. *J. B. A. Dumas.*

On the occasion of his eighty-ninth birthday, the biology class at the University of Colorado sent Dr. Alfred Russel Wallace a greeting, and to it the veteran naturalist replied:

The wonders of Nature have been the delight and solace of my life. From the day when I first saw a bee-orchis in ignorant astonishment, to my first view of the grand forests of the Amazon; thence to the Malay Archipelago, where every fresh island with its marvellous novelties and beauties was an additional delight—Nature has afforded me an ever-increasing rapture, and the attempt to solve some of her myriad problems an ever-growing sense of mystery and awe. And now, in my wild garden and green-house, the endless diversities of plant life renew my enjoyments; and the ever-changing pageants of the seasons impress me more than ever in my earlier days. I sincerely wish you all some of the delight in the mere contemplation of Nature's mysteries and beauties which I have enjoyed, and still enjoy. *Dr. A. Russel Wallace.*

Darwin, with whom Wallace shared the honour of building up the great principle of natural selection as the prime cause of organic evolution, found equal pleasure in Nature to the end of his life; and his chief regret was that he had not been able to contribute more to natural knowledge and human happiness. "As for myself," he said, "I believe that I have acted rightly in steadily following and devoting my life to science. I feel no remorse from having committed any great sin, but have often and often regretted that I have not done more direct good to my fellow creatures."

So little done, so much to do, is the first and last thought of the man of science. A short time before his death, Sir Isaac Newton expressed the memorable sentiment: "I do not know what I may appear to the world, but to myself I seem to have been only like a boy playing on the sea-shore, and diverting myself in now and then finding a smoother pebble or a prettier shell than ordinary, whilst the great ocean of truth lay all undiscovered before me."

This was Newton's estimate of his work, yet it is related that when the Queen of Prussia asked Leibnitz his opinion of Newton, Leibnitz said that taking mathematicians from the beginning of the world to the time when Newton lived, what he had done was much the better half.

After Sir William Herschel had discovered the planet Uranus he was commanded by King George III. to attend the court with his telescope. Writing to his sister Caroline he said: "Nothing now is talked of but what they call my great discoveries. Alas! this shows how far they are behind when such trifles as I have done are called great. Let me but get at it again; I will

make such telescopes and see such things—that is, I
will endeavour to do so."

The less a man knows, the more content he is with his
intellectual capacity and outlook: it requires a great
man to realise the imperfections of his knowledge. At
the jubilee of Lord Kelvin, celebrated at the University
of Glasgow in 1896, representatives of "light and leading" from all parts of the world assembled to do honour to him. In science and in invention his work belongs to the front rank of results of human thought
and ingenuity. Yet what did Lord Kelvin say in reply
to the congratulations expressed upon his service in
the cause of scientific progress?

"One word characterises the most strenuous of the efforts
for the advancement of science that I have made persever-
ingly during fifty-five years; that word," he said, "is *failure*.
I know no more of electric and magnetic force, or of the relation between ether, electricity and ponderable matter, or of
chemical affinity, than I knew and tried to teach to my
students of natural philosophy fifty years ago in my first
session as Professor." *Kelvin*.

Far more than anyone else in his day and generation,
Lord Kelvin contributed to the advancement of science
and the application of natural knowledge to the use of
mankind; yet in his mind the predominant idea was
not satisfaction at success but disappointment at the
failure of his persevering efforts during fifty years to
understand the omnipresent ether of the physicist and
the manner in which it is concerned in electric and magnetic forces. The achievement of ocean telegraphy,
the improvement of the compass and sounding-line, the
hundreds of papers on properties of matter, provide
sufficient justification for a score of scientific careers,
but to Lord Kelvin they seemed insignificant in comparison with the unsolved problem of the theory of

matter which would unify them all. He knew that when the key to the riddle of the relation between ether and matter is discovered, mankind will be able to enter the treasure-house in which Nature's secrets are stored.

Such men as Lord Kelvin are learners always, because they realise that for one problem solved, one principle discovered, one structure completely described, there are a thousand of which they understand nothing.

> All Nature is but art, unknown to thee
> All chance, direction which thou canst not see;
> All discord, harmony not understood;
> All partial evil, universal good. *Pope.*

Man as a physical being is but a microscopic part of the universe, yet his mind carries him ever upward, and with spirit bold and unconquerable he seeks to reach the summit of Mount Olympus. Infinite space remains to humble his pride in spite of the knowledge he has obtained of the starry heavens; yet he pursues his inquiries into the unknown, and his children's children will continue the search.

As we conquer peak after peak we see in front of us regions full of interest and beauty, but we do not see our goal, we do not see the horizon; in the distance tower still higher peaks, which will yield to those who ascend them still wider prospects, and deepen the feeling, the truth of which is emphasised by every advance in science, that "Great are the Works of the Lord." *Sir J. J. Thomson.*

It is said that Thales of Miletus, who was the first of the Greeks to devote himself to the study of the stars was on one occasion so intent upon observing the heavens that he fell into a well, whereupon a maidservant laughed and remarked, "In his zeal for things in the sky he does not see what is at his feet." Many men have been laughed at since then for gazing heavenward when their minds might have been occupied with affairs of earth. There will always be the mind that strives to reach to the skies, and the scoffer who regards all such aspirations as folly.

> Two men stood looking through the bars,
> One saw the mud, the other saw the stars.

CHAPTER II

TRUTH AND TESTIMONY

The first and last thing that is demanded of genius is love of truth. Goethe.

There is no lie in Nature; no discords in the revelations of science, in the laws of the Universe. C. Kingsley.

Nothing great in science has ever been done by men, whatever their powers, in whom the Divine afflatus of the truth-seeker was wanting. Huxley.

The greatest and noblest pleasure which men can have in this world is to discover new truths; and the next is to shake off old prejudices. Frederick the Great.

New occasions teach new duties; Time makes ancient good uncouth;

They must upward still and onward who would keep abreast of truth. J. R. Lowell.

We cannot command veracity at will; the power of seeing and reporting truly is a form of health that has to be delicately guarded. The penalty of untruth is untruth. George Eliot.

If God held enclosed in His right hand all truth, and in His left simply the ever-moving impulse towards truth, although with the condition that I should eternally err, and said to me, "Choose!" I should humbly bow before His left hand, and say, "Father, give! Pure truth is for Thee alone." G. E. Lessing.

DURING the celebration of the 250th anniversary of the Royal Society in 1912, a commemorative service was held in the ancient Abbey of Westminster, and the Right Rev. the Dean of Westminster, Dr. H. E. Ryle, delivered a short address, taking for his text the words:

"Truth abideth, and is strong for ever, she liveth and conquereth for ever more . . . Blessed be the God of truth . . . And all the people then shouted, and said, Great is truth and strong above all things" (I. Esdras, iv. 38, 40, 41).

The familiar proverb, *Magna est veritas, et praevalebit* is a slightly altered rendering of this text; and no more appropriate inspiration than it provides could be found for an address to an assembly of men of science. For the love of truth is the chief characteristic of the scientific mind.

It is the man of science, eager to have his every opinion regenerated, his every idea rationalised, by drinking at the fountain of fact, and devoting all the energies of his life to the cult of truth, not as he understands it, but as he does not understand it, that ought properly to be called a philosopher. To an earlier age knowledge was power—merely that and nothing more—to us it is life and the *summum bonum. C. S. Peirce.*

In the pursuit of truth the man of science spends his days; and for the defence of truth he is prepared to stand against the world. From his earliest instruction in the laboratory or the field to the end of his life, the student of science is learning that by nothing but faithful observation and truthful record can a satisfactory conclusion be reached. Regard for truth becomes part of his nature, and the investigations which lead to it purify his life. Read the biography of any man who gained distinction by his studies of Nature, and you will find that he valued truthfulness above all other qualities of a scientific mind. "There is," said Lord Kelvin, "one thing I feel strongly in respect to investigation in physical or chemical laboratories—it leaves no room for shady, doubtful distinctions between truth, half-truth, whole falsehood. In the laboratory everything tested or tried is found true or not.''

A truthful mind is necessary for the discovery of truth in Nature. There is often a vast difference between the result an investigator expects to find and what he does obtain, but he must put his hopes aside and follow the new light if he is to be a worthy contributor to scientific knowledge. By this method alone are the conclusions and principles reached which form the refined gold of science. Advance is made by the study of cases which cannot be embraced by a general principle, by the possession of an eye to detect exceptions and of a mind willing to examine them instead of putting them aside because they are not in harmony with pre-conceived ideas.

A particular characteristic of Charles Darwin was the receptive mind with which he faced Nature, and the power of seeing exactly how to deal with variations from a general rule. Sir Francis Darwin relates that his father had a favourite gardener, to whom he used to predict the result of an experiment. When, as often happened, the contrary result came out, it was only natural that the gardener should be pleased. On the other hand, Darwin, though he was disappointed, would say as he left the green-house, "The little beasts are doing just what I did not want them to do." He was not the least upset and very often this type of failure heralded quite a new discovery. His love of truth enabled him immediately to abandon his own hypotheses when they ceased to be supported by observation, and to proceed to inquire into the cause of the unlooked-for result.

Exceptions to rules are welcomed by a scientific investigator not only because the rules have been tested by them and found wanting, but also because they show that there is still further knowledge to be gained. In this respect the attitude of the man of science differs from that of ordinary life; for most people instinctively cherish convictions based upon experience of a few cases or conditions and are adroit in avoiding evidence contrary to what they wish to believe. They cannot understand the habit of mind which looks upon all truth as relative and temporary, and rejoices at the disclosure of a fact that refuses to fall within the limits of an accepted principle. It may be impossible for human intelligence to comprehend absolute truth, but it is possible to observe Nature with an unbiassed mind and to bear truthful testimony of things seen.

> To thine ownself be true;
> And it must follow, as the night the day,
> Thou canst not then be false to any man. *Shakespeare.*

"Nature," once remarked Goethe to a friend; "Nature knows no trifling; she is always sincere, always serious, always stern; she is always in the right, and the errors and mistakes are invariably ours." No one realises this more fully than the scientific experimenter or observer. He looks at Nature's countenance, and as a sworn witness before the tribunal of reality, testifies to what is revealed to him. Upon him is the responsibility of recording exactly what he sees, and by his gaze alone can that knowledge be obtained which will subdue Nature to the rule of the human intellect. Much that he sees may not be understood, but unless he has the love of truth his vision will be distorted. Hear what a great physicist says of the essential attributes of a scientific observer and the conquests to which they lead:

I value in a scientific mind, most of all, that love of truth, that care in its pursuit, and that humility of mind which makes the possibility of error always present more than any other quality. This is the mind which has built up modern science to its present perfection, which has laid one stone upon the other with such care that it to-day offers to the world the most complete monument to human reason. This is the mind which is destined to govern the world in the future, and to solve the problems pertaining to politics and humanity as well as to inanimate nature. It is the only mind which appreciates the imperfections of the human reason, and is thus careful to guard against them. It is the only mind that values the truth as it should be valued and ignores all personal feeling in its pursuit. *Prof. H. A. Rowland.*

This is the type of mind a scientific training is intended to cultivate; and it is easier for a camel to pass through a needle's eye than it is to enter into the kingdom of science without it. We use the simile with all reverence in this connection, because science is an uplifting gospel as well as a revelation. Huxley described himself as "almost a fanatic for the sanctity of truth." Truthfulness, in his eyes, was the cardinal virtue without which neither science nor society could possess stability. The motive of all scientific work is to arrive at the truth, and Huxley's life was the apotheosis of this passion for veracity.

If absolute loyalty to truth, involving complete self-abnegation in face of the evidence, be the ideal aim of the scientific inquirer, there have been few men in whom that ideal has been so perfectly realised as in Huxley. If ever he were tempted by some fancied charm of speculation to swerve a hair's breadth from the strict line of fact, the temptation was promptly slaughtered and made no sign. For intellectual integrity he was a spotless Sir Galahad. I believe there was nothing in life which he dreaded so much as the sin of allowing his reason to be hoodwinked by personal predilections, or whatever Francis Bacon would have called "idols of the cave." *John Fiske.*

The love of truth is the beginning and the end of wisdom. It is with the astronomer as he searches the

skies from his watch tower and it animates the naturalist as he scrutinises muds gathered from the ocean bed;
it is the heart of scientific life, a stimulus to high
endeavour and a standard of righteousness. In this
spirit must Nature be approached, and by it is admission gained to the temples of her learning.

You come to the chest of knowledge. It is shut, it is bolted,
but . . . you have the key; put it in steadily and home. But
what is the key? It is the love of truth; neither more or less;
no other key opens it; no false one, however cunning, can pick
that lock; no assault of hammer, however stout, can force it
open; but with its own key, a little child may open it; often
does open it. *John Brown.*

In northern mythology, the well of wisdom was
situated at one end of a rainbow. There also is truth
hidden, and he who would discover either must adventure by himself into the unknown. Though perfect
wisdom and absolute truth are as unattainable as the
rainbow-foot, the effort to reach them brings a rich
reward. No two people ever see the same rainbow;
and to each of us, therefore, is given a different goal,
but whether we set out towards it or not depends upon
ourselves. Wisdom will not come to us, but we may
gain it by experience; truth will not wait on our command, and yet will accompany us always while we are
faithful to her. We may catch only a glimpse of her
wondrous beauty after a life of devoted service, but
there is even more satisfaction in the anticipation of
this vision than in the actual attainment of the heart's
desire.

It is the successful, or even the unsuccessful, pursuit of
truth which gives happiness to each generation of scientific
men, and not the value of the truth itself—the energy, the doing, not the thing done. If a time could arrive when all was
known, when there could not be a new investigation or experiment, our keenest pleasure would be at an end. We may

therefore feel happy in the thought of how much is still un-known. *A. G. Vernon Harcourt.*

The pursuit of truth is likely to last as long as the generations of mankind, for rightly understood it sig-nifies the quest for knowledge. In scientific truth there is no finality, and there should, therefore, be no dog-matism. When this is forgotten, then science will become stagnant, and its high-priests will endeavour to strangle new learning at its birth as has been done by the guardians of orthodoxy throughout the ages.

Since life began upon the earth, there has been a gradual development into new and nobler forms. In size and strength, many animals are mightier than man; but he is supreme over them because of his knowledge. Every conquest of science brings the human race nearer the day when it will have complete control over the forces of Nature and be able to use them for its own purposes. There must be no resting satisfied with achievements, but persistent endeavour to enter the unknown and bring back trophies from it. The talents with which we are entrusted must be given up with increase; so that, as one generation succeeds another, its store of knowledge shall be greater. The man who neglects to assist the advancement of his race so far as in him lies is like the slothful servant who buried his talent in the ground; and he should receive a like condemnation.

If we merely pass on what we receive the human race cannot develop onward and upward until man is "a little lower than the angels." We shall be like certain little brachiopods or "lamp-shells," which have re-mained unchanged in form for millions of years, being practically the same in the seas of to-day as they were in those of early geological times. While throughout countless ages the living world has been unfolding from lower to higher forms of life, these molluscan types have merely carried on their kind, benefiting nothing by the past, gaining nothing for the future. That is not the kind of life by which evolution has proceeded. It is the desire to learn by experience—not only our own experience but also the experience of others—that has raised the human race to its present position. We owe it to ourselves and to future generations to do what we can to secure a further increase of that knowledge by which our redemption from brute creation has been accomplished.

> Let knowledge grow from more to more
> But more of reverence in us dwell. *Tennyson.*

The recognition that knowledge of the physical universe is only the bud of a flower which can never be seen in its perfection is the salvation of science. Nature acknowledges no exclusive claims to truth or right of dictatorship in her name either to this generation or the next. The scientific man has to work for truth so far as her ways can be comprehended by him, but he is never more than a trustee for posterity, and has no authority to define the functions or limit the freedom of those who follow him. When men believe that complete truth has been revealed to them they restrain inquiry and persecute those who fail to see the same light. This position should never be taken in science, which invites investigation, welcomes criticism, and rejoices at new truths to supersede or supplement the old.

When men are striving for the discovery of truth in its various manifestations, they learn that it is by correcting the mistakes of preceding investigators that progress is made, and they have charity for criticism. Hence persecution for difference of opinion becomes an absurdity. The labours of scientific men are forming a great body of doctrine that can be appealed to with confidence in all countries. Such labours bring people together, and tend to break down national barriers and restrictions. The scientific creed is constantly growing and expanding, and we have no fears, but rejoice at its growth. We need no consistory of bishops, or synod of ministers, to tell us what to believe. Everything is open to investigation and criticism. *Prof. Asaph Hall.*

Science does not say "Be my brother, or I will kill you," but, "Follow me, and light shall be given you." It does not ask for the acceptance of any statement or principle purely as matters of faith, but as truthful records or reasonable conclusions, capable of verification by all who care to investigate them independently.

Essential to a scientific spirit is a temper of mind which seeks for conclusions, but does not jump at them —which, as the late Lord Derby once said, is equally opposed to the stupid incredulity of ignorance that refuses to accept any idea which is not familiar; to the reverential credulity which accepts as true any statement coming down from old or high authority; and to the careless indifferentism which, so long as a theory looks and sounds well, and especially if it flatters some previously existing feeling of prejudice, does not care on what foundation of reality that theory rests. The scientific mind asks for reasons for its beliefs, and is unwilling to express an opinion upon any conclusion without personal knowledge of the evidence upon which it is based. It distinguishes between the statements made by others and the conviction derived from experience; and it is impatient of the petty differences which often make contentions for sects and party politicians.

Call belief
Belief indeed, nor grace with such a name
The easy acquiescence of mankind
In matters nowise worth dispute, since life
Lasts merely the allotted moment. *Browning.*

In the discussion of political questions, prejudice and party determine the view taken, and facts are selected and exploited not so much with the object of arriving at the truth as to confound the other side or support a particular opinion. The vulgar abuse and vapid sentiment which are the stock-in-trade of many political writers and speakers provoke only contempt in the minds of thinking men. A politician may place party before truth, a diplomatist will conceal it on behalf of his country, and an advocate in the interests of his client, but it is the duty of a man of science to strive to attain truth at all costs.

In direct opposition to the narrowness of thought, which views all subjects through the distorting mirage of party prejudice, stands the absolute freedom of mind of the man of science, who knows, or ought to know, nothing of party, and stands with open arms to welcome truth in however strange or unexpected guise she may present herself. In his writings the man of science has no lower aim than the diffusion of truth so far as it is known, and no desire to make converts to any opinion or .y. As opposed to the finality of party opinions, he proclaims that truth is but very partially attained by man on any subject, for we can see truth only imperfectly, as she appears altered by the perspective of our own standpoint. *Sir William Huggins.*

Most scientific work must be done without recognition or expectation of reward. Many men who devote their lives to the extension of knowledge continually find themselves without the means of obtaining the instruments or other material necessary for the pursuit of their researches. On the principle of "Nothing succeeds like success," assistance is offered when the work for which it would have been of service has been accomplished or to the man who is independent of it, instead of to the earnest investigator whose limited means leave little for science when social necessities have been satisfied. Newton himself was, at one time of his life, in such poverty that he asked to be excused from the weekly payment of one shilling which the Royal Society required of its members.

Patronage is not wanted, but encouragement in a practical form may be of the greatest service if given early. *Bis dat qui cito dat* is particularly applicable to the needs of young men trained for scientific investigation and eager to pursue it if the means which will permit them to do so are provided. The position is like that stated in Dr. Johnson's celebrated letter to Lord Chesterfield concerning his Dictionary. Johnson worked for seven years "without one act of assistance, one word of encouragement, or one smile of favour" from his lordship, who, however, when the Dictionary was on the eve of publication, made professions of friendship in the hope, it is said, that the work would be dedicated to him. Johnson wrote:

Is not a patron, my lord, one who looks with unconcern on a man struggling for life in the water, and when he has reached ground, encumbers him with help? The notice which you have been pleased to take of my labours, had it been early, had been kind; but it has been delayed till I am indifferent, and cannot enjoy it; till I am solitary, and cannot impart it; till I am known, and do not want it. I hope it is no very cynical asperity, not to confess obligations where no benefit has been received, or to be unwilling that the public should consider me as owing that to a patron, which Providence has enabled me to do for myself.

When men of science ask for funds for scientific research they do not wish to bury the talents they receive or to derive personal profit from them. Whatever amount is entrusted to them is returned a hundredfold in the results achieved. How many are the researches worthy of assistance, and how small are the

funds available for investigations having no obvious
practical application, are understood only by men of
science themselves?

It would be a revelation to people endowed with a
larger share of worldly riches to be present at a meeting of the Committee of the British Association for the
Advancement of Science concerned with the allocation
of grants for scientific purposes. Thirty or forty of
the leading men of science in the British Isles debate
for several hours how to divide the sum of about £1,000
which represents the amount available from the sale
of tickets at each annual meeting. There are many
applications for grants from committees of each of the
twelve sections of the Association, and the amount
required has usually to be whittled down to £5 or £10,
which often does not cover the expense of stationery
and postage of a research committee. Not one penny
goes into the pockets of the men who are conducting
the researches, yet claim after claim has to be passed,
or reduced to its lowest limits, because the fund is
miserably inadequate to meet the demands made upon
it.

The Royal Society was unable to find the money
required to print Newton's *Principia*—a work which
will always be regarded as one of the most remarkable
products of the human intellect that the world has ever
seen—and it was published at the expense of his friend
Halley. Our scientific societies are in little better
position to-day. Their members—most of whom possess but very slender means—pay by their own sub-
scriptions for the publication of the results of their
investigations. They sacrifice their leisure, and draw
upon their limited resources, not only that knowledge
may be increased, but also that the gain may be published to the world, which is free to make use of it.

It is difficult for the man of the world to understand the altruistic spirit which induces men of science to band themselves together in societies having for their sole aim the advancement of knowledge in particular directions; and that these men should themselves pay to enlighten and benefit others by the publication of their researches is almost incomprehensible to the selfish or money-making mind; yet such is the case. While the State grant made by Great Britain towards the expense of the publications of learned societies is limited to the sum of one thousand pounds annually to the Royal Society, several times this amount is expended each year upon stationery alone used by members of the House of Commons.

The politicians who pay themselves a salary for the time they devote to party tactics and personal persiflage, would be astounded if the proposal were made to provide for the support of Fellows of the Royal Society or of any other scientific institution, yet of the relative values to the nation of the work done in the two spheres of politics and science, there can be no question. In a splendid building and surrounded with all the appurtenances of precedent and dignity, months and years are wasted in a game of finding weak points in arguments relating to subjects many of which are of doubtful national importance; while the scientific elect of the country are crowded in modest apartments to discuss discoveries which it has cost them much time and frequently much money to complete, and for the publication of which they must themselves make provision. It requires the satire of a Swift to describe the disparity of support afforded to polemics and natural philosophy by a State that owes most of its modern advance to apostles of scientific truth.

CHAPTER III

THE SCIENTIFIC MIND

One use of physical science is that it gives definite ideas.
Sir Humphry Davy.

The man of science has learned to believe in justification, not by faith, but by verification. Huxley.

The future of our civilisation depends upon the widening spread and deepening hold of the scientific habit of mind.
Prof. John Dewey.

Ocasionally, and frequently, the exercise of the judgment ought to end in absolute reservation. We are not infallible, and so we ought to be cautious. Faraday.

To the natural philosopher, there is no natural object unimportant or trifling. From the least of Nature's works he may learn the greatest lessons. Sir John Herschel.

I do not know anything, except it be humility, so valuable in education as accuracy. Direct lies told to the world are as dust in the balance when weighed against the falsehoods of inaccuracy; and accuracy can be taught. Sir Arthur Helps.

Scientific thought does not mean thought about scientific subjects with long names. There are no scientific subjects. The subject of science is the human universe; that is to say, everything that is, or has been, or may be related to man. W. K. Clifford.

THE main qualities which go to make up a scientific mind are not peculiar attributes of the man of science; they may be recognized as belonging to men who have commanded or deserved success in other departments of intellectual activity. Science, as Huxley said, is

organised common sense; and all men who have been
drilled in the ways of common sense should, therefore,
possess the characteristics of a fruitful scientific mind
as defined by one in whom it was clearly manifest:

In the first place, above all things, his nature must be one
which vibrates in unison with that of which he is in search;
the seeker after truth must himself be truthful, truthful with
the truthfulness of Nature. For the truthfulness of Nature
is not wholly the same as that which man sometimes calls
truthfulness. It is far more imperious, far more exacting.
Man, unscientific man, is often content with "the nearly," and
"the almost." Nature never is . . . In the second place, he
must be alert of mind. Nature is ever making signs to us, she
is ever whispering to us the beginnings of her secrets; the
scientific man must be ever on the watch, ready at once to lay
hold of Nature's hint, however small, to listen to her whisper,
however low.

In the third place, scientific inquiry, though it be pre-emi-
nently an intellectual effort, has need of the moral quality
of courage—not so much the courage which helps a man to
face a sudden difficulty as the courage of stedfast endurance.

Sir Michael Foster.

Love of truth creates the habit of accuracy and
exactness in matters of fact which characterises a
scientific mind. Conviction counts for nothing, and
any knowledge arrived at as the result of observation
or experiment must be capable of being verified by
other investigators who will follow the same road.
Scientific truth is thus objective and not subjective;
it must be open to all eyes and not a vision limited to
the consciousness of one mind. The distinction between
this kind of truth which we can all examine for ourselves if we wish, and the truth which is a matter of
personal conviction, is fundamental. Knowing that
others may repeat his observations and that by the
confirmation of them or otherwise will he be judged,

the student of science learns that faithfulness to fact in every detail is required of him. The habit of mind thus acquired is never willing to base conclusions upon the flimsy evidence which satisfies most people. It is a mill that requires verifiable fact for its grist before it can deliver the good white flour of scientific conclusion into the hopper. This is the mind which a scientific education is intended to produce; and no substitute of words or symbols for things can give it.

Advocates of traditional learning cannot understand the educational difference between contact with natural fact and the study of allusions in classical literature. Theirs was the view taken by the old school of thought in the University of Cambridge when a demand was made for funds to build laboratories in the last third of the nineteenth century. Provision of opportunity for the development of an independent observational type of mind was opposed on the ground that it was not good to attach more importance to things seen and done than to things communicated to it by someone in authority. "If," said a leading mathematician of those days, "he does not believe the statement of his teacher—probably a clergyman of mature knowledge, recognised ability, and blameless character—his suspicion is irrational and manifests a want of power of appreciating evidence."

Everything depends upon the meaning to be attached to evidence. The only evidence of value in science, and the only testimony which a student of science is competent to give, is that derived from his own observations. Hearsay evidence is not admitted in a court of law or given any weight in a scientific discussion, even when the informant is a clergyman of blameless character. A witness is expected to give a truthful account of the facts of a case as they presented themselves to him; and at the tribunal of science he dare not offer false testimony. His observations must be exact if they are to stand the test of cross-examination; his evidence must be impartial if it is to have any weight; and his loyalty should be to truth alone, as understood by him, if it is to influence the verdict.

But the scientific man is a judge as well as a witness; his own investigations provide him with the evidence upon which he himself passes judgment; and when he is asked to accept conclusions or subscribe to convictions in support of which no facts are forthcoming, he declines to derogate his reason to his desire. As an example of this attribute of a scientific mind, which asks for evidence when earthly matters or historical records are under consideration, the view taken by Huxley in regard to the former narrow interpretation put upon the Mosaic record of creation is typical.

I find no difficulty in conceiving that, at some former period, this universe was not in existence; and that it made its appearance in six days (or instantaneously if that be preferred), in consequence of the volition of some pre-existent Being. . . . Far be it from me to say that it is untrue because it is impossible. I confine myself to what must be regarded as a modest and reasonable request for some particle of evidence that the existing species of animals and plants did originate in that way, as a condition of my belief in a statement which appears to me to be highly improbable. *Huxley.*

How can the mind which is continually working for exact knowledge, and is ready to reject any belief or revise any opinion when shown to be opposed to fact, occupy a different position? When facts are not available it is equally permissible to believe or to doubt. Nothing is impossible; but in the court of natural knowledge nothing is acceptable without proof. The duty of science is to obtain trustworthy evidence from every available source, and to arrive at conclusions from it. But clear and complete testimony is difficult to obtain even of the events and occurrences of every-day life; and it can only be elicited from Nature by the mind that hesitates to believe and requires positive impressions in order to be convinced. The man of science, by virtue of his training, is alone capable of realising the difficulties—often enormous—of obtaining accurate data upon which judgment may be based.

It is only the active worker—the original investigator—who, by personal appeal to Nature through artificially imposed con-ditions, *i.e.* experiment, or through observation, *i.e.* ready-made phenomena, has come to understand fully what a *fact* really means in the scientific sense; to realise how laborious is the process of wooing truth and how ambiguous are the answers often given by Nature to his cross-examinations. I have else-where recorded a humorous rejoinder by Darwin on one of the very few occasions when it was my never-forgotten privilege to have met him; as this reply bears so closely upon the present topic I will venture to repeat it. I had been dwelling upon this very point of the difficulty of getting Nature to give a definite answer to a simple question, when, with one of those mirthful flashes that occasionally lighted up his features, he retorted, "She will tell you a direct lie if she can." *Prof. R. Meldola.*

The great historian, Hume, referring to the inception of the Royal Society, said that it is the part of scientific men to lift the veil from the mysteries of Nature. The only mysteries with which the natural philosopher is concerned are those belonging to the material universe. In ultramundane matters conviction takes the place of observation. The poet and the metaphysician feel that certain thoughts are true, and the ideas thus conceived are to them as definite facts as any inferences depend-ing upon the use of the senses. Such feelings do not admit of objective demonstration and cannot, therefore, be measured by the standards of natural or physical science. They belong to another world, which the describer of phenomena may contemplate but is usually unqualified to enter.

It is possible that absolute truth will come by introspection rather than by studies of material conditions and things, but this need not discourage the scientific investigator from examining the facts of the physical universe and expressing the results as phenomenal knowledge whatever may be the ultimate Reality behind them. We shall not be judged by what we cannot know but by the use we make of the opportunity given us to work and to understand. "If each of us," said Berthollet, "adds something to the common domain in the field of science, of art, of morality, it is because a long series of generations have lived, worked, thought and suffered before us."

All labour that demands exactness, honest thought and steady application is worth doing, and all these things are required of a worker for science. Each stone chiselled for the temple of science has the mason's mark scribed upon it; and if it is not fairly and squarely fashioned it will be rejected by the builders. Remembering this, the scientific mind cannot be content with the perfunctory performance of any task before it; the work must be true if it is to stand the judgment of to-morrow as well as to-day; therefore it is sacred.

Devotion to science is a tacit worship—a tacit recognition of worth in the things studied; and by implication in their cause. It is not a mere lip-homage, but a homage expressed in actions—not a mere professed respect, but a respect proved by the sacrifice of time, thought, and labour. *Herbert Spencer.*

The gospel of work is the gospel of science. Go into the fields of Nature and labour if you would become a disciple of science; for not otherwise can the kingdom of natural knowledge be gained. By nothing but patient toil and the quiet thought which it brings can a scientific habit of mind be acquired. No amount of learning from books or of listening to the words of authority can be substituted for the spade-work of investigation. New treasures can never be secured from Nature without effort; "tribulation, not undisturbed progress, gives life and soul, and leads to success, when success can be reached, in the struggle for natural knowledge."

Success in science means the birth of new knowledge. Patient observation and productive thinking are what the world needs for progress, and what true scientific study demands. There are now so many opportunities of obtaining ready-made opinions that the habits of independent thought, caution in accepting assertions, and critical inquiry into evidence, are becoming atrophied by disuse. *Vox populi, vox Dei* may be a sound democratic principle for political platforms, but it stands for nothing in science. The men who have advanced the human race throughout the ages are those who have stood for individuality as against the conclusions of the crowd. Cultivate appreciation for beauty, the instinct for truth and the creative power, and all the rest shall be given unto you. In Nature.

> Beauty is truth, truth beauty; that is all
> Ye know on earth, and all ye need to know. *Keats.*

Truth, Beauty, Learning, Observation, Reason, Expression, Production, are powers which all of us possess in varying degrees; and the greatest of the seven is Production, whether it be applied to literature, art, or science.

The all-round liberally-educated man, from Palaeolithic times to the time when the earth shall become a cold cinder, will always be the same, namely, the man who follows his

standards of truth and beauty, who employs his learning
and observation, his reason, his expression, for purposes of
production, that is, to add something of his own to the stock
of the world's ideas. *Prof. H. F. Osborn.*

The power to produce is not the exclusive possession
of any particular class; and in the realm of science it
comes to all who will approach Nature with clear eyes,
will observe accurately, weigh the observations with
unprejudiced mind and weave them into a reasonable
web of interpretation. These qualities of a scientific
mind come not by believing but by doing; not from
contentment with things as they are but from a desire
to know something of the land beyond the hills.

Natural Science is a subject which a man cannot learn by
paying for teachers. He must teach it himself, by patient
observation, by patient common sense. And if the poor man
is not the rich man's equal in those qualities, it must be his
own fault, not his purse's. *Charles Kingsley.*

The true meaning of Nature can be understood only
by those in direct communion with her. Every devout
student has to learn to read the book of Nature for
himself; and when he has done so he cannot think
lightly of the wonders revealed to him.

The study of Nature is an intercourse with the highest mind.
You should never trifle with Nature. At the lowest her works
are the works of the highest powers, the highest something in
whatever way we may look at it. A laboratory of Natural
History is a sanctuary where nothing profane should be tolerated. I feel less agony at improprieties in churches than
in a scientific laboratory. *Louis Agassiz.*

At the beginning of his career, Agassiz wrote to his
father, "I wish to be a good son, a good citizen, and the
first naturalist of my time"; and his life realised these
aims. He was born in a little village in Switzerland in

1807, and attained the highest reputation as a naturalist in Europe before he removed to the United States of America when thirty-nine years of age. The nobility of his character, his untiring efforts to increase the knowledge of science, and his inspiring personality, brought him many friends and pupils. An active generation of Nature students was created by his work and influence. His fiftieth birthday was celebrated on May 28, 1857, at a club of distinguished men of which he was a member; and upon that occasion Longfellow read a memorable poem in which occur the well-known verses:

> And Nature, the old nurse, took
> The child upon her knee,
> Saying "Here is a story-book
> Thy Father has written for thee."

> "Come wander with me," she said,
> "Into regions yet untrod;
> And read what is still unread
> In the manuscripts of God."

> And he wandered away and away
> With Nature, the dear old nurse,
> Who sang to him night and day
> The rhymes of the universe.

The only qualifications required for the study of Nature's story-book are devotion to truth, and sincerity of spirit; all the other qualities will come to the possessor of these, and a habit of mind will be developed that tries to face all facts squarely and honestly, despises shams and false conventions, and exposes superstition whenever it is encountered. These are the standards of scientific integrity, and the man whose ideals are dominated by them has found the way to intellectual and spiritual salvation.

Science seems to me to teach in the highest and strongest manner the great truth which is embodied in the Christian conception of entire surrender to the will of God. Sit down before fact as a little child, be prepared to give up every preconceived notion, follow humbly wherever and to whatsoever abysses Nature leads, or you shall learn nothing. I have only begun to learn content and peace of mind since I have resolved, at all risks, to do this. *Huxley*.

Huxley's attitude towards the belief in a future life was at one time the cause of much bitterness against him; yet it is only another illustration of his reluctance to make a positive assertion about a subject upon which no evidence, or rather evidence which appealed to him, was available. The survival of the soul is beyond the bounds of our terrestrial experience; and much as Huxley may have wished to believe in it, he could not do so without being false to his personal convictions. His position was beautifully expressed in a pathetic letter which he wrote to Charles Kingsley in 1860, soon after the death of his first child.

My convictions, positive and negative, on all the matters of which you speak, are of long and slow growth and are firmly rooted. But the great blow which fell upon me seemed to stir them to their foundations, and had I lived a couple of centuries earlier I could have fancied a devil scoffing at me and them— and asking me what profit it was to have stripped myself of the hopes and consolations of the mass of mankind? To which my only reply was and is, "Oh, Devil! truth is better than much profit." I have searched over the grounds of my belief, and if wife and child and name and fame were all to be lost to me one after the other as the penalty, still I would not lie. *Huxley*.

What matters it if a man who will let such a creed as this control his life does not accept the beliefs of particular sects? Whether we are Christian or Mohammedan, Buddhist or idolater, there is a heaven awaiting us if we are faithful to the good that is in us. Speaking to Mr. John Fiske on one occasion, Mr. Alexander Macmillan said: "I tell you, there is so much real

Christianity in Huxley that if it were parcelled out among all the men, women and children in the British Islands there would be enough to save the soul of every one of them, and plenty to spare.''

The man who lives a moral life merely because he wishes to save his own precious soul is little better than an expectant Hedonist; for his motive is personal profit. He may be saved from punishment hereafter by being negatively evil, but his life will be of no benefit to the human race unless he is positively good. What existence awaits us across the dark river we cannot say; but we do know that here on earth each thread of life is intended to contribute to the web designed by its Creator.

Science may not be able to provide a complete code of ethics, but it does teach that every action carries with it a consequence—not in another world but in this—to be felt either by ourselves or by others, in our own time or the generations to come. The knowledge that effect inevitably follows cause in Nature makes the student of science circumspect in all his dealings with her. In the sublime words of Francis Thompson:

> All things by immortal power
> Near or far,
> Hiddenly
> To each other linkèd are,
> That thou canst not stir a flower
> Without troubling of a star.

The man who keeps this thought constantly before him, and understands the altruistic principle suggested by it, cannot act lightly towards others or himself. But neither this principle nor any other stimulus to high endeavour can have any significance in moral philosophy unless it is put into practice or creates a response in the form of action. Light is invisible until it strikes a material body, and a maxim of conduct has likewise no practical meaning until it is reflected in human life. The final test of a gospel is the influence it has upon those who follow it; and by that test the Spirit of Science is content to be judged. Let one who represented the Christian faith at its highest and best testify to the virtues of men who are faithful students of science:

Good men, honest men, accurate men, righteous men, patient men, self-restraining men, fair men, modest men. Men who are aware of their own vast ignorance compared with the vast amount that there is to be learned in such a universe as this. Men who are accustomed to look at both sides of a question; who, instead of making up their minds in haste like bigots and fanatics, wait like wise men, for more facts, and more thought about the facts. In one word, men who have acquired just the habit of mind which the study of Natural Science can give, and must give; for without it there is no use studying Natural Science; and the man who has not got that habit of mind, if he meddles with science, will merely become a quack and a charlatan, only fit to get his bread as a spirit-rapper, or an inventor of infallible pills. *Charles Kingsley.*

When King George III. appointed Herschel king's astronomer at a salary of £200 a year, Sir William Watson, Herschel's friend at Bath, exclaimed, "Never bought monarch honour so cheaply." But it is so unusual for a royal personage in England to give any practical support to scientific studies that this remark seems a trifle ungenerous, particularly as King George's action enabled Herschel to give up the teaching of music and concentrate his attention upon astronomy, and the construction of telescopes, in aid of which he afterwards obtained two grants of £2,000 each. "I spend money on war because it is necessary," said George III. on one occasion to Lalande, who had thanked him for his encouragement of astronomy, "but to spend it on science, that is pleasant to me. This object costs no tears; it is an honour to humanity."

The achievements of science represent increase of knowledge not alone for the man who makes it, not alone also for the nation or country to which he belongs, but for the whole human race. Power and glory gained by victory in war carry with them the humiliation and exploitation of the vanquished; and on both sides human life is sacrificed to causes which are often far from righteous. The conquests of science do not mean the aggrandisement of one country or people at the expense of another, but gifts to all who will receive them. The only domain which it is desired to penetrate is that of ignorance; and the fight is against the physical and mental death which is its heritage. For light instead of darkness, for truth in the place of error, for the fruit of the tree of knowledge of good and evil, the warriors of science carry on their continuous campaign. Probably no granite block will record their actions or marble monument declare the renown of their leaders, but neither will their spirits be disturbed by the moans of the widow and fatherless which must ever be associated with the victories of military commanders.

When a new city appeared on Asgard's Hill—the abode of the gods of the northern Sagas—after the destruction and renewal of the world, a new race of men came to it from Memory's Forest; and Loki, the disturber of law and order, as well as Fenrir the destroyer, had no place in it. The new race was typical of the scientific spirit which lives for ever, and of those who labour for new knowledge.

They are the salt of the earth, which keeps the world of man from decaying back into barbarism. They are the children of

Photo. Henry Dixon & Son.

II. THE SPIRIT OF THE SUMMIT.
Painting by Frederick, Lord Leighton, P.R.A.,
(1830-1896).

light. They are the aristocracy of God, into which not many noble, not many rich, not many mighty, are called. Most of them were poor; many all but unknown in their own time, many died and saw no fruit of their labours; some were persecuted, some were slain, as heretics, innovators and corruptors of youth. Of some the very names are forgotten. But though their names be dead, their works live, and grow and spread over ever fresh generations of youth, showing them fresh steps towards that temple of wisdom which is the knowledge of things as they are; the knowledge of those eternal laws by which God governs the heavens and the earth, things temporal and eternal, physical and spiritual, seen and unseen, from the rise and fall of mighty nations to the growth and death of moss on yonder moors. *Charles Kingsley.*

The scientific mind seeks continually for natural revelations whether they can be applied to arts and industries or not. The delight is in the chase, and it ceases with the capture. An Oxford professor once said that the one thing he valued in the system of quaternions was the certainty that it could not be defiled by any utilitarian applications. The spirit that prompted this remark was possibly obscurantist, and the prediction has proved to be incorrect, but it reflects the feeling of many scientific investigators, who work primarily to extend knowledge and to learn more of the mysteries of the universe, with little thought of the possible usefulness of their observations and discoveries. To men of this type of mind, science is sacred, and they bow their heads before the vastness of the unknown. Realising that the steps forward are very short in comparison with distance to be traversed by the human race in the future, they confess the truth of the stanza:

> Thou hast not gain'd a real height,
> Nor art thou nearer to the light,
> Because the scale is infinite. *Tennyson.*

Humility is indeed a distinctive quality of every scientific mind; not humility before man and man-made images, but before the marvellous universe in which the Earth is only a particle. By his devotion to Nature, the man of science is exalted above the planes occupied by those who pay no attention to her; and he is humbled by the greatness of the view presented to him.

The wisdom of God receives small honour from those vulgar heads that rudely stare about, and with a gross rusticity admire His works; those highly magnify Him, whose judicious enquiry into His acts, and deliberate research into His creatures, return the duty of a devout and learned admiration. *Sir Thomas Browne.*

The holy flame of wisdom burns brightly in a scientific mind and its rays are diffused for the benefit of mankind. The conviction that devotion to the study of Nature exalts the Creator gives courage and power to those who possess it; it is the Divine afflatus which inspires and enables the highest work in science. Novitiates in the temple of natural knowledge learn from their teachers this cardinal principle of their calling. Hearken to the high note struck by a pioneer of electricity in an address to his students:

Nothing but the conviction that our love of knowledge is an endeavour after a true reality, and that it is true life and true harmony, can give you a genuine enthusiastic love of wisdom. The conviction that when you diffuse knowledge you are instrumental in the consolidation of God's Kingdom on earth can alone give you a true and unalloyed desire to lead those around you towards a higher light and higher knowledge. This is the important vocation for which you have begun to educate yourselves. Continue your endeavours with holy seriousness, and you will become capable of participating in a joy which the world cannot bestow, and your works will be a blessing to your fatherland; yes, and will confer a benefit on the whole human race. *H. C. Oersted.*

The savage endows his images of wood and stone with divine attributes, and makes them objects of worship, and the Gods of all men and ages reflect the thoughts and aspirations of those who fall down before them. Volney wrote in *Les Ruines*: "Ce n'est point Dieu qui a fait l'homme à son image, c'est l'homme qui a figuré Dieu sur la sienne," but long before him Xenophanes had said "Men make gods in their own image," and had held that the representations of the gods in the human form by Homer and Hesiod were directly responsible for the moral corruption of the time. The image in which man makes God is determined chiefly by extent of knowledge of the universe; the shape that satisfies the common mind evokes no spirit of reverence in that which stretches out to the stars or studies the profound marvels of the life of the simplest organism.

Science alone can give us true conception of ourselves and our relation to the mysteries of existence. Only the sincere man of science—and by this title we do not mean the mere calculator of distances, or analyzer of compounds, or labeler of species; but him who through lower truths seeks higher and eventually the highest—only the genuine man of science, we say, can truly know how utterly beyond not only human knowledge but human conception is the universal power of which nature, and life and thought are manifestations. *Herbert Spencer.*

The mind that thinks in aeons and sounds the depths of interstellar space cannot be brought within the limits of a narrow religious formulary; yet it is essentially devout, and it influences for good all with whom it comes in contact. G. F. Watts exerted a remarkable power over others by his elevating personality. On one occasion a lad who was living a fast life owing to the dissolute and vicious company he met at his father's house, walked with Watts across a park in London, on a night when the dome of the sky was brilliant with

stars. From that time the life of the lad underwent a
change; and when some years later he was asked what
had been said to give him higher aspirations the answer was simply, "We talked of the stars." By the
light of the heavens he was able to see the dust in the
road he had been treading and to select cleaner paths
for his journey towards manhood.

Whether science is studied for its proximate value or
for the sake purely of increased knowledge, it creates
a consciousness which transfigures life. Neither it nor
philosophy can satisfy the religious instincts of the
plain man who requires a personal and social being to
worship. But though religion exists without science,
there is no science without religion; and the study of
the laws of Nature creates a respect for them and
reverence for their Maker of a far profounder kind
than the ordinary mind can conceive.

There cannot be any issue between faith and science, for
science and faith mutually exclude one another; not in the
sense that the one renders the other impossible, or *vice versa*,
but rather that so far as science extends faith does not exist,
and faith begins where science leaves off. It cannot be denied
that beyond this limit there may be real objects to be embraced
by faith. It is, therefore, not the object of science to destroy
faith, but rather to define the boundaries to which knowledge
extends, and within these to establish a uniform system.
Rudolf Virchow.

There is, indeed, no conflict between religion and
science; one is the expression of an instinct, the other
is a spirit of inquiry into the character and meaning
of all things visible and invisible in the universe.
"Science is bound," said Lord Kelvin, "by the ever-
lasting law of honour, to face fearlessly every problem
which can fairly be presented to it." It does not set
out to establish or depose any particular articles of
belief or substance of faith, but to examine critically

whatever comes before it in the natural world and to
testify faithfully to what is seen. The knowledge thus
gained may at times appear to undermine the foundations of belief, but that need cause no anxiety, for in
the course of years the truth will prevail and error
will be confounded, whether it comes from conviction
or observation.

The dogmatism of a few generations ago, both of
men of science and theologians, is giving way to a more
liberal spirit; and all who are searching earnestly for
truth are considered to be worshippers at the same
shrine. But any attempt to express traditional super-
naturalism in terms of objective reality, or to bring
modern science within the ambit of scriptural exegesis,
is to design a flimsy shelter for the destitution of the
semi-reasonable. Neither creed nor doctrine shall place
boundaries upon the field of inquiry. "Science," said
Carl Ernst von Baer, "is, in its source, eternal; in its
operation, not limited by time and space; in its scope
immeasurable; in its problem, endless; in its goal, unattainable." The study of science creates this feeling
of infinite greatness in all who follow it; and though it
may lead to imperfect interpretations, its motive cannot be irreligious.

By cherishing as a vital principle an unbounded spirit of
inquiry, and ardency of expectation, it unfetters the mind
from prejudice of every kind and leaves it open and free to
every impression of a higher nature, which it is susceptible of
receiving, guarding only against enthusiasm and self-decep-
tion by a habit of strict investigation, but encouraging rather
than suppressing everything that can offer a prospect or a
hope beyond the present obscure and unsatisfactory state.
The character of the true philosopher is to hope all things not
impossible, and to believe all things not unreasonable. He
who has seen obscurities which appeared impenetrable in
physical and mathematical science suddenly dispelled, and the

most barren and unpromising fields of inquiry converted, as if by inspiration, into rich and inexhaustible springs of knowledge and power on a simple change of our point of view, or by merely bringing to bear on them some principle which it never occurred before to try, will surely be the very last to acquiesce in any dispiriting prospects of either the present or future destinies of mankind; while, on the other hand, the boundless views of intellectual and moral, as well as material, relations which open to him on all hands in the course of these pursuits, the knowledge of the trivial place he occupies in the scale of creation, and the sense continually pressed upon him of his own weakness and incapacity to suspend or modify the slightest movement of the vast machinery he sees in action around him, must effectually convince him that humility of pretension, no less than confidence of hope, is what best becomes his character. *Sir John Herschel.*

"Blessing, and honour, and glory and power" are not the usual rewards of a life devoted to science. All the benefits of modern civilisation are due to the achievements of science or inventions based upon them; but neither the multitude nor its masters are familiar with the names of the men whose work has provided the comforts of the present day. If you seek fame and riches, enter not upon a scientific career; for they are easier won in politics or commerce or many other walks in life. If, however, you will be content with the satisfaction which faithful and unselfish work always brings, Nature offers a rich field in which you can exercise your intellect.

To qualify for admission into the temple of science it is necessary to offer sacrifices at the altar of knowledge; and only those with sincere regard for truth will find their gifts acceptable. Nature must be loved for herself and not for her dowry. The reward which the world can give may come; but the discoveries which may bring them can only be secured in the pure quest for the advancement of knowledge. To one alone of

King Arthur's knights, Sir Galahad, was a complete vision of the Holy Grail vouchsafed; and he was the single knight that could say:

> My strength is as the strength of ten,
> Because my heart is pure. *Tennyson.*

The secrets of Nature are likewise reserved for those who seek them purely for the love of truth and desire for understanding. The "just and faithful knight" can see Nature unveiled and pass into the spiritual city of science, where purer joys than all earthly fame can give will be his prize.

CHAPTER IV

PURSUIT OF KNOWLEDGE

Knowledge advances by steps, and not by leaps. Macaulay.

Prove all things; hold fast that which is good. St. Paul.

*We ourselves die, but the fair fame never dies of him who
has earned it. A Lay of Odin.*

*Knowledge is proud that he has learnt so much; Wisdom
is humble that he knows no more. Cowper.*

*When you call a thing mysterious, all that it means is that
you don't understand it. Lord Kelvin.*

*Where a spring rises, or a river flows, there should we
build altars and offer sacrifices. Seneca.*

*Knowledge comes by eyes always open and working hands;
and there is no knowledge that is not Power. Do
valiantly, and hope confidently and wait patiently.
Jeremy Taylor.*

"TAKE this fish," said Agassiz to a student who entered
his laboratory to study zoology, "and look at it; we
call it a Haemulon; by and by I will ask what you have
seen." In ten minutes the student thought he had seen
all that could be seen in the creature without a magnifying glass, but when he commenced to draw it he
discovered new features, and upon the return of
Agassiz several hours later he rehearsed what he had
observed. "You have not looked very carefully" was
the remark of the naturalist, "why, you haven't even
seen one of the most conspicuous features of the animal,
which is as plainly before your eyes as the fish itself;
look again, look again!"

For three days the student was kept examining the fish before Agassiz was satisfied that he had discovered for himself the essential points of its structure. On the fourth day, a second fish of the same group was placed beside the first and he was bidden to point out the resemblances and differences between the two; another and another followed until the entire family had been examined and the relationships of the members of the group could be brought in review. The student thus received that training in the observation of facts and their orderly arrangement which is characteristic of the scientific method. "Facts are stubborn things," Agassiz would say, "until brought into connection with some general law."

For successful work in science, or in any subject, the student must have interest as well as the faculty of distinguishing the relative value of things. Confucius, the great Chinese philosopher, used to send away his disciples who did not show sufficient ardour for study, or such as were not sufficiently intelligent to understand him. "When," he said, "I have shown a pupil one corner of the subject, and he is unable to discover the other three, I do not repeat my lesson." Devotion to a subject will lead to the acquisition of knowledge, but mastery is only secured when it is combined with insight.

The old French anatomist, Méry, said of himself and his colleagues that they were like the rag-pickers of Paris, who knew every street and alley, but had no notion of what went on in the houses. The accumulation of miscellaneous knowledge of useful things, copious, inexact, inapplicable, may, like rag-picking, leave us ignorant of the world in which we live. Let us try to reach the inner life of something, great or small. The truly useful knowledge is mastery. Mastery does not come by listening while somebody explains; it is the reward of effort. Effort, again, is inspired by interest and sense of duty. Interest alone may tire too quickly; sense of duty alone may grow formal and unintelligent. Mastery comes by attending long to a particular thing—by inquiring, by looking hard at things, by handling and doing, by contriving and trying, by forming good habits of work, and especially the habit of distinguishing between the things that signify and those that do not. *Prof. L. C. Miall.*

Success or failure at school or college supply no standards by which the promise of the future may be estimated. Originality of thought or achievement is not measurable by the same units as those of absorbing power of a prescribed pabulum, usually tested by a written examination. To be able to reproduce the words of others, or to shuffle mathematical symbols rapidly, may be creditable, but it is not to be compared with the power of originating ideas or devising new solutions to problems. A student may possess many examination certificates and yet be only a kind of text-book gramophone. Unless he acquires also the desire to see and do things independently he knows nothing of the scientific spirit which asks for new knowledge gained by individual inquiry.

The senior wrangler at Cambridge has often been an inferior man, from the point of view of productive mathematical science, to candidates lower on the list, because the examination tested merely the power of writing out the solutions of known classes of problems quickly and precisely. When Lord Kelvin was a student at Cambridge he produced several original papers in the higher branches of mathematics, yet he was beaten in the final examination and was placed second wrangler. The examiners themselves knew his great mathematical abilities, but the examination was a test of memory rather than of originality. Speaking of Kelvin (then named William Thomson), one of the examiners remarked to another, "You and I are just about fit to mend his pens." His genius was recognised, but the examination did not provide a way of showing it.

To be able to observe details and distinguish minute resemblances and differences are attributes of every scientific observer. In 1781 Sir William Herschel was "searching the skies" when he noticed that one star "appeared visibly larger than the rest." He came to the conclusion, after making several observations, that this object was not a star but a comet. Further studies of the body and its movements proved it to be a new planet—the first to be discovered in historic time. The other planets, Mercury, Venus, Mars, Jupiter and Saturn have been known back to the earliest days of the human race of which written records exist; and the discovery of this new planet, to which the name of Uranus was given, revolving round the sun with the rest, but previously unrecognized, aroused great interest. Other astronomers had examined at various times the parts of the sky occupied by Uranus, but they did not notice any difference of appearance between it and an ordinary star. By overlooking nothing in his field of view, Herschel became the discoverer of a world which proved to be nearly fifty times larger than the globe on which we live.

Herschel scrutinised everything; and this all-seeing eye, combined with sagacity of interpretation, is characteristic of all great observers. Of Charles Darwin it is recorded:

He wished to learn as much as possible from an experiment, so that he did not confine himself to observing the single point to which the experiment was directed, and his power of seeing a number of other things was wonderful. There was one quality of mind which seemed to be of special and extreme advantage in leading him to make discoveries. It was the power of never letting exceptions pass unnoticed.

Writing to *Nature* of September 29, 1892, Lord Rayleigh said, "I am much puzzled by some recent results as to the density of nitrogen, and shall be obliged if any of your chemical readers can offer suggestions as to the cause. According to two methods of preparation I obtain quite distinct values." It appeared from Lord Rayleigh's observations that while nitrogen derived from the air weighed 2.3102 grammes under standard conditions in a certain globe, nitrogen obtained as a chemical product from other sources than the air weighed 2.2990 grammes under exactly the same conditions. These values do not, of course, represent two experiments only, but are averages of many weighings carried out with the greatest possible care and precision. The difference between the two values is 11 milligrammes, or one-half per cent.

Expressed in British weight, the difference which puzzled Lord Rayleigh was about one-sixth of a grain. Small as this difference was, it exceeded the possible errors of the experiments, and gave rise to the conclusions that the natural nitrogen from the air was different in character from nitrogen manufactured from chemical substances. Later investigations with Sir William Ramsay led to the discovery of a new gas— to which the name Argon was given—in air; and this gas, which is nearly half as dense again as nitrogen, caused the discrepancy noticed by Lord Rayleigh.

Accurate and minute measurement seems to the non-scientific imagination a less lofty and dignified work than looking for something new. Yet nearly all the grandest discoveries of science have been but the rewards of accurate measurement and patient, long-continued labour in the minute sifting of numerical results. *Lord Kelvin.*

After argon had been isolated from the atmosphere, many sources of nitrogen were examined to see if they also contained the gas mixed with argon or with argon compounds. In the furtherance of this research, Sir William Ramsay was led to experiment upon cleveite —a rare Norwegian mineral—which had been found to give off, when boiled with weak oil of vitriol, two per cent. of a gas supposed to be nitrogen. The question to be decided was "Did this gas contain any argon, either free or combined?"; and the experiments showed that there was only a mere trace of nitrogen in it. To determine readily the character of the remainder, some of it was sealed up in a glass tube, through which an electric discharge was passed—this being the usual method of making a gas luminous, so that the quality of its light can be observed by means of the spectroscope.

The light from the luminous gas from cleveite passed into this marvellous instrument of analysis, and was sifted into its component parts by the glass prism. When the bright lines into which it was resolved were observed, they were found to comprise a number of prominent rays of which the origin was not known; in other words, the gas which had been believed to be nitrogen was something quite different. One of these rays was especially brilliant; and it was identified as a line due to helium—an element only observed previously in analyses of light from the sun.

During the total eclipse of the sun in 1868, the spectroscope showed that the red flames or solar prominences visible here and there around the sun's edge, when the dark body of the moon had cut off the dazzling light of the sun's visible surface, consisted of luminous gases, chief among which was hydrogen. Shortly afterwards Sir Norman Lockyer devised a method of observing solar prominences at any time when the sun is shining; and he then found that in addition to hydrogen, the light of these tremendous flames commonly exhibited in the spectroscope a line or ray which could not then be matched with light from any terrestrial substance. The enigmatical light appeared to be the exclusive possession of bodies at the intense temperature of the sun; and for this reason Sir Norman Lockyer gave to the substance emitting it the name helium —the element of the sun. It was not until twenty-six years later that helium was isolated by Sir William Ramsay; so that we have the remarkable fact of an element being actually discovered on the sun long before it was found on the earth.

Helium is now known to occur in many minerals, and fairly large quantities of the gas are brought annually to the earth's surface dissolved in the waters of deep-seated mineral springs, like those at Bath, being produced in all probability by the disintegration of that wonderful element—radium. The minute differences between the weights of atmospheric and chemical nitrogen observed by Lord Rayleigh in 1892 are thus seen to be connected, link by link, with the marvellous properties of radioactive minerals.

The diligence and persistence shown by men of science in the pursuit of knowledge are as remarkable as acuteness of vision and quickness of understanding. When Herschel was constructing the great mirror for his telescope, he had to do all his polishing by hand, and he found when once the final stage had begun, it was necessary that it should never stop even for a moment. His sister, Caroline, relates how she was kept busy in attending on her brother when polishing: "Since by way of keeping him alive I was constantly obliged to feed him by putting the victuals by bits into his mouth. This was once the case, when, in order to finish a 7 ft. mirror, he had not taken his hand from it for sixteen hours together.

Herschel undertook the stupendous task of surveying with his telescope the whole of the heavens visible from his observatory. With his instrument the field of view visible at one setting was about one-quarter the apparent size of the full moon, and Herschel had to observe more than 300,000 of such fields in order to make his census of the stars in a hemisphere of space. The method of observation is described by Von Magellen in a letter to Bode, from which the following are extracts:

He has his 20 ft. Newtonian telescope in the open air. It is moved by an assistant who stands below it; near the instrument is a clock. In the room near it sits Herschel's sister, and she has Flamsteed's Atlas open before her. As he gives her the word, she writes down the declination and right ascension. In this way Herschel examines the whole sky; he is sure that after four or five years (from 1788) he will have passed in review every object above our horizon. Each sweep covers 2 deg. 15 min. in declination, and he lets each star pass at least three times through the field of the telescope, so that it is impossible that anything can escape him. Herschel observes the whole night through; for some years he has observed every hour when the weather is clear, and this always in the open air.

Another astronomer whose diligence in observation was astonishing was S. H. Schwabe, a native of Dessau, who began to observe the sun in 1826, with the idea that the labour "might be rewarded by the discovery of a planet interior to Mercury," and was led to inquire into the rotation of the sun as indicated by the spots which appear from time to time. Each spot was noted and numbered in the order of its appearance, and when this system of registration had been carried on to the end of 1843, Schwabe modestly remarked that the number of spots visible upon the sun varied periodically, waxing

and waning in what seemed to him to be a period of
about ten years. But the subject attracted little attention, and it was not until 1851 that astronomers realised
its importance. In 1857 the gold medal of the Royal
Astronomical Society was presented to the indefatigable observer of Dessau.

"Twelve years," remarked the President of the Society in
his address, "he spent to satisfy himself, six more years to
satisfy, and still thirteen more to convince mankind. For
thirty years never has the sun exhibited his disc above the
horizon of Dessau without being confronted by Schwabe's im-
perturbable telescope, and that appears to have happened on an
average about 300 days a year. So, supposing that he observed
but once a day, he has made 9,000 observations, in the course
of which he discovered about 4,700 groups. This is, I believe,
an instance of devoted persistence (if the word were not equivocal, I should say pertinacity) unsurpassed in the annals of
astronomy. The energy of one man has revealed a phenomenon
that has eluded even the suspicion of astronomers for 200
years! . . . I can conceive few more unpromising subjects
from which to extract a definite result than were the solar
spots when Schwabe first attacked them."

Everyone can add something to knowledge if he will
make use of the opportunities richly offered by Nature.
He is a bad workman who grumbles at his tools, and the
student of science who neglects research because he
does not possess apparatus ready-made and varnished
by the instrument-maker, lacks the spirit of the investigator. Test the efficiency of the things at your disposal is good advice; for the knowledge and experience
gained by direct communion with Nature, even through
the roughest apparatus, is a very valuable educational
training. Tradition says that a foreign savant, who
had heard of the fame of Dr. Wollaston, the great
chemist and physicist who was President of the Royal
Society in 1820, called upon him one day and asked to

see his laboratory. "Certainly," said Wollaston, and rang the bell. "John," he said to the attendant who entered, "bring up my laboratory." Whereupon John went out and returned in a few moments with all Wollaston's apparatus on a tea-tray.

Prof. E. C. Pickering, director of the Harvard College Observatory, says that people used to ask if the Observatory possessed the largest telescope in the world. He would answer, "No, but we have the smallest that is doing useful work." The instrument to which he referred was constructed for measuring the light of the bright stars; and its object-glass was only two inches in diameter. With this, during the years 1880-1882, a hundred thousand measures were made of four thousand stars, mainly visible to the naked eye. Similar instruments have since been constructed with larger lenses capable of bringing fainter stars into view, but throughout the work for which Harvard College Observatory is famous in the astronomical world, the principle has been to obtain the maximum efficiency from the instruments available.

This plan of making the best use of whatever is at hand must always be followed if scientific work is to be done. While the dreamer sighs for opportunities, the inquirer works with things as he finds them. Difficulties to the man of science engaged in research are only problems to be solved; they may hinder progress but never prevent it entirely. "The way I get over a difficulty," remarked an Irishman, "is to go round it"; and that represents the frame of mind by which advance is made in every branch of human activity.

For certain scientific purposes "gratings" are required on which about a hundred thousand parallel lines have to be ruled within the width of an inch. All the parts of the machine by which a surface as hard as steel has thus traced upon it, by means of a diamond, a furrow several miles long, have to be made with extreme accuracy. A screw to rule a "grating" six inches wide required two years or more to make; and almost ten years were occupied in making one to rule a "grating" fifteen inches wide. From beginning to end the process of producing a perfect optical grating is beset with difficulties, and only an indomitable spirit can overcome them. Nothing must be left to chance; and the slightest disregard of a possible disturbing influence during the grinding of the screw or the ruling of the grating means that months or years of work will be completely wasted.

Prof. A. A. Michelson, who devoted many years to the perfection of a machine for producing accurate optical gratings, has compared it to an antagonist who was always ready to take advantage of a mistake, yet always played fair.

One comes to regard the machine as having a personality— I had almost said a feminine personality—requiring humouring, coaxing, cajoling, even threatening! But finally one realises that the personality is that of an alert and skilful player in an intricate but fascinating game who will take immediate advantage of the mistakes of his opponent, who "springs" the most disconcerting surprises, who never leaves any result to chance, but who nevertheless plays fair, in strict accordance with the rules of the game. These rules he knows, and makes no allowance if you do not. When *you* learn them, and play accordingly, the game progresses as it should. *Prof. A. A. Michelson.*

In order to test certain conclusions he had reached as to the effect of the earth's atmosphere in absorbing particular rays of sunlight, a French astronomer, Dr. Jules Janssen, wished to make observations at the summits of high mountains, where the layer of air interposed between him and the sun would be less than at lower levels. He was lame, but that did not prevent him from attaining his object; he first ascended the Faulhorn, then the Pic du Midi, and afterwards undertook several ascents of Mont Blanc. His lameness made mountain climbing particularly difficult, and in order to reach the summit of Mont Blanc he had to be carried either on a litter or on a sledge. He not only achieved his original purpose, but created the observatory which now stands upon the snow of the very top of this famous peak of the Alps. The observatory is a monument to his energy and tenacity of purpose. Referring to the realisation of the project, he once said, "I have always thought that there are very few difficulties which cannot be surmounted by a will strong enough or by study sufficiently profound."

When Newton was actively engaged in completing one of his important works, a lighted candle which he left in his room burned down, setting fire to papers which represented the results of much labour, and destroyed them. The story of the fire having been caused by a little dog called "Diamond" upsetting the candle, and that the papers related to the famous *Principia,* is shown by Brewster to be fabulous. The fire did, however, destroy twenty years' work upon light and colour, which Newton had almost brought to a conclusion, and it was said at the time by a student at Cambridge, where Newton was a Fellow of Trinity College, "everyone thought he would have run mad, when he had seen what was done; he was so troubled thereat that he was not himself for a month after." All that Newton himself said of the loss thus caused, when asked about it by a friend, was that he was obliged to work the calculations all over again. To have to reconstruct an intricate work from the very beginning was sufficient to appal the strongest mind, but he set about the task and accomplished it.

The man who has the spirit of science in him is ever ready to sacrifice personal comfort or convenience to it. It is told of Dr. Robert Grant, who was professor of zoology in University College, London, and devoted to his subject, that he spent eight or ten hours of a sleety day in February wading in the shallows of the Firth of Forth, in order to secure some specimens of a certain small aquatic creature which can best be studied in a living state, as its beautiful and varied colours disappear when the animal is dead and immersed in spirit. When showing to his class the specimens he had obtained he said: "I had no companion, I had nothing to eat or drink, I was wet through, my hands were half frozen, and I was chilled to the marrow; but, gentlemen, I was amply rewarded; I became the happy possessor of no less than three of these beautiful little creatures, these Dorises," and he held up a phial containing three scarcely visible little bladder-like animals.

If there is one branch of science more than another in which the infinite patience of genius is required, it is that of the study of insects; not of insects pinned in boxes or arranged in cabinets, but of the living creatures, with the view of discovering something of their life-history or of understanding a type of mental life on lines different from ours. It is much more exciting to catch insects and to kill them with cyanide or chloroform, so as to convert them into specimens for a collection, than it is to watch their individual characteristics as living things, unravel the complicated thread of changes they undergo, and observe their domestic economy. On this account there are many insect-hunters and collectors, but few who have an intimate acquaintance with the habits of insects in the life.

One such open-eyed naturalist was Réaumur, born at La Rochelle in 1683, and as diligent and accurate an observer as ever lived. Réaumur's *History of Insects* occupies six large volumes, and though issued so long ago as between 1734 and 1742 they are still a rich mine of information upon all aspects of insect-life observable with the naked eye or a simple lens. Referring to his accounts of the change from a caterpillar into a chrysalis, and of the chrysalis into a moth, Prof. L. C. Miall says: "These luminous descriptions are now reproduced with cruel abridgment in all popular works which treat of insect-transformations . . . The only important additions which naturalists have made to Réaumur's account of the transformations of Lepidoptera relate to the internal changes, and these demand a minute acquaintance with insect anatomy."

The geometrical or mechanical properties of Nature are far more easily defined with precision than are any of the processes of organic life. Five hundred years before the commencement of the Christian era, Pythagoras observed that the three angles of every plane triangle together make up two right-angles; and this conclusion stands now as it did then. Two and a half centuries later Archimedes proved that an object immersed in a fluid is buoyed up with a force equal to the weight of the fluid displaced; and this principle admits of no alteration whether it is applied to the flotation of a ship in water or the buoyancy of a balloon in air. Hipparchus, the founder of astronomical science, who lived in the second century B.C., determined the periods of revolutions of the planets with remarkable accuracy, and his values differ very slightly from those accepted at the present day, but

it was not until eighteen hundred years later that
Newton discovered the law of gravitation by which the
movements of these and other bodies in the solar system are governed.

An accurate observation remains unaltered throughout the ages. Its scientific value is determined by its
truth to Nature; and the more complete the testimony,
the less room is there for elaboration by investigators
in succeeding generations. Whatever precise knowledge exists of natural things and operations has been
obtained by patient labour. It is so much easier to
accept traditional views upon the structure, habits and
functions of the various forms of life around us than
it is to inquire minutely into them by personal observation that mistaken ideas often pass currency for
hundreds of years before they are detected. Aristotle in his natural history makes a king-bee the
governor of a hive, and this view is reflected in Shakespeare's lines:

> For so work the honey-bees,
> Creatures that by a rule in nature teach
> The act of order to a peopled kingdom,
> They have a king and officers of sorts;
> *King Henry V.* i. ii.

It was a country parson, Charles Butler, who, in the
early years of the seventeenth century, took the trouble
to study bees themselves instead of reading books
about them; and he found that the queen-bee was the
dominant factor in the hive community. Milton possibly knew of Butler's work when he wrote in *Paradise Lost*, published half a century later, of "The
female bee, that feeds her husband drone Deliciously,
and builds her waxen cells With honey stored."

J. J. Swammerdam, son of an apothecary at Amsterdam, carried the investigation of the hive-bee much further than any naturalist before him, though he did not exhaust it. He proved definitely that the so-called "king of the bees" was really a queen and the only effective female in a hive. The chief part of his work was done in 1673, when the dykes were cut to save Amsterdam from the French invasion, so that the hives in Holland were ruined, and scarcely any queens could be procured. Swammerdam spent many months upon the investigation of bees, and took scrupulous pains in examining their structure and habits. Referring to his *Biblia Naturæ,* in which the hive-bee is described, Prof. Miall says:

The life-history, the anatomy of the male, female and neuter bees in every stage, and the whole economy of the hive, are carefully described . . . The engraved figures would do credit to the most skilful anatomists of any age. This, the first extensive and truly scientific memoir on the hive and its inhabitants, carries the exploration a long way at a single bound, and biology can hardly produce a second example of a research so comprehensive and disfigured by so few faults.

Réaumur extended the knowledge of the honey-bee still further by studies of the living insect in observation hives; Schirach, in 1771, proved that worker-bees are imperfect females, and the history of the wedding-flight was first correctly described by Huber in 1814. Finally, Dzierzon, in the middle of the nineteenth century, showed that the eggs laid by unwedded queens give birth to drones; that the fertilisation of the queen takes place within a few days of her quitting her cell, and lasts for life; and that female bees (queens and workers) proceed only from eggs fertilised by drones. Queens and workers are respectively produced from female bees by being fed on different foods while in their larval state. The future queen is fed on "chyle food" by the nurses until it assumes the chrysalis change, from which it emerges a perfect female. The future worker is weaned upon the fourth day, and fed henceforth on honey and digested pollen, with the result that it remains an undeveloped female.

This wonderful history of the hive-bee represents the results of work done by naturalists of many countries and at different times. There have been hundreds of practical bee keepers from ancient to modern times, but they have contributed almost nothing to this knowledge of the structure and functions of the complicated social community of a hive; and for the actual fact we have to go to Butler, Bonnet, Swammerdam, Réaumur, Huber, Dzierzon, and other inquiring naturalists whose names are unfamiliar not only to general readers but also to a large part of the scientific world.

Three hundred years ago little was known of the transformation which insects undergo from the egg to the fly emerging from the larval skin. Harvey, the discoverer of the circulation of the blood, was so far mistaken as to teach that insects were generated by chance, and that the change from a pupa to the winged form was a transmutation like that of a base metal into gold, or the flying nymph of Ovid into a laurel tree. He regarded the pupa as an egg; and even now the pupa of ants are popularly called ants' "eggs." Swammerdam persistenly pointed out the errors of this belief, and by his studies disposed of it completely. He proved that all the parts of an insect are beneath the larval skin long before the insect emerges; that, in fact, the larva or pupa is not transmuted into a butterfly but is the butterfly itself in another form.

By his laborious studies in the latter half of the

seventeenth century, Swammerdam worked out the complete transformation of insects, and recognised the chief types of development. For his facts he went direct to Nature, and he was rarely deceived by her. Upon most of the subjects studied by him, philosophers and other schoolmen had been content to pass on fantastic ideas without inquiry into their veracity. Aristotle, Vergil, Pliny and other early writers, all agreed that certain bees, which may sometimes be seen carrying small stones as they fly, do so to prevent being blown out of their course in windy weather. The conclusion was childish, but it was sufficient for writers who had not watched the habits of this insect —the mason-bee. When actual observation was made by Swammerdam, nearly two thousand years later, he found that the stones were used by the bee to strengthen its hive.

Aphids, or plant-lice, are familiar to every gardener, yet how few know anything of their life-history or of the patient work of investigators who revealed it. When, toward the end of the seventeenth century, the ever-curious naturalist, Antony Van Leeuwenhoek, began to study the insects, he sought for their eggs, but without success. Later, he made the surprising discovery that aphids brought forth their young alive, and upon opening an aphis only a fortnight old, he found no fewer than sixty young ones in it. Réaumur extended Leeuwenhoek's observations, and showed that both the winged and wingless aphids could produce living young. He tried to isolate aphids from birth to see if they would still continue to increase their kind, but was prevented by accidents from concluding his observations. When, therefore, Charles Bonnet (1720-1793) asked him to suggest a subject of investigation, the unfinished experiment was proposed as one likely to lead to interesting results. Bonnet was only twenty years of age when he undertook this task.

He filled a flower-pot with earth, and plunged it into a phial of water, intended to supply the food-plant. A new-born aphis, whose birth had been observed, was placed on the plant, and all was covered up by a bell-jar, which was pressed into the earth, so as to exclude other insects. An aphis found upon the spindle-tree was selected for the first trial, which began on May 20, 1740. Bonnet kept an exact diary of his observations, which were made hourly or oftener during the day; a good lens was continually employed. The aphis changed its skin four times, and came to maturity on June 1, when the first young one was born. By June 21, the unfertilised female had produced 95 aphids, all born alive. *Prof. L. C. Miall.*

A similar result was obtained the next year, when two new-born aphids, isolated in the same way, produced respectively 90 and 49 young. Five successive generations of aphids were then bred without the participation of a male insect, and the result, which was contrary to all that was then known of reproduction in nature, was received with lively interest not unmixed with incredulity. The life-history of these insects differs indeed from all pre-conceived ideas. Bonnet's observations established it to be as follows: both winged and wingless aphids produce young alive while food is plentiful, but as the winter approaches this mode of reproduction ceases; small winged males then appear, and the females lay fertilised eggs from which young aphids emerge in the following spring. Aphids are thus born without the participation of the male insect during mild weather, and their race is carried on from one year to another by the eggs laid by fertile females near the end of the season.

The discovery of this intricate course of events is far more wonderful than the achievement of any Arsène Lupin or Sherlock Holmes of fiction. There

are winged and wingless females both producing live
young without any eggs or the intervention of the
male, winged insects which produce no young, and
eggs from which young emerge; and the problem was
to find the clue which connected these various threads
into a skein of evidence. Leeuwenhoek, Réaumur and
Bonnet were the chief detectives in this case, and their
work, though unknown to the world at large, claims
the admiration of all who will consider it.

The mantle of the French naturalist, Réaumur, fell
upon J. H. Fabre, and in these two faithful observers
France can claim possession of the greatest students
of insect-life the world has ever seen. Fabre, born in
poverty and earning for himself and family a salary of
£64 a year as a schoolmaster, "less," as he says,
"than a groom in a well-to-do household," produced
works on the habits of insects which stand by themselves, whether we consider them as science or literature. So long ago as 1871, Darwin, in his *Descent of
Man,* referred to Fabre as "that inimitable observer,"
and Maurice Maeterlinck has happily named him "The
Insects' Homer." In his *Souvenirs Entomologiques,*
Fabre recorded in ten volumes the results of fifty years
of observation, study and experiment on living insects
of the South of France.

In 1843, when eighteen years of age, Fabre, with his
teacher's certificate, was appointed to take charge of
a primary school at Carpentras, at a salary of £28 a
year. He there met for the first time the black mason-
bee which makes nests of clay on pebbles or a wall and
fills them with honey. Réaumur dedicated one of his
studies to this interesting insect, but Fabre did not
then know of it. He spent a month's salary in the
purchase of a standard work on insects, and thus provided food for the mind at the expense of food for the

body. "That which I bestowed on the one I re-
trenched from the other—a balance of accouuts to
which whoever takes science for a livelihood must
needs resign himself." Fabre devoured the book, and
the delight he derived from it was a compensation for
the parsimony he had to exercise to obtain it. "There
I learned," he says, "the name of my black bee, and
there I read for the first time details of the habits of
insects, and found, with what seemed to my eyes an
aureole round them, the venerated names of Réaumur, Huber, Léon Dufour; and while I turned the
pages for the hundredth time, a voice whispered vague-
ly, 'Thou too shalt be a historian of animals.' "

The entomological studies thus started, and further
excited by reading a pamphlet by Dufour upon the
habits of a wasp-like insect, a species of Cerceris,
which feeds its progeny upon certain kinds of beetles,
were continued by Fabre with unabated enthusiasm
and conspicuous success. With supreme contempt for
riches and remarkable indifference to worldly honours,
in his lifetime he built up a more solid and durable
monument than was ever made by hands. His stories
of insects are full of dramatic situations and romantic
interest.

As a naturalist he sacrificed everything to his work
and gained a knowledge of insect life unequalled by
any other observer; as a writer he possessed a style
that enabled him to disclose convincingly to others the
scenes enacted before his eyes and commanded the
admiration of masters of literature. In an age of
haste and money-making, when few will devote time
to studies which offer little prospect of direct or indirect reward, Fabre quietly continued his observations of Nature's ways with the sole object of becoming intimately acquainted with them. So long as the

world shall last his works will be an inspiration to naturalists, and an exemplar of what can be accomplished by the observer, however limited his worldly means may be, who seeks for knowledge in the spirit of humility and truth.

Most people are now familiar with fossil shells and similar remains found imbedded in many rocks. Such objects were known in very early times, and some philosophers—notably Leonardo da Vinci and Bernard Palissy—realised that they were the relics of life that once existed at the places where the fossils were found. It was generally believed, however, that marine shells found inland were deposited there by the Deluge; and that strange animal remains were "freaks of Nature" unworthy of serious study. An English land-surveyor, William Smith, was the first to show, toward the end of the eighteenth century, that fossils provide the key by which the relative ages of the beds of rock which make up the earth's crust can be determined.

Before Smith commenced his work, fossils were supposed to be scattered in haphazard fashion in the rocks. As the result of many years spent in examining rocks in all parts of the country, and collecting the fossils from them, he was able to conclude that each stratum has its own particular fossil population, and that the strata lie upon one another in a regular order. Fossils were thus shown to be the trade-marks of the rock-layers in which they occur. This conclusion enabled a natural system of classification of strata to be introduced, and was the foundation of scientific geology.

Rocks can be classified according to their appearance or structure, but these features give no information as to the period of the earth's history at which the rocks were formed. The only trustworthy test of geological age is that afforded by fossil remains, and this principle, established by William Smith, is now used by all geologists as a guide to the order in which deposits were laid down in any part of the earth. The oldest rocks in Great Britain are those in the west; and as we pass eastward, we traverse beds of rock formed in successive epochs of the earth's history until we come to the relatively recent formations of Essex and other parts of the east coast. Relics of elementary forms of life are found in the older rocks and are succeeded in regular order by remains of fishes, amphibians, reptiles, birds and mammals, until at last deposits are reached containing human remains and evidence of man's handiwork.

Though the biological significance of this development of life from the simple coral to the complex structure of man was not realised by Smith, it was he who gave the first complete proof that there was a regular succession of forms of life in the beds of the earth's crust. "To effect his object," said Sir Andrew Ramsay, "Smith traced the English formations from end to end of the country with unwearied devotion, and at length, in 1815, produced his great geological map of England. He struggled long, almost unrecognised in his labours, but when they were well-nigh at an end, men began by degrees to realise that a master was among them."

The insight which a naturalist can acquire into the forms of life of the past, by studies of the records of the rocks, is well illustrated by an episode in the life of Louis Agassiz. At a meeting of geologists in England, Agassiz was once asked what kind of fish would be found in fossil form in a particular stratum of the earth's crust. He thought for a moment and then made a sketch of the fish which he believed would live at the time this geological stratum was formed. He did not understand the cheer with which his drawing was received by the company, until someone brought forward an actual fossil specimen which had just been found and showed that it agreed perfectly with the sketch which Agassiz had created from his own knowledge of what characteristics a fish belonging to a particular stratum ought to possess.

Facts known to everyone often have to wait hundreds of years before their true significance is understood. A remarkable instance of this is the relation of the flower of a plant to the fruit which follows it. In very early days men must have noticed that when the blossom on a tree or bush was destroyed no fruit could be expected from it. First the flower, then the fruit, has been a matter of common knowledge from time immemorial, yet the causal relationship between the two stages was not established until the seventeenth century. Herodotus, in the middle of the fifth century B.C., had observed that in Assyria the female tree of the date-palm was made fertile by dusting it with the branches of the male, but he did not pursue his inquiries any further. Other Greek philosophers who followed him taught that fertilisation is unnecessary, that both male and female date-palms bear fruit, and held like beliefs which a single experiment would have shown to be erroneous. So it was with other plants; nothing was accurately known of the functions of the various parts of the flower concerned in the production of the fruit, and no serious attempt had been made to secure precise knowledge.

If a common apple blossom be examined, slender filaments or stamens will be seen bearing golden pollen on the anthers at their tops. This pollen produces the fertilising element of the plant, and without it no fruit can be formed. It is carried to the sticky stigmas of other apple blossoms by wind or insects, and then starts changes which result in fruit and seed. The anthers are, in fact, the male organs of flowering plants, and the dust they shed is the quickening influence by which a new generation is produced. In some plants such, for example, as the date-palm, mulberry-tree, and willow, the male and female organs are borne on different trees, but in most cases the flower contains both stamens bearing the pollen on their anthers, and stigmas to which the pollen adheres.

No plant can ripen its fruit unless pollen is supplied to the female organs. The pollen may come from the male organs of the same flower, be borne by wind or insects from another flower of the same species, or be supplied artificially, but in any case it is essential to fertilisation. This was suspected long before anyone made the crucial experiment of isolating a female plant from the pollen of the male in order to test whether fruit bearing the seeds of another generation would then be produced.

Prof. L. C. Miall describes, in his *Early Naturalists*, the conclusive observations and experiments by which the doctrine of the sexuality of plants was established by Prof. R. J. Camerarius, professor of botany at Tübingen, toward the end of the seventeenth century. Experiments were first made with the Annual Mercury, in which the sexes are usually represented by different plants, one of which carries the fertilising stimulus while the other bears the fruit and seeds. Two female plants, when isolated, were found to produce only abortive or unfertile seeds; and, in like manner, when the parts of the flower of maize which receive pollen were cut away, the cobs which afterwards appeared were found to be devoid of seed.

By these and other experiments Camerarius converted into scientific truth the conjectures as to sexes of plants held by gardeners and botanists almost from the days of the Garden of Eden. Science had to wait, however, nearly one hundred and fifty years longer before the mechanism of fertilisation was completely analysed. It was Dr. Robert Brown who showed in the first half of the nineteenth century that when pollen grains reach the stigma of a plant they send out tubes which penetrate openings in the outer skin of rudimentary seeds and set up the changes that result in the formation of seeds or embryos.

It is to the credit of science that many notable advances have been made by men who have not been professionally occupied with scientific work, but have devoted their leisure hours to the study of Nature. Sir Joseph Prestwich was a man of this type. His knighthood at the age of eighty-three, a few months before his death, was a tardy recognition of scientific services of the highest value to the nation. For forty years Prestwich was a busy merchant in Mark Lane, London, yet during the years of his City career his contributions to geological knowledge were so many and important that almost every hour of his time out of business must have been occupied with them.

As a youth, Prestwich's inclinations were all for science, but when it became his duty to enter upon a City career he applied himself to business with all the conscientiousness and earnestness of his nature.

"Perhaps," says his biographer, "there are few endowed as he was who would have had the moral courage to resist the fascinations of science. At the outset he planned out his life, and resolved that there should be no interruption to his geological work. The hours at his disposal he allotted, as before, to the identification of fossils and to the analysis of minerals.

Time for that work, and for practical chemistry, as well as for his mathematics and reading, had to be found in the early morning before breakfast and after his return from the City at six or seven in the evening, when each hour had its appointed subject. . . . The youth seemed to have an intuitive consciousness that there was something for him to do, that he himself might aspire to demonstrate some truth in God's nature; and henceforward every hour he could call his own was set apart to train and gird himself for the task.''

This devotion to truth and knowledge remained with Prestwich to the end of his long life, and led to results of the highest value both to the nation and to science. He was the first to insist upon the importance of geological knowledge in dealing with questions of water-supply, and he became the leading authority upon this subject in England. Water-diviners suggest that some occult influence enables them to locate underground springs or water-courses; but without expressing any opinion upon their claims we can assert that geological conditions alone determine the presence or absence of underground water, and when these conditions are precisely known the geologist can state without hesitation what the possibility is of finding water.

A striking instance of the application of geological knowledge to the subject of water supply is given in Prestwich's *Life*. Having acquired a site for a house overlooking the valley of the Darent above the village of Shoreham, Kent, Prestwich engaged two well-diggers to sink a well 168 feet deep. The boring proceeded, but when a depth of 166 feet was reached, the well-diggers went to the city and sought an interview with their employer, whom they found at his desk. They explained that there was no sign of water, and that in their opinion, it was useless to bore to a greater depth. ''Go on,'' was the quiet rejoinder, ''you will come upon water to-morrow. You are within two feet

of it." Next day it proved as Prestwich had foretold. He knew the exact level of the springs in the
valley, and that water must be found when that depth
was reached.

Another direction in which Prestwich's work found
practical application was in connection with British
coalfields. When only twenty years of age, he produced a memoir on the coalfield of Coalbrookdale which
was a model of completeness. He spent his holidays
examining the surface geology of the district, and
descending pits to see the underground structure of
the coal seams, and the fossil plants they contained.
By minute and patient study he produced a geological
map covering an area of about a hundred square miles
on the scale of one inch to a mile; and it was so true
to detail that when the Geological Survey mapped the
same district later no very important differences were
found from this work done by a youth who was practically a City clerk when he accomplished it.

F. W. Bessel, renowned among astronomers for
epoch-making works in many departments of the astronomy of precision, was also a merchant's clerk at
Bremen when he calculated the orbit of the celebrated
comet of Halley. This youth of twenty, self-taught
and occupied with commercial pursuits, solved unaided
a problem of high order in mathematical astronomy.
He sent his work to H. W. M. Olbers, a physician at
Bremen, who for half a century devoted all his spare
hours to studies of the skies and the movements of
comets. Olbers received Bessel's work with delight,
and secured its publication. Two years later he induced Bessel to accept a post as chief assistant in
J. H. Schröter's observatory at Lilienthal.

It was not without a struggle, that Bessel resolved to exchange the desk for the telescope. His reputation with his

employers was of the highest; he had thoroughly mastered the details of the business, which his keen practical intelligence followed with lively interest; his years of apprenticeship were on the point of expiring, and an immediate and not unwelcome prospect of comparative affluence lay before him. The love of science, however, prevailed; he chose poverty and the stars, and went to Lilienthal with a salary of a hundred thalers yearly. Looking back over his life's work, Olbers long afterwards declared that the greatest service he had rendered to astronomy was that of having discerned, directed and promoted the genius of Bessel. *Miss A. M. Clerke.*

Many men have made immense fortunes, but few have had the ambition to devote their riches to the advancement of knowledge. Dr. Heinrich Schliemann was one of the few. Before he was ten years old, he had made up his mind that the mighty walls of Troy could not have disappeared, but must have been buried by the dust of ages; and that he would himself some day bring them to light. This object was before him in all his early struggles with poverty. Even when working in an office in Amsterdam for a salary of £32 a year, he spent half that sum on living and the other half on self-education, his dinner costing him two-pence, and a fire being an unknown luxury. Under these conditions, and with the Homeric story in his mind, he began the study of modern languages, and became master of seven or eight tongues besides his own, including ancient and modern Greek. By sheer business talent he rose from poverty to great wealth, and he used his fortune to carry out the purpose of his life.

In 1871 Schliemann began his career as an explorer by an attack on the hill of Hissarlik, near the mouth of the Dardanelles, where he expected to find the city of his dreams. For seventeen hundred years archaeologists had been in academic dispute as to the precise position of the city, but Schliemann sought for evidence by actual excavation. He was somewhat of a visionary, but he had sufficient knowledge and insight to know which sites to explore, and he passed all the earth from the site through a sieve, so that nothing of significance should be overlooked. Literary genius, it has been said, is erratic and incalculable, but genius works in science through clear discernment of means and by infinite pains. By these methods Schliemann was able to secure a splendid collection of antiquities, and to disclose a fortress which he believed to be the Pergamos of Troy. Later investigations by Dr. Dörpfeld have shown that the Troy of Homer's epic was a more extensive city than that identified by Schliemann, and that as many as nine different towns or villages existed at various times on or around the mound of Hissarlik; but it was Schliemann who began the accumulation of scientific evidence that enabled the site of the city to be determined.

In geographical exploration the spirit of adventure has, perhaps, been the stimulating influence more often than the desire to increase scientific knowledge, but whatever the aims, the results have been for the benefit of mankind. Columbus sails west into unknown seas and reaches the Bahamas; John and Sebastian Cabot land on North America and open a new world to Merchant Venturers; Vasco da Gama, by sailing round the Cape, reaches India and shows the door to the East; and Magellan's ship circumnavigates the globe, though the daring explorer did not live to complete the voyage. Of a somewhat different type of maritime explorer was Captain James Cook, whose energy and steadfastness of purpose, joined to his mastery of every detail of his profession, enabled him to carry through the journeys which elucidated the questions as

to the amount and extent of the lands in the Southern
Ocean, the answer to which had eluded many less competent and persevering explorers. Cook was the first
to take scientific preventative measures against scurvy
—the disease which had wrecked the hopes of many
intrepid seamen—and for his splendid work in this
direction he was elected a Fellow of the Royal Society
—a distinction attained by few geographical explorers.

In modern times the spirit of scientific exploration
is best exemplified in the work of Fridtjof Nansen.
In June, 1881, an American exploring ship called the
Jeanette foundered in the Arctic at a point north of
the New Siberian Islands. Three years later a number of articles which had belonged to the ship were
found on the south-west coast of Greenland, having
been carried from one side of the Arctic regions to the
other by drifting ice. From an examination of the
facts relating to this, and one or two similar instances
of a similar character, Dr. Nansen arrived at the conclusion, in 1891, that "a current flows at some point
between the pole and Franz Josef Land from the
Siberian Arctic Sea to the east coast of Greenland."
He determined, therefore, to organise an Arctic expedition upon the basis of his conclusion. A strong
ship was to be built on such principles as to enable
it to withstand the pressure of the ice, and was then
to be taken up to the Siberian Islands where the *Jeanette* foundered, and moored between suitable ice-floes
in the hope and conviction that she would be carried
to the other side of the North Pole.

The suggestion met with little encouragement from
geographers, but Dr. Nansen persisted in his plans,
and sailed from Norway in his famous vessel the *Fram,*
with a crew of twelve, in July, 1893. He disappeared
from the civilised world a few weeks later and was

not heard of again until June, 1896, when he was met
by Major F. G. Jackson on the ice to the south-south-
east of Cape Flora.   Nansen and his companion, Lieut.
Johansen, had left the *Fram* in March, 1895, in latitude 84° N., with the object of exploring the sea to the
north, to reach the highest latitude possible, and then
go to Spitsbergen *via* Franz Josef Land.   These two
hardy men spent fifteen months together amid the
Arctic ice, and reached a point in lat. 86° 14′ before
they returned and were met by members of the Jack-
son-Harmsworth expedition.   The *Fram* drifted a
little northwards after they left it, and remained in
the ice until August, 1896, when she was steered
through the last ice-floes out into open water.   Shortly
after Nansen reached Norway, the *Fram* touched at
Spitsbergen, and a week later the leader and his men
met again.

Since Nansen's journey the North Pole has been
reached by Rear-Admiral Peary, but the attainment
of this geographical point though it appeals to popular sentiment, is not of such scientific interest as
Nansen's voyage in which inferences derived from
observations were proved to be correct.

The pursuit of knowledge in Polar regions has cost
many lives, and the dangers of the ice have enriched
heroic literature with the stories of the efforts of many
great men, "The famous ones of old."

How of the field's fortunes?   That concerned our Leader!
Led, we struck our stroke, nor cared for doings left and right:
Each as on his sole head, failer or succeeder,
Lay the blame or lit the praise: no care for cowards: fight!
                                        Robert Browning.

Among the names of explorers who lost their lives
in endeavouring to increase our knowledge of Arctic

regions that of Sir John Franklin is most prominent, partly on account of his noble character and heroic death.[1] In 1845 Sir John Franklin sailed in the *Erebus* and *Terror,* with a party of 129 men, for the purpose of completing a survey of the Arctic coast of Canada, upon which he had been engaged previously. The expedition vanished from the world's ken almost at once, and as nothing had been heard of it three years later a search was begun.   In 1859, at Point Victory, on the north-west coast of King William Land, the chief relic of the Franklin expedition was found in the form of a record of successful exploration up to May 28, 1847. But round the margin of the paper containing this record was a second message in a different handwriting:

April 25th, 1848: the ships were deserted on April 22nd, having been in the ice since September 12th, 1846. Sir John Franklin died June 11th, 1847, and the total loss to this date has been nine officers and fifteen men. The rest (105 in number) landed here and start to-morrow for the Great Fish River.

The ships had been provisioned for a period ending July, 1848, and in April of that year the retreat by land was begun. Not a soul survived. Franklin had succeeded in his object, the North-West Passage had been discovered; but the ice had taken its toll. Not until 1906 did any ship traverse the North-West Passage, but in that year the *Gjoa,* under Roald Amundsen, reached the haven of San Francisco, having left Christiania in May, 1903.

In the interests of scientific investigation it was arranged that from August, 1882, simultaneous observations should be taken in a series of international circumpolar stations. The United States expedition

[1] The toll of the ice here counted is chiefly that of an article by B. C. W. in *The School World* for March, 1913.

to Lady Franklin Bay was under the command of Lieutenant A. W. Greely, who established his camp in that high latitude, and made many arduous sledge journeys. On account, however, of the failure of the relief ships to reach him after his work had been accomplished, he had to depend entirely upon his own efforts in returning homewards. In 1884 the few men left were only just alive when they heard the whistle of a steamer. Two men struggled out from the camp, and the search party, entering the cove by boat, saw one of them make a signal and approach; twice he fell. When the rescuers reached Greely's tent they cried, "Greely, is that you?" In a faint, broken, hesitating voice came the answer, "Yes—yes—seven of us left—here we are—dying—like men. Did what I came to do—beat the best record."

The map of Greenland contains two names along its northern shores—Peary Land and Mylius Erichsen Land. Rear-Admiral R. E. Peary attained the North Pole as a crowning result of twenty-three years' devotion to Arctic exploration; but one of his most remarkable and hazardous journeys is commemorated in the name *Peary Land*. He explored the north-west coasts of Greenland, and crossed the interior in its neighbourhood. This success left only the north-east coast unexplored, and in 1906-8 a Danish expedition, under the leadership of Erichsen, proceeded thither for the purpose of scientific exploration. Erichsen and two companions on a sledge journey were confined during the summer of 1908 to a small territory near Denmark Fiord. By the middle of the summer their food was exhausted, and they had no footgear. They attempted to reach a depot; daily they crawled out of dilapidated sleeping bags and pushed forwards barefooted over the inland ice in the hope of leaving their records where

their comrades could find them.   Brönland was the last
survivor; he crawled the last few miles to the depot,
ate some of the food there, wrote his last report,
wrapped himself in his fur and died.   His report con-
cludes:

I perished in 79° N. lat., under the hardships of the return
journey over the inland ice in November. I reached this place
under the waning moon, and cannot go on because of my
frozen feet and the darkness. The bodies of the others are
in the middle of the fiord. Hagen died on November 15th,
Mylius Erichsen some ten days later.

The records of the scientific work of these three
heroes were retrieved by an expedition under the leadership of Einar Mikkelsen, which reached Greenland
in 1909.   They were found in a cairn near Erichsen's
summer camp.

But the records of polar exploration contain no more
inspiring story than that of the way in which Captain
Scott and his companions of the British Antarctic
Expedition met their death in returning from the
South Pole early in 1912.   Captain Scott, Dr. Wilson,
Capt. Oates, Lieut. Bowers and Petty Officer Evans,
after pulling their sledges alone for 147 miles, reached
the Pole on Jan. 18th, 1912.   When they began the
return march, the season was unduly advanced, and
progress delayed by the sickness and subsequent death
of Evans.   Yet, despite this and exceptionally severe
weather and difficulties of travel, they persisted in
carrying their collection of specimens, though this
must have increased their labours.   Captain Oates
suffered severely from frostbite, and his companions
delayed their progress to help him.   Capt. Scott wrote:

He was a brave soul. He slept through the night, hoping
not to wake, but he awoke in the morning. It was blowing a
blizzard. Oates said, ''I am just going outside and I may

be some time." He went into the blizzard, and we have not seen him since.

Oates felt death upon him, and knowing he held his companions back, went from them to meet it. No more appropriate epitaph was ever written than "Hereabouts lies a very gallant gentleman," marked upon a post near where Oates walked to his death amid the Antarctic snows.

On March 21st, 1912, Capt. Scott, Dr. Wilson and Lieut. Bowers were forced, on account of a blizzard, to camp in latitude 79° 40′ S., eleven miles from a depot where there was at least a ton of stores. They had food for two days and fuel for one hot meal. The blizzard prevented them from leaving their tent, and when they had been imprisoned for four days, Capt. Scott wrote his last message and his final appeal on behalf of those who are left behind. He wrote:

We took risks—we know we took them. Things have come out against us, and therefore we have no cause for complaint, but bow to the will of Providence, determined still to do our best to the last.

The message signed, Capt. Scott placed it with his diary between his head and the tent-pole, and, leaning against the pole, met the end. The remains of Capt. Scott and his two companions were not found until the following November, when the heroes were reverently laid to rest. But though they have entered into their long sleep, from the solitude of the polar waste of snow and ice where they lie their spirits have risen triumphant to testify to the world the greatness of human endeavour and the glory of self-sacrifice for the purpose of increasing knowledge.

CHAPTER V

BELIEF AND EVIDENCE

We see only what we know. Goethe.

Science is, I believe, nothing but trained and organised common sense. Huxley.

Let us first understand the facts, and then we may seek the cause. Aristotle.

The work of science is to substitute facts for appearances, and demonstrations for impressions. Ruskin.

And Reason now through number, time, and space
Darts the keen lustre of her serious eye;
And learns from facts compar'd the laws to trace
Whose long procession leads to Deity. J. Beattie.

I hope that my children, at least, if not I myself, will see the day, when ignorance of the primary laws and facts of science will be looked upon as a defect, only second to ignorance of the primary laws of religion and morality.
C. Kingsley.

THERE is a common impression that the conclusions arrived at by men of science are of the nature of beliefs, and have, therefore, no firmer basis than that of conviction. Nothing could be farther from the truth. From his earliest days the student of science is trained to ask for evidence before arriving at a judgment; and he should hesitate to pass an opinion upon a subject with which he is not familiar. Any beliefs he may hold as to natural phenomena belong to quite a different category from that of knowledge gained by the

92

critical examination of observed facts. No subject is too trivial for inquiry, and no relationship must be regarded as impossible from *a priori* considerations, but the scientific mill must have material to work upon before the value of the product can be estimated. It is permissible to doubt whether the grain is worth grinding, but not to deny it a trial; for without a test any belief may be held as to its quality. Whether you doubt or believe is of no consequence whatever in scientific things if you cannot give reason for the position you occupy. There must be facts and there must be thought about them before any statement of substantial value can be made as to natural objects and phenomena.

Popular impressions and beliefs relating to weather are often based upon casual observations, and have little foundation in fact. Yet every belief of this kind is worthy of examination, and if it has not been investigated no man of science is justified in asserting that it is untrue. But when such an inquiry has been made, and the evidence has failed to support popular opinion, we cannot do other than state that the case has not been proved. Two such examples may here be given; one as to alleged change of climate and the other as to a connection between the moon and the weather.

Many people believe that the British climate has undergone considerable changes in comparatively modern times. "The winters (or the summers) are not what they were when I was young," is a statement frequently made; but when meteorological records are examined, they show that the temperature, rain, snow, frost and like atmospheric phenomena are much the same at the present time as they were in the early days of the declining generation. Going back so far as trustworthy observations with meteorological instruments exist, no evidence can be found to justify the common belief that the climate of England has changed. When there were few instruments, or none, the tendency of writers or diarists of those days would be to pass ordinary weather conditions unnoticed, and to refer only to unusual experiences.

The diaries of Evelyn and Pepys provide faithful chronicles of noteworthy aspects of the weather during the latter half of the seventeenth century; and a careful examination of them has been made with the view of discovering whether any marked differences exist between the seasons then and now. Consider the winter season, for example. The instances of snow recorded by Evelyn and Pepys are surprisingly few, being only mentioned in thirteen winters in the period covered by the diaries (1648-1703), and only three of these falls appear to have been exceptional. At least eleven very mild or wet winters occurred in Evelyn's lifetime, and prolonged or severe frosts—including that of 1683-84, when coaches plied to and fro on the Thames—were experienced in about ten of the winters.

The conclusion arrived at, after considering all the information available, is that cold winters were not more frequent, or mild winters less so, in the latter half of the seventeenth century than they have been in the last fifty years. Spring, summer and autumn have also preserved much the same general characteristics, with occasional noteworthy variations. An inquiry into the facts, therefore, affords no ground for the belief that the seasons of our time are sensibly different from those of our proximate forefathers.

Belief in an old-fashioned Christmas weather, with snow six feet deep, and skating for weeks on end, is fostered by most writers and artists who describe and depict Christmas scenes. Snow is apparently as essential a part of every Christmas story or picture as the ghost or the haunted chamber, yet our own experience tells us that one is almost as rare as the other, and that the association of snow with that day is more a matter of imagination than of fact. If, however, we look further back, a reason may be found for colder weather at Christmas than that now usually experienced. On account of the change from the Julian to the Gregorian Calendar in 1752, Christmas now occurs eleven days earlier than it did. Old Christmas day, Jan. 7, marks the date upon which the festival was formerly celebrated; and there have been considerable falls of snow after Christmas which would have occurred at Christmas or before if the Julian Calendar had been still in use.

Tradition, and general impressions of elderly people, are, indeed, of little value in deciding whether any permanent change of climate has taken place. The only trustworthy test is provided by records of rainfall, temperature or other meteorological observations made systematically with suitable instruments. Such records go back for 150 years or so, and when they are examined critically they are found to give no decided indication of any progressive change, either for the better or worse. From an examination of old records, and of the long series of observations made at Greenwich, Sir John Moore was able to show to the British Association in 1908 that no appreciable change has taken place in the climate of the British Isles during the past six centuries. It is of no use to place a popular belief in such a change by the side of such a conclusion arrived at as the result of open-minded and careful inquiry. The responsibility of proving that a change of climate has occurred lies with those who believe in it.

The origin of the belief in a permanent change of climate is probably to be found in the fact that weather everywhere has a tendency to vary in a cycle of about thirty-five years, referred to long ago by Francis Bacon, and established in detail by Prof. E. Brückner, of Berne, in our own times. In his essay "Of Vicissitude of Things," Bacon remarks:

> They say it is observed in the Low Countries (I know not in what part) that every five and thirty years the same kind and suit of years and weathers comes about again; as great frosts, great wet, great droughts, warm winters, summers with little heat, and the like; and they call it the "Prime." It is a thing I do the rather mention, because, computing backwards, I have found some concurrence.

Neglecting individual years, it may be stated that for about half this cycle the weather is warmer and drier than the average, and for the other half colder and wetter. Or, expressed in another way, wet and cold periods, or warm and dry periods, occur at intervals of about thirty-five years. It is impossible to predict whether any particular year will be colder or warmer than usual, or whether the rainfall will be above or below the average, but Brückner's cycle certainly does express a general truth, though not very precisely, when applied to the whole earth. In the seventies of the nineteenth century there was a series of very wet years in the British Isles, culminating in the black year of 1879, memorable to all who were then engaged in agriculture. Much the same phase of the cycle was reached in 1912, and that year proved almost as bad for many British farmers as the ruinous year thirty-three years earlier.

An interesting instance of the application of this

cycle and how it led to a belief in the change of climate, is contained in the following statement:

The time of the "boom" in western Kansas and Nebraska, and in eastern Colorado, in the decade 1880-90, followed one of Brückner's wet periods, and the collapse of the "boom" came when the drier period advanced. Farmers who went out on to the high plains in the years of slightly greater rainfall preceding the "boom," and who lost all their capital, and more too, in the vain attempt to raise their grain in the years which followed, could with difficulty be convinced that the climate of the plains had not permanently changed for the worse. The impression left upon their minds, and upon the mind of anyone who saw the country later, was one of decreasing rainfall, unsuccessful agriculture and financial ruin. Within more recent years, in this same region of Kansas, with a somewhat increased rainfall during a wetter cycle, but without any permanent change to a wetter climate, the intelligent choice of cereals better adapted to the soil and climate, and the rational use of the available water supply, have wrought a wonderful change in the aspect and economic value of the State. *Prof. R. de C. Ward.*

As with the farmers of Kansas, so many other people have arrived at their conclusions as to a progressive and permanent change of climate, from general impressions produced by a succession of several bad or good years. In the perspective of the past the individual years are not seen separately when viewed from another stage of a lifetime, and characteristics of periods of weather in youthful days are apt to be used as comparison with individual years of middle life or old age. However firm may be the belief that this generation experiences different weather from that of its fathers or grandfathers, the fact remains that no such change in historic times has been established.

Beliefs in the influence of the moon upon the weather are enshrined in the folk-lore of all countries. We cannot attempt here to classify and analyse the hundreds of proverbs which express the views of different peoples in different provinces as to lunar influence upon weather, but it is worth while to give the results of a few inquiries into alleged connections. Until similar studies have tested the various assertions as to the dependence of weather upon changes of the moon, science is not justified in denying the existence of any such relationship. Honest doubt is commendable, but when it leads to dogmatism it passes outside the realm of scientific thought.

One widespread belief for which no justification has been found is that "La Lune mange les Nuages," or, in the language of sailormen, "the full moon eats up the clouds." Sir John Herschel refers to the tendency of clouds to disappear under the Full Moon as a meteorological fact for which it is necessary to seek a cause, but his conclusion has found no support from systematic observations. To obtain information upon the subject, the Rev. S. J. Johnson compared the state of the sky at moonrise and at midnight on the day of Full Moon for fifteen years; and his observations, communicated to the Royal Astronomical Society in 1894, confirmed the opinion now held by almost every astronomer, namely, that the Full Moon has no effect in breaking up clouds. Mr. W. Ellis made a detailed examination of Greenwich observations with the view of discovering whether any such effect exists. The results of the inquiry showed that there is in general a maximum cloudiness in the forenoon and a minimum in the evening, but this has no relation to the position or phase of the moon. A change from a cloudy to a clear state in the evening sky is much more likely to attract attention when occurring near to Full Moon, and this may have given rise to the popular belief that the moon itself possesses the faculty of clearing away clouds.

The subject has been investigated in other countries than Great Britain. Observations of the night sky at Potsdam for the six years from 1894 to 1900 failed to show any cloud-dispersing power for the Full Moon. It was found, indeed, that there was a maximum amount of cloud visible shortly after Full Moon and a minimum about the time of New Moon. This result is to be expected if the moon has no influence upon clouds; for moonlight makes clouds visible. At Kenilworth (Kimberley) Mr. J. R. Sutton has found that certain clouds appear to dissolve at sunset, but the rising moon makes them visible again. Observations made at 8 p.m. over a period of seven years show considerably more cloud between the third and eighteenth days of the moon's age than between the eighteenth and third, so that here again the evidence is opposed to the popular view. At any rate, we are justified in declining to accept the power of the moon to disperse clouds until proof of this capacity is forthcoming from those who believe in it.

As the moon is chiefly responsible for the rise and fall of the tides, it seems reasonable to suppose that the earth's atmosphere is affected in the same way, and that there are air-tides which may vary through the lunar month, like the spring and neap tides of the sea. Daily atmospheric tides due to the moon have, in fact, been detected in records of barometer readings made at Brest, St. Helena, Cape Horn, Batavia, and Singapore. In 1895 M. Bouquet de la Grye proved that the curves of atmospheric pressure obtained at these places show clearly a regular, but minute, ebb and flow twice a day in accordance with the position of the moon. Dr. S. Chapman has recently (1919) been able to detect a similar lunar effect in records of atmospheric pressure at Greenwich, Batavia and Hong-kong. The

whole range of the effect, however, that is, the difference of height of the atmospheric tide from crest to
trough, is at Greenwich appreciably less than that represented by a difference of one-thousandth of an inch
in the reading of a mercury barometer, and about five-
thousandths of an inch at Batavia. An air-tide range
equal to a difference of a few thousandths of an inch
of mercury level is scarcely worth considering as a sign
of change of weather, yet that is the greatest amount
for which the moon can be held directly responsible.

The only definite association that can be regarded as
established between changes of the moon and weather
relates to the occurrence of thunderstorms, and it is
noteworthy that this is overlooked completely in pro-
verbial philosophy. Thunderstorms are found to be
slightly more frequent near New Moon and the First
Quarter than near Full Moon and the Last Quarter.
This is clear from the adjoining table, which is given
as much to show that the lunar influence has been the
subject of many investigations in different countries
and extending over long periods of years as to illustrate the kind of result obtained. Prof. W. H. Pickering, who brought the results together, remarked:

The number of observations here collected seem to be large
enough to enable us to draw definite conclusions, without fear
that further records will revise or neutralise them. From
these observations we conclude that there really is a greater
number of thunderstorms during the first half of the lunar
month than during the last half; also, that the liability to
storms is greatest between New Moon and the First Quarter,
and least between Full and Last Quarter. Also we may add
that while theoretically very interesting, the difference is not
large enough to be of any practical importance.

So far, then, as earnest investigations have been
carried out with the purpose of associating the weather

with the various phases and positions of the moon, no connection has been found definite enough to be of

THE MOON'S PHASES AND THUNDERSTORMS

Station.	Authority.	Years.	New and First Quarter. (per cent.)	Full and Last Quarter. (per cent.)
Kremsmünster	Wagner	86	54	46
Aix-la-Chapelle	Polis	60	54	46
Batavia, Java	Van d. Stok	9	52	48
Gotha	Lendicke	9	73	27
Germany	Köppen	5	56	44
Glatz County	Richter	8	62	38
N. America	Hazen	1	57	43
Prague	Gruss	20	51	49
"		20	53	47
Göttingen	Meyer	24	54	46
Greenwich	MacDowall	13	54	46
Madrid	Ventatasta	20	52	48
Providence, R. I.	Seagrave	6	49	51

service in the actual work of weather prediction. Any observer who can bring forward evidence which will establish such a connection will make a notable contribution to meteorological science, and at the same time confer a benefit upon humanity. Meteorologists are prepared to adopt any rule or relationship which is of assistance in preparing their weather forecasts; and the fact that they take no account of lunar phases or the directions of the moon's horns—which can be determined many years in advance for any latitude on the earth—shows that lunar influence has not yet been brought within the sphere of practical science.

There is a vast difference between forecasts based upon substantial truths of science and those made by irresponsible weather prophets in almanacs popular in agricultural districts and among credulous people. Appropriately can it be said of such predictions: "The prophets prophesy falsely and the priests bear rule by

their means; and my people love to have it so." No
doubt some of the forecasts made by "Zadkiel," "Old
Moore" and "Raphael" in their almanacs, and by
other soothsayers who think they have discovered
weather cycles and causes which have eluded the wisest
meteorologists in the world, do prove to be correct;
but it would be strange if these coincidences of prediction and realisation did not occur.

No man of science familiar with the many variable
factors which determine the character of the weather
would have the temerity to make such predictions as are
put before an indulgent public by these oracles, whose
theories break down immediately they are faced with
facts.   Caution comes with knowledge; and confident
assertion as to the weather to be expected day by day
even next week, in a particular part of the country,
must lead to discomfiture when promise is made to face
performance.   The predictions in most popular almanacs are based upon the time of day the moon enters
into one of its four quarters; and any success achieved
by them may be ascribed to the laws of chance.

In addition to the moon, the stars and planets are
believed by some people to exert an influence upon the
weather, the belief being a survival of the days of
astrology.   So far as the stars are concerned, the
positions they will occupy at 10 o'clock to-night will be
practically the same as will be presented at the same
time a hundred years hence.   Moreover, on account of
the earth's rotation on its axis, every star in the heavens
shines upon some part of the earth every day.   No one
who has considered the facts that the apparent movements of the stars are entirely due to the daily spin of
the earth, and the annual journey round the sun, is able
to believe that the weather can be determined by the
aspects of the stellar heavens at any time of day or year.

Certain groups of stars are visible at particular seasons, but they have nothing whatever to do with the cause of the seasons, which would, indeed, be of precisely the same character as they are now, even if every star in the sky ceased to shine. The stars are, in fact, much too far removed from the solar system to take any part in causing weather changes.

The nearest of all the stars is a quarter of a million times farther away from us than is the sun; and the heat we receive from a star is so small in amount that it can only be detected with instruments of extreme delicacy. Whatever the temperatures of the stars may be, the stellar heat that reaches the earth is almost inappreciable. The best measurements available, made by Prof. E. L. Nichols at the Yerkes Observatory, near Chicago, with an instrument capable of detecting a difference of temperature of less than the ten-millionth part of a degree on a Centigrade thermometer, shows that a square foot of the earth's surface receives from the bright reddish star Arcturus only as much heat as would be received from a standard candle nearly six miles away, even if none of the heat of the candle were absorbed during the passage of the rays through the air. To produce the same heating effect as the brilliant bluish-white star Vega, a standard candle would have to be taken to a distance of nearly nine miles.

Dr. S. Chapman estimates that the total starlight is only about equal to that of a one candle-power lamp at a distance of nearly twelve yards, or of a sixteen candle-power lamp at 47 yards' distance; so that the heat received from the whole of the stars is far too small to have any observable influence upon the atmospheric movements which produce changes of weather.

As regards heating effect, the planets are in the same case as the stars. From the planet Jupiter, the heat received is nearly five times more intense than from the star Vega, but even that is next to nothing, and is altogether negligible in comparison with solar heat. It is, therefore, not remarkable that no amount of juggling with planetary conjunctions and oppositions has ever revealed a combination of the slightest service in weather prediction. It is possible, of course, that rays of an undiscovered kind are received from certain celestial bodies, and that these are operative in producing weather changes, but the fact remains that no relationship of practical value has been made out between the movements—apparent or real—of the moon, stars, or planets and the weather of any part of the earth.

Animals depend so much upon weather for their supply of food, that their sensitiveness to weather changes, which may deprive some of them of a meal, is not strange. It is unnecessary to assume that they have any special sense in this respect—any prophetic instinct that enables them to foretell the character of coming seasons. They may be affected by atmospheric conditions which are not detected by human nature in general, and they respond to these conditions by their actions, but these signs only indicate the weather to be expected in the immediate future. Sufficient for living creatures to know what the proximate weather will be, and their prescience goes no farther than that, as is shown by the myriads of birds and other animals that are destroyed every year by severe storms and untoward changes.

Plants even more than animals show by their condition the weather of the past or present rather than that of the future. Variations of the temperature, moisture and electrical state of the air are doubtless reflected readily by some plants and flowers, but the same variations can be detected by other means. Whether we interpret the closing of the scarlet pimpernel — the ploughman's weather glass — the trembling of aspen leaves, or the increased odour of flowers, we must recognise that these are only signs of possible showers coming soon, and that no indications can be given of the weather to follow afterwards.

The conditions of trees in the spring, whether the oak comes into leaf before the ash, or the ash before the oak—as it is sometimes said to do—are determined entirely by past performances of the weather, and have nothing whatever to do with the future. Similarly, when bushes have plenty of berries, it is because conditions were favourable for the production of their fruit when they were in flower, and not because the coming winter is to be severe. The temperature, sunshine. rainfall, abundance of particular insects, and other past causes which affect the birth and growth of plants, decide whether the berries shall be few or many, and not the future conditions.

In some years, no doubt, popular confidence in the supply of beneficent berries for hungry birds is justified, while in other years it is not, but people forget their failures and remember only their successes, and this infirmity of human nature causes many beliefs to endure which can find no support in the results of critical study. Records of the behaviour of plants and animals under different atmospheric conditions and in different seasons are of interest to the meteorologist, but they have not yet been found of any service in making forecasts of weather over periods longer than those which at present limit his predictions.

Relationships may be found long before they are understood, but in all cases it is desirable to be assured of their truth before attempting to explain them. The evidence for the beliefs mentioned already is altogether insufficient to satisfy any critical mind, yet many "wise-saws" which serve for making estimates of weather changes a few hours, or even a day or two, in advance, are contained in the accumulated wisdom of ages, often enshrined in proverbs and folk-lore. The shepherd and the sailor, the hunter and the tiller of the ground, learnt to read the face of the sky and to interpret its promises and warnings long before any scientific foundations for their beliefs had been discovered.

There is no better example of this than the numerous proverbs of different times and nations referring to the weather outlook foretold by a red sunset or red sunrise. "When it is evening, ye say, 'It will be fair weather: for the sky is red.' And in the morning, 'It will be foul weather to-day: for the sky is red and lowring.'" So spake Christ to the Pharisees and Sadducees; and He used this common belief of His day as an illustration of the self-satisfying spirit which is content with the obvious and seeks not to discern the "signs of the times."

As a general rule for weather prognostication it is as true in the British Isles as it was in Palestine that

> "Sky red in the morning
> Is a shepherd's sure warning;
> Sky red at night
> Is the shepherd's delight."

The connection between the weather which usually follows redness of sunrise or sunset is a statement of fact derived from long experience; the explanation could only be given when the effects of atmospheric dust and moisture as filters of sunlight had been studied. Sunlight is white light, and when we see the sun red, it is because the blue rays in the original beams have been dissipated by the intervening air, or rather by the dust particles in the air and the water droplets which surround them.

A red sky in the evening indicates that there are plenty of dust particles in the air, and that water-vapour is beginning to be condensed upon them, but relatively few water droplets are being formed, and it is unlikely that they will increase sufficiently to cause rain during the succeeding twenty-four hours. A red sky in the morning shows, however, that the droplets around the dust particles are being protected from becoming smaller by a blanket of overlying moisture, otherwise they would soon be driven into vapour again by the rising sun's rays. The conditions are, therefore, favourable to the growth in size of the droplets, and rain will probably fall during the day.

The association of a red sky with weather thus admits of complete physical explanation, but it is not at all necessary that the reason should be forthcoming for every fact. It is, however, desirable to distinguish between accurate observation and traditional belief which asks for acceptance without inquiry into the evidence of its truth.

In the prediction of good and bad seasons, meteorologists are to-day little in advance of the priests and astronomers of ancient Egypt or Assyria; for the only forecasts that can be made are based upon the recurrence of cycles of changes. Unfortunately, this is true to a great extent because, although the knowledge of periodic changes in the earth's meteorology over a cycle of years is of a more exact nature than formerly, the fundamental cause of the variations from year to year has yet to be found. Ancient astronomers were able to predict eclipses with fair accuracy, because they knew the eclipse cycle, though they did not understand the true relationships existing between the sun, moon and earth as members of the solar system, or the law of gravitation. The discovery of this law was the key to all cycles caused by the movement of members of our system, and in the light of its predictions of eclipses are now made. On the other hand, no master-key has been found which will enable the cycles extricated from meteorological records to be seen as consequences of natural laws.

The sun is responsible for the great movements of the atmosphere which circulates around the solid earth. The various kinds of messages which its rays bear to the earth are being accumulated in solar observatories, and persistent efforts are being made to understand the code in which they are written. Little by little the language of the sun is being pieced together, but we still await the discovery of an inscription which will provide a key to solar influences, as the Rosetta stone did for Egyptian hieroglyphs. When this key has been found, it will be possible to predict the seasonal weather from year to year in advance; but that time is not yet.

To an observer unfamiliar with the game of chess, the movements of the different pieces upon the board by the players are unintelligible. A master of the game sees, however, not only the disposition of the pieces at a given moment, but also for several moves ahead. As regards weather prediction, meteorologists are at present in the position of a spectator knowing one or two simple moves in the air and these limited to a small portion of the board. They do not see the whole board at one time, though this is essential for an estimate to be made of the effect of a change of position of one piece upon the future relationship of the others.

Though there is always comfort in prayer—the comfort that comes from trust in a power other than our-self—it would be just as reasonable to pray that the moon should change its course in order to give additional light when required, that the sun's heat should increase or decrease to suit particular needs, or the earth's rotation be altered from time to time, as to pray that the circulation of the atmosphere should be adapted to the wants of a particular country or district. Because we can predict the positions of the moon, sun, earth and other bodies we do not pray to alter them, but the movements of the air are subservient to like law and in the course of time will be predicted in like manner.

A clergyman who was asked to pray for rain is said to have replied, "My good friends, what is the use of praying for rain whilst the wind is in the east." It may be said, of course, that everything is possible to Omnipotence behind the universe; and the only answer to this must be that it would be equally illogical to pray for changes in the aspects of the heavens as that winds should have their movements altered for the benefit of particular people or interests.

Belief in works rather than faith in prayer is responsible for the attempts to produce rain in drought-stricken districts by means of explosives. It has been shown that such experiments are a useless expenditure of money, and they have been condemned by the best meteorologists of Europe and America. In 1908 a meteorologist who was ordered to watch the result of rain-making experiments carried out in a district of New Zealand reported that "the explosions had apparently no more effect on the vast expanse of the air than would the striking of a match in a room." The belief has been shown over and over again to have no foundation, yet rain-wizards still exist even in civilised countries.

The possibility that rain or drought can be produced by human means is never questioned by barbarians, who have their professional rain-makers and great medicine men, and superstitiously attribute to them all power over Nature. A few years ago elaborate experiments to determine whether rain could be caused by explosion were made in connection with the United States Government, at an expense of thousands of pounds, but the results proved that nothing of the nature of rain was produced by the bombardment. In fact, rain falls according to the general weather conditions existing at a place, and is altogether independent of the puny efforts of man to change the nature of the clouds. When rain does occur in the wake of a rain-wizard, a glance at the meteorological chart will show that it is a natural consequence of the distribution of temperature and pressure.

Many educated people believe that rain follows great battles, the general opinion being that the noise of the guns or the combustion of the explosives in some way affects the clouds, and causes them to precipitate their moisture. The belief is, however, much older than artillery, and is referred to by Plutarch in his life of Caius Marius (155-86 B.C.) in the words "They say that extraordinary rains generally follow great battles." The human tendency to forget facts or events which are contrary to a cherished conviction, and remember only those which support it, is responsible for the existence of this and many other like beliefs. During the first ten weeks of the European War, when there was little rain, though heavy gun-firing was almost continuous, nothing was heard of the belief, but when this was followed by an excessively wet period we were again assured by the newspapers that big battles invariably produce rain.

So firm is the fallacy as to explosions causing rain that in the year 1911 a member of the House of Commons asked the First Lord of the Admiralty in Parliament "whether he would arrange for the fleet to carry out their heavy gun-firing practice round the coast at some other period of the year than in the middle of the harvest-time, when the resulting heavy rain may cause serious loss to the farming community." The reply was that "there is no evidence that the firing causes heavy rain," but this only meets belief with denial. Though the argument is not strictly scientific, perhaps the most convincing form of reply to those who profess to believe, or do believe, in the efficacy of gun-firing to produce rain, is to point out that the firing of big guns is carried on at Shoeburyness more frequently than at any other point on the coast, yet the mean rainfall at Shoeburyness, and on the coast of Essex generally, is the lowest in the British Isles.

It is commonly believed that during severe thunderstorms a bolt is sometimes discharged from the clouds and reaches the earth as a solid mass of stone or metal. There is, however, not a particle of material evidence in support of this belief. No thunderbolt originating in the clouds has ever been found, and none exists, whatever conviction may be held to the contrary. What are mistaken for thunderbolts as popularly understood are peculiar mineral objects, meteorites, or particles of soil or rock which have been fused by lightning striking the earth through them.

Masses of a metallic or stony nature do fall from the sky occasionally, but they have nothing to do with thunderstorms, and really reach the earth from outer space. In its annual journey around the sun the earth now and then encounters stray fragments of cosmic matter, and draws them toward itself by the force of gravitation. When the mass reaches the earth's atmosphere, friction against the air makes it white hot, and like a moth flying into a flame it is consumed, the streak of light thus produced being a shooting star or meteor. Sometimes the piece of cosmic material is so large that it is not completely consumed as it traverses the atmosphere; and in this case it reaches the earth as a solid mass—a meteorite—which may weigh a few ounces or several tons. Many of these meteorites are preserved in our museums, but though they may make a noise or a series of explosions as they hurl themselves toward the earth, they are not connected in any way with thunderstorms, and cannot correctly be termed thunderbolts.

Other objects often mistaken for thunderbolts are known to geologists as fulgurites, and are produced by the fusion of grains of loose sand by a lightning discharge. At the mouth of the river Irt, in Cumberland, fulgurites have been found extending to a depth of forty feet in the sand, and a fulgurite found in a sandy stratum at Macclesfield reached to a depth of twenty-two feet. It is perhaps natural to conclude that tubes or patches of fused rock, found after lightning has been seen to strike the earth in a place where only loose sand could be seen, actually came from the clouds, but here again the view that "seeing is believing" leads to an erroneous conclusion.

In the absence of any precise knowledge of the nature of globular or ball lightning, it may be undesirable to assert that nothing solid can come from a thundercloud; nevertheless, it can be stated with confidence that no so-called thunderbolt has ever proved to be one, so that the possessor of a true specimen would have an object of unique value and interest. In the absence of such a specimen, it is permissible to state

III. SCIENCE.

Lunette, painted by Kenyon Cox. In the Congressional Library, Washington, D. C.

that no thunderstorm has ever discharged a thunderbolt which was afterwards picked up and is preserved
in a museum, or among a private collection of curiosities.

Uncritical observation and hasty conclusion are responsible for the reports of the occurrence of living
frogs and toads enclosed in blocks of coal or other hard
rock many feet below the surface of the ground. A
stone is being broken by a quarryman, a frog is seen
hopping about close to the place, and forthwith the
lively imagination of the labourer persuades him that
he has seen it actually come out of a cavity in the rock.
Dean Buckland made experiments for the purpose of
ascertaining how long frogs and toads could live shut
up in cavities of stone and excluded from air and food,
with the result that most of them were dead within a
year, and none survived more than two years. Yet
frogs are alleged to have been found enclosed in rocks
which, geology teaches, were deposited under water
millions of years ago, and afterwards subjected to a
pressure which has crushed all the fossils contained in
them as flat as paper. If geology is right, the frog
stories are utterly incredible. Or, as a distinguished
geologist once said, the blow of the hammer that disclosed a live frog inside a block of stone without an
opening would at the same time destroy not only
geology but the whole fabric of natural science.

Critical examination of evidence, and cautious consideration of conclusions, are characteristic attributes
of a scientific mind. There is a tendency in the present
age to make sensational announcements upon a slender
basis of fact; but science suffers by such premature
publication. *Festina lente* must be the motto if the
steps forward are never to be retraced. Test all things,

and you will then be in a position to hold fast by that which is true.

When about the middle of the nineteenth century, evidence was being found of man's existence upon the earth for a period long anterior to the seven thousand years or so of the Semitic tradition, it was regarded with suspicion by men of science as well as the world in general. M. Boucher de Perthes, antiquary, archaeologist, and gentleman of France, announced in 1846 that an ancient flint implement had been found associated with bones of elephant, rhinoceros, and other extinct animals in gravel exposed during excavations for the construction of a canal at Abbeville. When three years later he asserted that numbers of rudely worked and chipped flint implements had been found with remains of extinct mammals in the same undisturbed beds of gravel, geologists gave no heed to his announcement, and he was regarded as an amiable visionary. Dr. Rigollot, of Amiens, appears to have been the only naturalist in France who took the trouble to examine the ground personally, with the result that he came away convinced of the accuracy of M. de Perthes' observations. The conclusions of both observers were either scorned or discredited by the rest of their countrymen for several years; and it was an Englishman, Joseph Prestwich, who ultimately proved them to be correct.

Dr. Hugh Falconer saw M. de Perthes's collection of flint implements, including a flint hatchet, in 1858; and he wrote to Sir Joseph Prestwich asking him, as a geologist who would inquire into their origin and associations *con amore*, to take an early opportunity of visiting Abbeville. Prestwich had made the gravels of England the subject of particular study, and was, therefore, well qualified to examine the proofs of the antiquity of man yielded by similar deposits in France. It was said of him, in mingled earnest and raillery, "point out a broken pebble amongst a thousand others in a gravel pit, and there is one who will tell you the point of the compass from which it came, the stratum which yielded it, the distance it had travelled, the amount of rolling it had undergone, and the time it had occupied in its journey."

Prestwich went to Abbeville and Amiens in 1859 and, with Sir John Evans, examined both beds of gravel and flint implements, with the result that he convinced himself of the following facts: (1) that the flint implements are the work of man, (2) that they were found in undisturbed ground, (3) that they are associated with the remains of extinct mammals, (4) that the period represented by the deposits containing the flint implements was late in geological time, and preceded that in which the surface assumed its present outline.

In these conclusions we have definite statements of fact in which no attempt is made to account for them or consider their significance. It was certain that primitive man existed in the north of France at the same time as animals which had become extinct, for his flint weapons were found associated with their bones. Also, the old valley-gravels in which the relics occurred must have been deposited before the ground took its present configuration; that is, long before historic times. Whether the gravels with their flint implements and other remains represented an epoch thousands or tens of thousands of years ago could not then be decided, but in any case the period was long anterior to that in which man was supposed to have been created.

The importance of these discoveries was readily recognised by geologists; but such revolutionary views as to the remote antiquity of man naturally met with much opposition from the guardians of traditional teaching. Prestwich was a devout Churchman, and he cautiously abstained from making any pronouncement upon the necessity of extending current chronological ideas as to the existence of man, but he could not be false to the facts before him, and the truths which they revealed have since been placed beyond criticism. Geologists, have now no hesitation in stating that it must have been at least ten thousand years ago since man the hunter made the flint implements found mingled with the remains of various animals in the valley-gravels of Abbeville and elsewhere.

It is to Prestwich more than to any other geologist that we owe the establishment of the fact that man co-existed with a number of now long extinct mammals, and that his advent on the earth must be relegated to a far higher antiquity than that which had previously been accepted. *Sir Archibald Geikie.*

We have described these observations and conclusions somewhat fully because of the excellent example they afford of the difference between belief and evidence. No one now supposes that only a few thousand years have elapsed since man made his appearance upon the earth, yet that was the belief until accurate observations, cautiously interpreted, proved it to be untenable. It is not surprising that facts which led to such revolutionary ideas as to man's antiquity should have had almost to force their way to attention. Until scientific observation had provided incontrovertible evidence of the existence of prehistoric man in an early stage of culture, it was easy to believe anything as to human origins.

It was the absence of methods of accurate observation and critical inquiry, and the subservience of mind to authority, that led to many fables and beliefs being handed down as natural truths for hundreds of years. Among such beliefs mentioned by Prof. L. C. Miall in his *Early Naturalists* are: that the crocodile weeps when it has eaten a man; that the hedgehog sticks ripe grapes upon its prickles, and so carries them home to its children; that the crab waits till the oyster gapes and then puts a stone between the shells, so that he may gnaw the oyster's flesh; that an oar dipped into water seems to be broken because of the swift moving of the water; that the chameleon feeds on air; that during the winter swallows lie hidden at the bottom of lakes and rivers, two together, mouth to mouth, and wing to wing; that buried crabs produce scorpions; that the hind legs of the frog are formed by the splitting of the legs of the tadpole; that barnacles are transformed into geese, goats are milked by the nightjar, and that gryphons, harpies, phoenixes, rocs, and like legendary creatures actually exist.

Most of these beliefs probably had their origins in the casual observation and hasty conclusion which are antithetic to scientific methods of inquiry and thought. The literature of the ancients is full of fabulous statements and misinterpretations of natural things; and many of the paradoxes and fallacies contained in it persist to the present day.

The belief that when a horsehair is left in a stream or lake for a little while it assumes life, and finally becomes an eel, is an instance of an error due to superficial observation. There is a species of thread-worm which develops in stagnant pools and somewhat resembles a horsehair in appearance, and as a dry horsehair when placed in water may twist about somewhat in the fashion of this parasite, one was supposed to be produced from the other, after which the transition from the thread-worm to the eel became easy to a credulous mind. This simple way of explaining the origin and development of the common eel satisfied the uncritical observer, but the truth was much more difficult to discover.

From the days of Aristotle onward the actual mode of development of the eel was a mystery. It was known that large eels pass from rivers into the sea at certain seasons, and that diminutive young eels, called in this country elvers, ascend the rivers in enormous numbers. But until Profs. Grassi and Calandruccio, of Rome, investigated the matter in 1895, no one in any country had been able to discover how the elvers were produced. These naturalists proved that the eels which annually descend the rivers travel very long distances, until they reach the ocean. It is not known exactly in what part of the ocean spawning takes place, but the eggs develop into strange, colourless, transparent, thin-bodied creatures, which were thought to be a special family of fishes, but are now known to be really the larvae of eels. After attaining a certain size the larva ceases to feed, its body shrinks, and it assumes the very different form of the elver which ascends our rivers. A more wonderful series of changes than that thus revealed would be difficult to find. The whole story of the eel and its spawning reads almost like a romance instead of scientific reality.

Another curious case of deceptive appearance gave rise to the widespread belief in the production of honey by bees in the carcasses of dead animals, and principally from those of oxen, whence the term Bugonia—oxen-born—used in Greece to describe it. Vergil referred to the legend in his Fourth *Georgic,* but the earliest appearance of the belief in literature is found in the Biblical story of Samson, who had killed a lion in the vineyards of Timnath on his way to his bride: "And after a time he returned to take her, and he turned aside to see the carcass of the lion; and behold there was a swarm of bees and honey in the carcass of the lion,'' The story leads up to the riddle propounded by Samson: "Out of the eater came forth meat, and out of the strong came forth sweetness.''

Many professors of scriptural exegesis have commented upon these passages, and offered explanations of the appearance of the cleanly hive-bees in the carcass of a lion. Linnaeus once said that the progeny of three blow-flies would devour the carcass of an ox as quickly as would a lion; and on this principle, commentators who insist upon literal interpretations have concluded that "after a time" may mean a sufficient interval for the carcass to be reduced to a clean skeleton and the bees to have made a hive in it. We are not concerned here, however, with exegetic difficulties, but with the fact that the belief in the Bugonia legend was current among the people of Samson's time.

So far back as the latter half of the seventeenth century, Swammerdam suggested that the insect supposed to be bees in a decaying carcass were really flies which resembled bees, but his desire for a literary interpretation of a scriptural passage prevented him from taking the last step that was needed. Réaumur, the French naturalist, showed clearly in 1738 the resemblance between the drone-fly and the honey-bee, and remarked: "such resemblances have made people believe that honey-bees, hornets and wasps originate in putrescent matter upon which those other flies occur.''

Towards the end of the nineteenth century, Baron Osten Sacken proved that the Bugonia fable had its origin in the fact that the drone-fly lays its eggs upon carcasses of animals, that its maggots develop within the putrescent mass and resemble bee-larvae, and finally change into a swarm of flies which, in their shape, hairy covering and colour, look exactly like bees, although they belong to a totally different order of insects. "Thinking is difficult, and acting according to reason is irksome," said Goethe. For more than two thousand years people overlooked the likeness between the drone-fly and the honey-bee, and believed in a tradition which a single experiment would have shown to be without the slightest foundation.

We may forgive most people for holding such beliefs, because they may have had no easy opportunity of testing them by personal observation; but it is remarkable that writers on natural history should be content to hand down statements of traditional authorities without troubling to look for evidence of the beliefs they accepted, or to examine for themselves the commonest natural facts. Perhaps the most extraordinary case of this mental blindness is that of the colours of the rainbow. In *De Proprietatibus Rerum*, written by Bartholomew of England before the middle of the thirteenth century, and translated into English in 1397, the succession of colours in the rainbow is given as red, blue and green. "The succession," says Prof. Miall, "had a mystical meaning; red was a symbol of fire, blue of water, green of earth. For more than five hundred years men went on repeating an error which might have been corrected at once by observation of an actual rainbow."

Misconception as to the cause and character of many common phenomena in Nature; the tendency to accept statements without inquiry into the credentials of the author or independent investigation of the facts; and the view that science is an esoteric study beyond the comprehension of most people, are almost as prevalent now as they were in former times. The book of Nature is open for all to read, yet few look into it and fewer try to understand what is written.

The sun rises and sets at different points on the horizon every day, yet it is believed by the unobservant to rise in the east and set in the west throughout the year; the starry heavens may be seen majestically swinging around a point near the North Star every fine night, but this apparent movement has escaped general notice; the horns of the new or old crescent moon always point away from the sun, yet artists continually paint the moon in unnatural positions at sunrise and sunset; rising and setting new or old moons are described at impossible times by authors who ought to know better; the centre of a rainbow is always opposite the sun, and there is always a regular succession of colours from red to deep blue, the red being on the outside of the arc and the blue inside in the case of a single rainbow, and in the reverse order in the additional or secondary bow sometimes seen; yet the colours are often wrongly described or depicted, and a halo seen when facing the sun is mistaken for a rainbow, which can only be seen when the observer has his back to the sun.

Hasty conclusions are responsible for many mistaken interpretations of natural incidents, even when phenomena have been accurately observed. Before the days of Copernicus, nothing seemed more obvious than that the sun actually moved round the earth every day; for "seeing is believing" was considered as cogent an argument than as it is now. But every one knows in these days that the conclusion was incorrect, and that the apparent daily motion of the sun is an effect produced by the real motion of the earth upon its axis, the sun being practically a fixed body as regards the earth.

To inhabitants of the northern hemisphere, unfamiliar with the cause of the seasons, it is perhaps natural to conclude that the earth is nearer the sun in the northern summer than in winter, whereas the earth is three million miles nearer the sun at the beginning of January than it is at the beginning of July.

Most of these facts are known to all observant people, but judging from statements commonly made in newspapers—not only in daily papers but also in weekly periodicals in which greater accuracy might reasonably be expected—there are few literary people who have a knowledge of natural objects and phenomena equivalent to that of children in the State schools. It is scarcely too much to say that, omitting signed articles written by experts, few newspapers make any announcement relating to a scientific subject without committing a mistake. Either terms are wrongly used, or a matter of common knowledge among men of science is regarded as a remarkable discovery, or observations of a sensational kind are presented to the public as if they were established truths, though they await confirmation from the scientific world, and are mostly unworthy of serious consideration.

Almost every newspaper report of a volcanic eruption contains a reference to "flames and smoke" issuing from "the burning mountain," though this description of the phenomena is completely inaccurate. During an eruption there is practically no flame, and certainly none that can be seen except close to the crater; no smoke such as issues from a chimney is ever produced; and there is no burning in the ordinary sense of combustion as in a fire. These elementary facts have been taught to thousands of school children for the past twenty years, yet popular writers and journalists seem still to be unaware of them.

A volcanic eruption may be compared not inaptly to a series of boiler explosions. The dense clouds projected from the vents at each paroxysm of the eruption consist of steam and fine dust, and the light of the molten rock in the crater flowing down the flanks of the volcano as lava streams, illuminates the clouds so brilliantly as to give the appearance of flames. As the lava flows it also emits water vapour copiously and seems to burn and smoke, though what looks like smoke is really steam, and the flame is reflected light. Whatever may be the ultimate cause of volcanic action, the sudden transformation of water into vapour is the active agent of an eruption, and by far the most abundant product ejected is steam. A few inflammable gases are produced, and as they burn they give rise to true volcanic flames, but their pale and flickering light cannot easily be distinguished when a volcano is in active eruption.

It may be too much to expect men of letters to possess an elementary knowledge of science, or to have any sympathy with scientific precision, but it is not unreasonable to ask for accuracy of description when they are dealing with natural facts and phenomena. They may reply that Shakespeare was often at fault in matters pertaining to natural history; but he at any rate reflected in his works the best knowledge of his time, which is more than can be said of most writers to-day.

We are often told that men of science should cultivate the art of literary expression, but the stronger necessity for literary men to have at least a nodding acquaintance with the outstanding facts of natural knowledge is overlooked. A well-known author has unkindly said, "The man of science appears to be the only man in the world who has something to say, and he is the only man who does not know how to say it."

The retort invited by this remark is that the man of letters frequently has nothing to say, and he says it at great length. The first business of the man of science is to create new knowledge, and not necessarily to clothe his discoveries in a pleasing dress, though he may do so. The facts of science provide material upon which literary art may be exercised, but the two functions of exploration and fine expression are rarely found together.

The methods of accurate observation and cautious interpretation demanded of scientific investigators do not readily lend themselves to attractive description, and the results require more mental concentration to understand them than is usually demanded of a literary performance. A writer of romance can let his imagination have free play, but when natural occurrences enter into the story they should be presented accurately, if the material is to be used rightly. Nothing is easier than to be deceived by appearances, or to accept a belief without inquiry into its foundations; the scientific plan of asking for evidence, and of limiting statements to those for which good justification can be produced, is much more tiresome, yet it is the only way by which truth can be attained; and that after all is the highest aim.

CHAPTER VI

INQUIRY AND INTERPRETATION

Science commits suicide when it adopts a creed. Huxley.

The philosophy of one century is the common-sense of the next. H. W. Beecher.

Forgetting those things which are behind, and reaching forth unto those things which are before. St. Paul.

For nothing is so productive of elevation of mind as to be able to examine methodically and truly every object which is presented to thee in life. Marcus Aurelius.

The patient investigation and accurate methods required to obtain desired results in the school of experimental and technical science, cannot fail to impress, refine, and ennoble the characters of those who work in this direction. Sir Wm. Mather.

MANY people find satisfaction in the words of the preacher "there is no new thing under the sun"; they delight in tracing suggestions of modern scientific discoveries in the works of Greek, Roman and other philosophers, and in showing that classical literature contains all that is required for the making of a good citizen or for intellectual equipment. Well, in regard to logic, mathematics, metaphysical philosophy, jurisprudence, or any subject in which words or symbols make up the mosaic, and in ethical teaching, humanists are possibly right in attaching supreme importance to the thoughts and doctrines of other times. In observation also, and to some extent in mechanical ingenuity, the works of many of the ancients command the esteem of the modern scientific world. What is peculiarly

125

modern is the experimental investigation of natural
phenomena; and the looking for mere rules of sequence
in the phenomena rather than transcendental causes
is of still more recent growth.

The art of observation and that of experimentation are very
distinct. In the first case, the fact may either proceed from
logical reasons or be mere good fortune; it is sufficient to have
some penetration and the sense of truth in order to profit by
it. But the art of experimentation leads from the first to the
last link of the chain, without hesitation and without a blank,
making successive use of Reason, which suggests an alterna-
tive, and of Experience, which decides on it, until, starting
from a faint glimmer, the full blaze of light is reached. *J. B.
A. Dumas.*

The merit of scientific observation lies in the direct
appeal to Nature for truth instead of to authority.
Whenever man has seen things for himself, and has not
been content with vicarious observation, he has taken
a decided step towards the emancipation of the human
race from the trammels of traditional doctrine. But
modern science demands something more than an open
eye for its advancement; it requires the kinetic quality
of mind that tests by experiment the things which might
be, as well as observes things as they are.

The method which our race has found most effective in
acquiring knowledge is by this time familiar to all men. It is
the method of modern science—that process which consists in
an interrogation of Nature entirely dispassionate, patient,
systematic; such careful experiment and cumulative record as
can often elicit from her slightest indications her deepest
truths. That method is now dominant throughout the civilised world; and although in many directions experiments
may be difficult and dubious, facts rare and elusive, science
works slowly on and bides her time—refusing to fall back
upon tradition or to launch into speculation merely because
strait is the gate which leads to valid discovery, indisputable
truth. *F. W. H. Myers.*

Scientific observations of natural phenomena were recorded four thousand years or more ago, but recognition of the essential importance of experimental science of the modern type is only about three centuries old, though the method was adumbrated at an earlier epoch.

As an observer and a recorder Aristotle surveyed the whole realm of Nature in his works, and had familiar knowledge of a thousand varied forms of life. He brought together an immense amount of accurate observation and examined it with skilful reasoning, but he was often led astray by pre-conceived ideas, and based his conclusions upon reports which were more curious than important. But he and other ancient philosophers particularly lacked the scientific method of inquiry by experiment. It is true that Pythagoras, in the sixth century B.C., is credited with the use of monochord, or single stretched string, of which the length and tension can be varied, to determine by experiments the law that the pitch of a note is inversely proportional to the length of the vibrating string, and to discover numerical relations between the various notes on the musical scale. It is also true that Ptolemy, in the second century A.D., determined by experiment the refraction or amount of deviation which a beam of light undergoes, from its original direction, when passing from air into water, or into glass. But these determinations, with the work in acoustics by Pythagoras, and Galen's proofs, by the dissections of animals, of the relation between the brain and the nerves, represent the sum total of experimental research in Greek science.

There was an interval of a thousand years between Ptolemy's investigations in optics and the experiments made by Alhazen, whose substantial studies of reflection, refraction, vision, the human eye and related subjects are the outstanding contributions of Arabia to physical science in a period during which the Arabs were in advance of the whole world in intellectual and industrial activity. It was chiefly upon the researches of Alhazen that Roger Bacon based the principles of optics expounded by him. This Franciscan Friar of the thirteenth century anticipated many later discoveries in physics and chemistry, and though he did not actually discover the telescope, he described in detail, in his *Opus Majus* (1276), the properties of lenses and how they could be used to make objects appear nearer, as in the case of a simple magnifying glass.

Adelard of Bath, who translated Euclid's *Elements of Geometry* from Arabic into Latin early in the twelfth century—four hundred years before the Greek text was recovered; Robert Grosseteste, the illustrious Bishop of Lincoln and author of an encyclopaedic *Compendium Scientiarum*; Peter Peregrinus of Maricourt, of whom Bacon said: "Through experiment he gains knowledge of natural things, medical, chemical, indeed of everything in the heavens or earth," all preceded Bacon in their scientific observations and writings and influenced his thought. He was not really a great experimenter, and his positive additions to natural knowledge are few, but he was one of the first philosophers to insist upon the value of experiment in scientific investigation. "We have," he said, "three means of knowledge—authority, reasoning, experiment. Authority has no value unless its reason be shown; it does not teach: it only calls for assent." Again "Armed with experiment and calculation, science must not be content with facts, though these may have their utility; it seeks truth; it wants to find out the laws, the causes —*canones, universales regulae*."

In the bold appeal which Roger Bacon made to experiment and the observation of Nature, he stood out as the champion of unlettered inquiry in a period of scientific stagnation, and he suffered persecution, banishment and imprisonment for his temerity. In popular esteem the memory of this champion of experimental science and advocate of positive knowledge has always been cherished; and after seven hundred years, in 1914, Oxford commemorated the birth of this—one of her greatest sons—described by Humboldt as "the greatest apparition of the Middle Ages," by erecting a statue to him.

Two hundred years after Roger Bacon, appeared that prodigy of Nature, Leonardo da Vinci (1452-1519), whose curiosity was insatiable, and whose methods were to search out all things, to experiment and verify, to let his eyes test and his reason judge. Another Italian philosopher who saw that the appeal should be from authority to Nature and urged that all true knowledge came from data given by the senses, was Bernardino Telesio (1509-1588). Leonardo himself had the clearest ideas as to the scientific method of inquiry.

In treating any particular subject I would first of all make some experiments, because my design is first to refer to experiments and then to demonstrate why bodies are constrained to act in such a manner. This is the method we ought to follow in investigating the phenomena of Nature. Theory is the general, experiments are the soldiers. Experiment is the interpreter of the artifices of Nature. It is never wrong; but our judgment is sometimes deceived because we are expecting results which experiment refuses to give. We must consult experiment and vary the circumstances, till we have deduced general laws, for it alone can furnish us with them. *Leonardo da Vinci.*

Leonardo was by profession an engineer, but he was also sculptor, musician and poet, and his fresco representing the Last Supper places him among the most illustrious artists of the world. He investigated thoroughly the laws relating to the movement of water and hydraulics generally, and anticipated many of the theories for which credit is often given to men of science who lived many years after him. Hallam, in his *Introduction to the Literature of Europe,* says that the discoveries which made the names of Galileo, Kepler and others famous, the system of Copernicus, and the theories of modern geologists, were anticipated by Leonardo within the compass of a few pages; not perhaps in the most precise language, or in the most conclusive reasoning, but so as to strike us with something like the awe of preternatural knowledge. In his work as an engineer he followed truly scientific methods. "Those," he said, "who are infatuated by practice without science, are like the navigator who sails a ship without helm and compass; he never knows with certainty whither he goes. Practice must always be built upon theory. Study science first, then follow the practice which is born of science."

Bernard Palissy, the potter who sacrificed everything, even the furniture of his cottage, in the production of a glaze for earthenware, was also one of the earliest followers of the experimental method of studying other aspects of Nature. His life extended over nearly the whole of the sixteenth century, and his contributions to agriculture, chemistry, mineralogy and geology disturbed the schoolmen and provided a new foundation for science. He was the first to give a true explanation of the origin of springs, and like Leonardo da Vinci, he understood that fossils represented past forms of life and were not freaks of Nature or relics of the world before Noah's flood. Buffon said of him, about a century and a half later, "a simple potter of the end of the sixteenth century was the first to dare to tell Paris and the doctors that marine fossils were true animal remains, were deposited in a sea in the place where they are now found, and were born of their respective animal parents. This he defied the Aristotelians to deny.''

Palissy offended the alchemists and astrologers of his time, as well as the priests and philosophers, by his ridicule of cherished opinion regarding natural objects and phenomena; and he died in prison in consequence of his appeal to observation and experiment for the basis of every speculation. He was an apostle of the inductive method, and demonstrated its application to large audiences in Paris, during the three years which Francis Bacon spent there in his youth; it has indeed been suggested by Sir Clifford Allbutt that Bacon first derived his ideas of inductive philosophy from the collections and contentions of Palissy, whose observations and influence are, however, rarely mentioned in the history of scientific thought.

Dr. William Gilbert (1540-1603), of Colchester, known to most students of magnetism and electricity as the founder of these branches of science, also practised the experimental method of investigation before Francis Bacon wrote about it. He is, indeed, repeatedly mentioned by Bacon in the *Novum Organum,* and elsewhere he is praised both for his industry and his method, but censured for endeavouring to build a universal philosophy upon a narrow basis; and not without reason. Gilbert was largely indebted in his work on magnetism to the observations of Peter Peregrinus made three centuries earlier, and he was so dominated by the notion that magnets possessed some sort of soul or spirit that he should perhaps be considered as a sort of connecting link between medieval superstitions and the modern spirit. He did, however, make better use of the experimental method than any natural philosopher who preceded him, and his work did much to break down the barrier raised by traditional belief against independent investigation.

In the discovery of secrets, and in the investigation of the hidden causes of things, clear proofs are afforded by trustworthy experiments rather than by probable guesses and opinions of ordinary professors and philosophers . . . To you alone, honest and true men of science, who seek knowledge, not from books only, but also from things themselves, do I address these magnetic principles and this new sort of philosophy. If any disagree with my opinion, let them at least take note of the experiments and discoveries which have been worked out and demonstrated by me, with many pains and vigils and expenses. Let them rejoice in these, and employ them to better use if they are able. *W. Gilbert.*

The ancients used only two methods of investigation —the philosophical and the mathematical; the third method, by experiment, was put into deliberate practice by Palissy, Gilbert and Galileo. By offering experimental evidence against what was believed to be the teachings of Aristotle, Galileo established the modern experimental method of inquiry in Nature. The authority of Aristotle as the arch-priest of natural science had been questioned before the time of Galileo, but no attempt had been made to confound it with truths secured by direct appeal to Nature. The high regard in which Galileo held the facts obtained by experiment, in comparison with the conclusions of peripatetic philosophy, in reflected in a letter written by him in 1615:

I would entreat these wise and prudent fathers to consider diligently the difference between opinionative and demonstrative doctrines, to the end that they may assure themselves that it is not in the power of professors of demonstrative sciences to change their opinions at pleasure. *Galileo.*

Francis Bacon is sometimes called the Father of Experimental Philosophy, but it may be doubted whether he merits the title; indeed, he disregarded in his own works the very principles of scientific investigation expounded by them. What Bacon did was to form into a system the method of investigation which consists in asking questions of Nature herself, of making observations with great care, carefully arranging them, and cautiously arriving at conclusions from them, Aristotle had long before insisted upon the collection of facts, and urged that we must "first classify them, bring particular facts under general heads and coordinate them into theories." He collected so-called "facts" by hundreds, and proceeded to speculate upon them as if they were unalterable truths, whereas in many cases they were merely old women's tales or other hearsay evidence. His method was a logical machine which could produce reasonable results when provided with sound material to work upon, but not otherwise. Aristotle and the school of thought he dominated for nearly two thousand years, knew nothing of the experimental method of inquiry; and by proclaiming that "our only hope is in the regeneration of the sciences by regularly raising them on the foundation of experience" Bacon became the apostle of a new school of philosophy, though not the founder of it.

Bacon's influence in establishing this inductive process of inquiry is often over-estimated, and he owes his prominence to the fact that his works appeared at the right psychological moment, when the age was ripe to receive a new philosophy. As we have seen, three centuries before the time of Francis Bacon, the main doctrines he promulgated had been proclaimed by Roger Bacon, and not only announced as articles of scientific belief but also followed in practice.

It is clear, therefore, that modern methods of observational and experimental science were not founded by
the works of Francis Bacon. Before his day, Tycho
Brahe had gone to the heavens for his astronomical
facts instead of to Greek philosophy, and had earnestly
urged his pupil Kepler "to lay a solid foundation for
his views by actual observation, and then by ascending
from these to strive to reach the cause of things."
Leonardo da Vinci had advanced science and engineering in many directions; and Palissy had collected and
studied a large variety of natural things. Gilbert had
made his memorable experimental researches on magnetism, while Galileo had confounded orthodox philosophy by his investigations in mechanics and observations of celestial objects.

Bacon drew up the rules by which he considered
Nature should be studied, but he treated almost with
contempt all progress accomplished without the use of
his prescription, and he persistently rejected the Copernican theory, though it formed the best possible example of the application of his own system of collecting
observations and arriving at conclusions from them.
Few natural philosophers who came after him took
heed of his artificial process of discovery; and there is
little evidence that the method assisted in the advance
of science in any way. Newton never mentioned Bacon
or his system, though he was born and educated after
its publication; and a study of the progress of science
fails to furnish sufficient reason for believing that
Bacon's *Novum Organum* has been either a powerful
source of inspiration or has provided the formula by
which natural knowledge has been increased.

It is, indeed, a mistake to suppose that all scientific
investigation must proceed from the general to the
particular according to a prescribed formula, or be

determined by any like hard-and-fast principle. Devotion to such doctrines has often led men astray and is always an undesirable obsession.

The maxim which should guide us in our work is not *from the simple to the complex,* nor yet, as some philosophers have taught, *from the more needful to the less needful,* but *from the known to the unknown,* from truths either discovered by steady effort or stumbled on by accident to new truths springing out of past acquisitions, and verified by observation or experiment. Biologists, like other scientific discoverers, have a rugged peak to climb, and are often urged to try this or that infallible method of Bacon, Descartes, or Comte, a method which generally turns out to be either misleading or impracticable. There is but one way—to wriggle up as you can, sometimes taking to the right, sometimes to the left, sometimes turning back, because what looked like a promising opening proves to lead nowhere. It is a great thing to possess natural aptitude for the work, a great thing too to be obstinately bent on getting to the top, but the successful climber often owes much to good-luck wisely turned to account. *Prof. L. C. Miall.*

In his *New Atlantis,* Francis Bacon planned in somewhat fanciful language a palace of invention, a great temple of science, where the pursuit of knowledge in all its branches was to be organised on principles of the highest efficiency. He argued that for a nation to apply a substantial part of its material resources to the equipment of scientific work and exploration, a share of its resources which should grow greater with the growth of population and the increasing complexity of knowledge, was the surest guarantee of national glory and prosperity. We still await in the United Kingdom the realisation of this institution. The Royal Society of London, which was founded for the furtherance of the experimental philosophy which Bacon wished to see pursued, had no endowment from King or country, and even now the subvention which it receives annually from the State for its own requirements amounts to only a thousand pounds towards the cost of scientific publications, together with the use of its rooms at Burlington House.

The experimental method of research represented the spirit in which the Royal Society was founded and became an organised association with a Royal Charter in 1662. No subject was considered too trivial for study by observation and experiment; and advantage was taken of every opportunity of advancing knowledge. Among the subjects brought forward at one of the earliest meetings of the Society were:

Experiments with wires of severall matters of ye same size, silver, copper, iron, &c., to see what weight will breake them. Experiment concerning the force that presseth the aire into lesse dimensions; and it was found that twelve ounces did contract 1/24 part of Aire. Experiment to show how much aire a man's lungs may hold, by sucking up water into a separating glasse after the lungs have been well emptied of Aire. Experiment of Animal engrafting, and in particular of making a Cock spur grow on a Cock's head. Whether there bee any such thing as sexes in trees and other plants; some instances were brought of Palme trees, plum trees, hollies, Ash trees, Quinces, pionies, &c., wherein a difference was said to be found, either in there bearing of fruit or in their hardness and softness, or in medical operations.

At that time and later some of the foremost men of letters exercised their powers of wit and ridicule and sarcasm upon the men who were devoting their time to the patient investigation of Nature. None of the common people, and few of the writers and scholars, could understand why valuable time should be given up to the study of "beasts, fishes, birds, snails, caterpillars, flies," and as to making experiments on the air, even Charles II., who took great interest in the Society, is said by Pepys to have "mightily laughed

at Gresham College, for spending time only in the
weighing of ayre, and doing nothing else since they
sat.''

At that time much more attention was given to the
human body than to the sciences of physics and chemistry. The great Italian anatomists of the sixteenth
century had bridged the gulf which separated them
from the time of Galen (130-200 A.D.), the first physiologist and the last of the Greek physicians. Though
Galen's conclusions were derived solely from his dissections of animals, for many centuries his authority
and that of Aristotle were considered sufficient for all
time upon every question relating to man. Dialectic
and dogma, mysticism and tradition, dominated the
science of medicine, and physicians lived upon the
knowledge—mostly illusory—handed down to them
from antiquity. Vesalius (1514-1564) corrected Galen's description of the human body; and the observations made by him on the valves of the heart, by Fab-
ricius (1537-1619) on the valves of the veins, and by
other anatomists at Padua, paved the way for the discovery of the circulation of the blood by William Harvey (1578-1657).

Harvey takes a place with Gilbert and Galileo as an
experimental philosopher and an apostle of the scientific method. He observed things for himself, experimented in order to see Nature at work, and did not let
the views of Galen or Aristotle influence his conclusions. ''I sought to discover,'' he says, ''the motions
and uses of the heart from actual inspection and not
from the writings of others; at length, and by using
greater and daily diligence and investigation, making
frequent inspection of many and various animals, and
collating numerous observations, I thought I had attained to the truth.''

For nine successive years Harvey expounded his views on the circulation of the blood, and demonstrated the anatomical and experimental evidence on which his conclusions were based, in his lectures at the Royal College of Physicians. Only after this probationary period, did he give his discoveries to the world in a little book of 76 pages, published in 1628, on the *Movements of the Heart and of the Blood.* In this treatise Harvey established absolutely the fact of the circulation of the blood, and the fact that muscular action of the heart causes this movement. But he was unable, from his want of a microscope, to indicate the precise path along which the blood travels from the terminal arteries to the commencing veins.

The large artery from the heart gives off branches to various parts of the body, and these branch off again into small arteries in different organs. Similarly, small veins carrying blood back to the heart unite to form large veins. How the blood passed from the small arteries to the small veins could only be conjectured by Harvey, and was not discovered until three years after his death. He concluded that the blood passes from the arteries to the veins mainly by percolation, as water, to use his own illustration, percolates the earth and produces springs and rivulets. No microscope in his time was powerful enough to enable him to see the meshwork of very minute tubes —the capillaries—which can now be observed easily.

Improvements in the microscope enabled Malpighi in 1660 and Leeuwenhoek in 1688 to demonstrate the completion of the circuit of the blood by microscopic observations of the movement from arteries to veins through the capillaries, and it can now be seen easily by any student who will examine the web of a frog's foot. The largest blood vessels seen are the small arteries bringing the blood from the heart, the finest are the capillaries through which the blood passes into the small veins which carry it back to the heart and thus complete the circuit.

Harvey's work was an excellent example of the application of the inductive method of study laid down by Francis Bacon as the essential principle of scientific progress; but Harvey did not begin to teach the circulation of the blood until 1619, and as Bacon died seven years later he may be forgiven the omission of any reference to it in his writings, though he must have known of it. Harvey's opinion of Bacon's doctrines is represented by his remark, "He writes philosophy like a Lord Chancellor."

John Hunter, who was born exactly a hundred years after the publication of Harvey's work on the circulation of the blood, paid no heed to Bacon's mechanical system of arriving at scientific truth. This great anatomist, biologist and surgeon, whose studies of the human frame raised surgery from the art of the barber-surgeon to the dignity of a science, and whose observations and experiments embraced every object which he could secure in the animal and vegetable kingdoms, did not trouble about Baconian principles in his inquiries and interpretations. He had a passion for knowledge, and possessed the creative and constructive attributes which enabled him to make discoveries and to coordinate them. Writing to Jenner about certain observations and experiments he desired him to make, he said, "Be as particular as you possibly can"; and that sentence epitomises his scientific method. He was rationally sceptical and critical of so-called facts, and was always ready to put them and principles to the test of experiment.

The principles of our art are not less necessary to be understood than the principles of other sciences; unless, indeed, the surgeon should wish to resemble the Chinese philosopher whose knowledge consisted only in facts. In that case, the science must remain unimproved until new facts arise. In Europe, philosophers reason from principles and thus account for facts before they arise. *John Hunter.*

On one occasion there was a discussion at a meeting at which Hunter was present as to the structure of certain organs in the digestive system of birds. The meeting adjourned without settling the question, and on the next assembly quotations from the works of Aristotle, Hippocrates, Galen and other authorities were brought forward by the advocates of particular views in support of their opinions. Hunter had not gone to the early masters for confirmation, but had dissected the organs and exhibited them on a plate. All the books in the world and all the speculations of philosophers throughout the ages are but featherweights in comparison with ocular evidence of this kind.

The desire to test and measure for himself instead of accepting the observations and systems of ancient astronomers as fixed standards of reference led to the foundation of modern astronomy of precision by Tycho Brahe (1546-1601). While a boy of thirteen at the University of Copenhagen this young Danish noble was impressed by the observation of a partial eclipse of the sun, which had occurred punctual to prediction. He then determined to train himself for an astronomer, and when a youth of seventeen we find him making measurements of a conjunction of the planets Jupiter and Saturn on August 17, 1564, by means of an ordinary pair of compasses. For a few years after, his attention was given to other scientific subjects, but the appearance of a remarkable new star in the constellation of Cassiopeia in 1572 re-awakened his activity and fixed his career.

Thenceforth, he devoted his life to the accurate determination of the positions and motions of celestial bodies, and started a renaissance of astronomical measurement. Until he began observations at his observatory at Uraniborg on the island of Huen, the astronomy of the ancients had remained practically undisturbed. No advance had been made in the knowledge of the positions of the fixed stars or of the moon's motion—so important for navigation; and the positions of the planet could not be foretold with anything like reasonable accuracy.

No astronomer had yet made up his mind to take nothing for granted on the authority of the ancients; but to determine everything himself. Nobody had perceived that the answers to the many questions which were perplexing astronomers could only be given by the heavens, but that the answers would be forthcoming only if the heavens were properly interrogated by means of improved instruments capable of determining every astronomical quantity anew by systematic observations. The necessity of doing this was at an early age perceived by Tycho Brahe. *Dr. J. L. E. Dreyer.*

For twenty-five years Tycho Brahe patiently and diligently measured the positions of stars and other bodies upon the celestial sphere, using instruments of his own design and attaining an accuracy of observation little short of marvellous. Upon the basis of these observations Kepler constructed his three famous laws of planetary motion.

Johann Kepler was born at Weil, in the Duchy of Würtemberg, in 1571. Refused as a divine, he pursued the study of mathematics and was appointed professor at Gratz in 1594, where he wrote his first work in support of the Copernican theory. Five years later he went to join Tycho Brahe at Prague, where for a number of years he endeavoured to fit Tycho Brahe's wonderfully accurate observations into the theories then held as to motions of bodies in the solar system.

In the process of discovery of the three fundamental laws known by his name, Kepler was led to make many fantastic hypotheses. But all through he was guided by the principle that God who made the world had established fixed laws throughout his works, laws that are often so definite as to be capable of expression in exact numerical terms. In accordance with these views he sought for numerical relations in the disposition of the planets and their arrangement, in respect to their number, their times of revolution and their distances from one another. Each hypothesis he made, however fanciful, he tried by a rigorous test whenever possible, and as soon as he found that the facts were not in accordance therewith he abandoned it, and without hesitation proceeded to try others, which he submitted to the same severe ordeal, to share perhaps the same fate. He says, "After many failures, I was comforted by observing that the motions in every case seemed to be connected with the distances; and that when there was a great gap between the orbits there was the same between the motions." He was at length led to the discovery of his well-known "Harmonic" law (the squares of the periodic times of revolution of the planets are as the cubes of their mean distances from the Sun).

The misery in which Kepler lived forms a painful contrast with the services which he performed for Science. The pension on which he subsisted was always in arrears; and though the three emperors, whose reigns he adorned, directed their ministers to be more punctual in its payment, the disobedience of their commands was a source of continual vexation to Kepler. When he retired to Silesia, to spend the remainder of his days, his pecuniary difficulties became still more harassing. Necessity at length compelled him to apply personally for the arrears which were due; and he accordingly set out in 1630, when nearly sixty years of age, for Ratisbon; but in consequence of the great fatigue which so long a journey on horseback produced, he was seized with a fever, which put an end to his life. *Sir David Brewster.*

The astronomical views of early Greek philosophers were summed up by Aristotle in the fourth century B.C. There were many speculations as to the form of the earth and the nature of celestial phenomena, but few have any scientific significance. "Some say," remarked Aristotle in one of his works, "that the earth rests on water. We have ascertained that the oldest statement of this character is the one accredited to Thales the Milesian [639-546 B.C.], to the effect that it rests on water, floating like a piece of wood or something of that sort." Aristotle himself stated plainly that the earth is a round globe, and Pythagoras (566-470 B.C.) is believed to have taught that the earth moves in the heavens, but Aristarchus of Samos, in the third century B.C., was the first philosopher to suggest that the sun is the centre of our system and that the earth revolves around it in a year. When, however, four hundred years later, Ptolemy of Alexandria built up his system of astronomy, he adopted the doctrine of an immovable earth in the centre of the universe, and this was accepted as true until the time of Copernicus.

The earliest serious criticism of the views of Aristotle and Ptolemy appear to have been made by Oresmus, who became Bishop of Lisieux, Normandy, in 1377, and died at that place in 1382. In a translation of the four books of Aristotle, Oresmus commented

upon Aristotle's contentions for an immovable, central
earth, gave numerous reasons and arguments against
this hypothesis, and showed it to be unsound. The
work in which this was done was never published,
though several manuscript copies exist. Probably
other thoughtful inquirers had the same dissatisfaction with the theory of a fixed central earth, but were
unwilling to publish any criticism of what was then
the orthodox view. It was perhaps fortunate for
Copernicus himself that the work in which he finally
dethroned the earth from the position it had held for
so long and following Aristarchus, made the sun the
centre of our system, was not published to the world
until he was on his death-bed in 1543.

In the plan of the solar system conceived by Copernicus, the planets Mercury and Venus are nearer the
sun than is the earth; and in the course of their revolutions around the body to which they owe their light
they must, therefore, exhibit phases like those through
which the moon passes monthly. Copernicus knew
that these phases were a consequence of his theory,
and predicted that they would be found to exist. One
of the first uses to which Galileo put his telescope in
1610 was the observation of Venus, and he wrote a full
account of the changes seen by him in the appearance
of the planet, from the fully-illuminated disc to the
crescent form and then through the half-moon aspect
to full again. The discovery of these phases provided
an unanswerable argument for the Copernican theory.

From the observation of these wonderful phenomena we are
supplied with a determination most conclusive, and appealing
to the evidence of our senses, of two very important problems,
which up to this day were discussed by the greatest intellects
with different conclusions. One is that the planets are bodies
not self-luminous (if we may entertain the same views about

IV. URANIA - THE MUSE OF ASTRONOMY.
From the engraving by R. Earlom, (1742-1822),
after G. B. Cipriani (1727-1785).

Mercury as we do about Venus). The second is that we are absolutely compelled to say that Venus (and Mercury also) revolve round the sun, as do also all the rest of the planets. A truth believed, indeed, by the Pythagorean school, by Copernicus, and by Kepler, but never proved by the evidence of our senses as it is now proved in the case of Venus and Mercury. *Galileo*.

The discoveries made by Galileo with his telescope excited the hostility of the expounders of Aristotelian philosophy; and they supported the Copernican doctrine to such an extent as to bring him under the ban of the Catholic Church. He was denounced to the Inquisition in 1612, but it was not until 1633 that proceedings were taken which resulted in the observer of seventy years of age being bound by oath to abjure the doctrine "that the sun is at the centre of the universe and is immovable, and that the earth is not the centre and is movable," and being treated as prisoner for the last nine years of his life. During this time, in his exile at Siena and Arcetri, his interest in science never waned, despite his infirmities, and he devoted himself to dynamical problems on which he was still at liberty to express opinions.

The Copernican doctrine was believed to be contrary to Holy Scripture, and therefore Galileo was compelled to renounce it and to do penance for teaching it. Whatever was in his mind as he rose from his knees before the ten Cardinals in the Convent of Minerva, Rome, on June 22, 1633, we cannot know, but it is unlikely that he muttered *"Eppur si muove"*—and yet it moves—as is related in the familiar anecdote associated with his abjuration.

The action of the Inquisition in forcing Galileo to deny the evidence of his own senses cannot be condemned too strongly; but the fact that the Church of

Rome was responsible for the recantation may almost be said to have been incidental. Had the Salvation Army or a council of politicians possessed the same powers in those days, they would probably have been just as active in crushing what was believed to be a pestiferous doctrine for which the people were not prepared and which was, therefore, a danger to the State. We need not go back three hundred years to find scientific workers who have been deprived of their posts, or whose careers have been ruined, because of their convictions. The man who to-day dared to teach doctrines so revolutionary as those held by Galileo, so opposed to conceptions of what is sacred, and contrary to what public opinion considers to be true, may not be tortured or imprisoned, but he would assuredly suffer social ostracism and would lose position and friends as sadly as Galileo did in his old age.

Copernicus put forward his doctrine of the arrangement and movements of bodies in the solar system hesitatingly, and merely as a hypothesis by which the different positions of the sun and planets as seen from the earth could be explained much more simply than on a system involving an immovable earth in the centre of the universe. Of a different type of mind was Giordano Bruno, who had arrived at a like conception of the cosmic system by intuition, and not only went beyond Copernicus in his ideas but also in his fearless advocacy of them. Thirty-three years before Galileo had been brought before the Inquisition, Bruno had declared to the same body his philosophical creed in unmistakable terms.

I believe in an infinite universe, the effect of the infinite divine potency, because it has seemed to me unworthy of the divine goodness and power to create a finite world, when able to produce besides it another and others infinite; so that I have declared that there are endless particular worlds similar to this of the Earth; with Pythagoras I regard it as a star, and similar to it are the moon, the planets, and other stars, which are infinite, and all these bodies are worlds, and without number, constituting the infinite all (*universita*) in an infinite space; while the latter is called the infinite universe, in which are innumerable worlds; so that there are two kinds of infinity, one in the magnitude of the universe, the other in the multitude of worlds, by which indirectly the truth according to the faith may be impugned. In this universe I place a universal providence, in virtue of which everything lives, grows, moves, and comes to and abides in its perfection. *Giordano Bruno.*

For teaching these doctrines Bruno was handed over to the governor of Rome in 1600, with the usual recommendation that he be punished "with as great clemency as possible, and without effusion of blood"— an equivocal form of words which signified burning at the stake. He had been eight years a prisoner of the Inquisition and could have secured his release at any time by forsaking the truth as it had been revealed to him, but an unbending sense of right kept him steadfast to the end. When his sentence was pronounced he uttered the memorable words, "You who sentence me are in greater fear than I who am condemned."

The fear of death was no part of Bruno's philosophy. "I have fought," he said, "that is much—victory is in the hands of fate. Be that as it may with me, this at least future ages will not deny me, be the victor who may—that I did not fear to die. Yielded to none of my fellows in constancy, and preferred a spirited death to a cowardly life." For liberty of thought and freedom of science he perished, and his executioners believed they were preserving Truth from desecration when they burned the body of the man who willingly offered himself up as a living sacrifice to her.

The fundamental principles of the Copernican system are: (1) That the apparent daily motion from east to west of the celestial sphere and the bodies in it, is due to the daily rotation of the earth on its axis from west to east; (2) That the earth is one of a family of planets revolving round the sun. Neither of these propositions were established by conclusive proof until long after the time of Copernicus. It was understood that if the earth moves around the sun, the stars ought to undergo an apparent annual displacement of position on account of being viewed from different positions. Tycho Brahe endeavoured to detect such a displacement, but unsuccessfully, and on that account he rejected the doctrine of the earth's motion. Great improvements had to be made in astronomical instruments before the difference of position of a star as seen from opposite sides of the earth's path around the sun could be measured. Not until about 1840 were observations of sufficient accuracy made to establish this kind of displacement, from which also the distance of a star could be determined.

It is not strange that the displacement should have escaped detection for so long now that we know how very minute is the difference of position due to the earth's annual motion. Imagine a circle an inch in diameter to be drawn somewhere on an extensive plain; let this circle represent the path which the earth traverses around the sun annually; and let there be a luminous point—representing a star—four miles away from it. What the astronomer has to measure is comparable to the difference of the apparent position of this point of light as viewed from different parts of the one-inch circle four miles distant. Suppose two lines were drawn from the light to the circle at points as far apart as possible; the angle between these lines represents the dimension which has to be measured in order to find the distance of the nearest star.

The minuteness of the angle may be understood by considering the movement of the minute hand of a clock or watch. If the hand moves at a perfectly uniform rate there will be a difference of position at the beginning and end of a second or any smaller interval of time. The angle between two positions separated by about the five-hundredth part of a second represents the angle due to the movement of the earth around the sun when the nearest star is observed; and this notwithstanding the fact that the earth is ninety-three millions of miles from the sun, so that by its revolution around the sun its position with regard to the stars is changed by nearly two hundred million miles.

Using an illustration due to Prof. E. C. Pickering, the apparent change of position of the nearest star, as the earth moves to points nearly two hundred million miles apart, is equal to the height of a man at a distance of two hundred miles. In other words, the problem of determining the apparent displacement due to change of the earth's position in its orbit is like measuring the height of a man two hundred miles away. So accurate are the methods now used by astronomers that the height of the man could be determined with an uncertainty of only one inch. Yet in spite of the marvellous precision with which measurements can be made, only about forty stars have been found near enough to our system for any angular displacement to be detected sufficiently large to admit of the determination of their distances. Few stars are less than a million times farther from us than the sun, and most of them are probably thousands of times more distant than the nearest.

The fact that stars undergo a measurable annual

displacement upon the vault of heaven is an indirect proof of the revolution of the earth around the sun, but a direct proof of this movement is available in the "aberration of light." The observations which led James Bradley (1693-1762) to the discovery of this important astronomical effect were made in the coal cellar of a house at Wanstead in the early part of the eighteenth century. Those were the days when very long telescopes were used as a means of avoiding the coloured fringes which appear around the images produced by an object-glass consisting of a simple lens. The lens of Bradley's telescope was on the roof, and the eye-piece end was placed in the coal cellar, so as to be as far away as possible; holes being cut in the intervening floor to allow the instrument to pass through.

Bradley used this instrument to measure the position of a star with the view of discovering the apparent effect, known as "parallax," which must be produced by the change in the earth's point of view—an effect sought for by Tycho Brahe and other astronomers, but not then established beyond question, though its existence was a fundamental consequence of the Copernican theory. Bradley did not find what he expected, but his observations showed that all stars seemed to shift slightly from their true places in periodic fashion and by the same amount. The paths followed were similar to what would be produced if the earth's orbit around the sun were projected in miniature upon the background of space. This wandering or aberration could not be confused with the parallax due to the change in the point of view, for the shift was the same for all stars, whereas apparent displacement due to parallax would differ for stars at different distances.

Bradley pondered over his observations for two or

three years before he was able to interpret them. The solution, when found, proved to be very simple, and may be illustrated by a familiar example of a similar effect. Suppose we are seated in a train or motor car, and that rain is falling vertically, or nearly so. The lines followed by the rain-drops are seen upright while the carriage is at rest, but immediately it moves they seem to be tilted forward at the top; and the faster we travel the greater is the deviation from the vertical. If we did not know that the rain was falling in vertical lines, we might think it was falling from points ahead of us, but we know that the slant is only apparent, and is due to the motion of the train or car. The effect is produced by a combination of the velocities of the carriage and the falling rain, and is precisely similar to that observed by Bradley in the case of the stars. The earth travels around the sun at a rate of nearly nineteen miles a second, and the stream of light coming to us from every star has a velocity of 186,000 miles a second. Consider the earth to be the carriage of the illustration and light-waves to be the rain, and it is easy to understand that the combination of the two velocities must cause every star to be seen slightly ahead of its true position.

As the velocity of light is about ten thousand times that of the earth, the amount of the deviation due to aberration may be represented by two lines each nearly three hundred yards long drawn from the observer's eye toward a star and separated at the upper ends by the length of an inch. The angle between these two lines is equivalent to the "constant of aberration" discovered by Bradley by observations in a coal-cellar in 1726. Bradley afterwards became Astronomer Royal, and the improvements he effected at Greenwich during his tenure of the office provided astronomers with a mine of exact knowledge of the positions and movements of stars. The lesson taught by his life is that perfection should be aimed at, and the best use made of the instrumental means available, even though the significance of the observations may not be understood.

Many men of science have built better than they knew for future generations because of their attention to this principle of precision throughout their investigations. About the middle of the eighteenth century L. Euler, a Swiss mathematician, showed that, assuming the earth to be a truly rigid body, it should oscillate slightly with reference to its axis; that is to say, the direction of the axis should vary in a period which was calculated to be about three hundred days, and therefore the positions of the north and south poles, which are the extremities of the axis, and the latitudes of all places, should be subject to a like periodic variation.

Observations of sufficient precision to establish this variation of latitude were not made until one hundred and fifty years later, when S. C. Chandler, at Cambridge, Mass., and F. Küstner, at Bonn, proved that the variation amounted to a few tenths of a second of angular measurement. On account of this, the north pole of the earth is not a fixed point, and may sometimes be nearly thirty feet distant from the average position. Euler assumed the earth to possess no elasticity, and in that case the period of variation of latitude would be about 305 days. The results of prolonged observations give, however, unmistakable evidence of a period of 428 days, which is what would be expected if the earth possesses a certain amount of elastic yielding. The conclusion of the whole matter is that the observed effects can be accounted for by regarding the earth as a little more rigid than a globe of steel of the same size. Here, again, theory had to be adapted to the results of accurate observation.

Scientific theory is established or modified by cumulative evidence of this kind. The Copernican theory is held to be true, because it accounts completely for the varying aspects of the heavens as seen from different parts of the earth and at different times; it describes the movements of the celestial machinery, and when the law of gravitation had proved to be the mainspring, the two principles combined provided astronomers with everything required for the construction of an accurate time-table of the heavenly bodies in the past, present or future. The powerful instrument which has thus been placed in the hands of astronomers, and the use made of it, has been described in impressive words.

Supply any man with the fundamental data of astronomy, the times at which stars and planets cross the meridian of a place, and other matters of this kind. He is informed that each of these bodies whose observations he is to use is attracted by all the others with a force which varies as the inverse square of their distance apart. From these data he is to weigh the bodies, predict their motion in all future time, compute their orbits, determine what changes of form and position these orbits will undergo through thousands of ages, and make maps showing exactly over what cities and towns on the surface of the earth an eclipse of the sun will pass fifty years hence, or over what regions it did pass thousands of years ago. A more hopeless problem than this could not be presented to the ordinary human intellect. The men who have done it are therefore in intellect the select few of the human race. The astronomical ephemeris is the last practical outcome of their productive genius. *Prof. Simon Newcomb.*

Observation, interpretation, prediction, realisation, are successive stages of scientific theory. Astronomy, being the oldest branch of science, can furnish the most perfect links in this chain of reasoning, but remarkable examples are found in other departments of natural knowledge.

By acute reasoning from observed facts relating to the character and arrangement of the coal-fields and associated rocks of Somersetshire and South Wales on the west, and of the Belgian and North French coal-fields on the east, Lieut.-Col. Godwin-Austen showed in a memorable paper to the Geological Society of London in 1856 that, in all probability, similar coal-fields were buried beneath the newer strata of the intervening region. Combining all the observations then available, he finally concluded that there were coal-fields in the south-east of England sufficiently near the surface to allow of their being of great economic value.

This prediction of the existence of coal, based upon purely geological considerations, has been fulfilled, and it affords a striking example of the application of scientific reasoning. Whether the quantity and quality of the coal in Kent will make its working a profitable undertaking has yet to be proved, but in spite of this, it is little short of marvellous that geologists should be able to see in imagination the coal seams extending underground from England to Belgium and France, and should be able to say so confidently, "Seek, and ye shall find," to the prospectors who have followed them. The prediction of the existence of coal in Kent, hundreds of miles from the great coal-fields, is a remarkable example of successful scientific induction based upon careful observations.

New results and new ideas often meet with severe criticism in the scientific world. Newton's experiments with a glass prism were marvels of accurate study and cautious conclusion, yet they brought him more trouble than praise. He proved that white light is not homogeneous but consists of rays which are

refracted or bent by different amounts when they pass
through a prism, the deviation from the original direction increasing gradually from red light successively
through orange, yellow, green, blue and indigo to
violet, which is the light which undergoes the greatest
amount of refraction. He concluded from his researches "That the colours of all natural bodies have
no other origin than this; that they are variously qualified to reflect one sort of light in greater plenty than
another"; but no sooner was this and like truths as to
the nature of colour announced than they were bitterly
assailed by philosophers who were unfamiliar with the
experiments upon which they were based, or held other
views upon light and colour.

No wonder such opposition was disturbing to Newton, and that it almost made him decide to do no work
except for his private satisfaction.   "I was so persecuted with discussions arising out of my theory of
light," he wrote in 1675, "that I blamed my own im-
pudence for parting with so substantial a blessing as
my quiet to run after a shadow"; and a year later he
remarked, "I see a man must either resolve to put out
nothing new, or to become a slave to defend it."

Everyone is now so familiar with electrical phenomena that the explanation of lightning as an electric discharge between two clouds, or a cloud and the
earth, and of thunder as the sound of the discharge,
is readily intelligible.   Before the eighteenth century,
when experiments with various machines for producing electric and other curious effects had excited great
attention, many strange conjectures had been made as
to the nature of lightning and thunder.   Anaximander
considered the phenomena as "caused by the wind enclosed in a thick cloud, which, by reason of its lightness,
breaketh forth violently, the rupture of the cloud mak-

eth a crack, and the divulsion by reason of the blackness causeth a flashing light."

This represents an early attempt to account for the phenomena on a naturalistic basis, instead of referring them to Jove and his thunderbolts. Clouds crashing together instead of cracking seem to the child to provide sufficient reason for the cause of thunder—a view expressed by Milton in the lines:

> As when two black clouds,
> With heaven's artillery fraught, come rattling on
> Over the Caspian; then stand, front to front
> Hovering a while, till winds the signal blow
> To join their dark encounter in mid-air.

Later views were that lightning and thunder were caused by the explosion of gases in the air, or by the spontaneous combustion of particles of "a subtle sulphur." No means existed for the production of long "electric sparks" and, therefore, no suggestion could be made of any relation between such discharges and those taking place in the clouds. Early experimenters with electrical machines did not overlook the resemblance between the flash and crack of their electric sparks and the similar effects observed during thunderstorms. Benjamin Franklin, in 1749, stated the points of similarity between the electric discharges and lightning to be: (1) Giving light, (2) Colour of the light, (3) Crooked direction, (4) Swift motion, (5) Being conducted by metals, (6) Crack or noise in exploding, (7) Subsisting in water or ice, (8) Rending bodies it passes through, (9) Destroying animals, (10) Melting metals, (11) Firing inflammable substances, (12) Sulphurous smell.

It remained to establish the identity of the machine-made electricity with lightning flash and thunderclap, and Franklin suggested a means of doing this by fixing a pointed rod at the top of a high tower or steeple and using it to draw down the lightning for the purpose of comparing its effects directly with those produced by electricity. Before Franklin could raise the money for the erection of his pointed rod on a tower, Dalibard had obtained electricity from the clouds by means of a rod about forty feet long, fixed at the ground level upon an insulated stand near Paris. He instructed an old dragoon to try to obtain electric sparks by bringing a brass wire fixed in a glass bottle near the rod when thunderclouds were seen.

After several days' waiting, a thundercloud appeared on May 10, 1752. The dragoon approached the wire to the rod, and there was a lively crackling of sparks. The flame and sulphurous odour were evidently infernal. The terrified dragoon dropped the wire and shouted to his neighbour to send for the village priest. The latter was braver than the dragoon. He began to experiment for himself, and drew sparks from the rod. He communicated the results to Dalibard, who wrote, "Franklin's idea ceases to be a conjecture. Here it has become a reality." *Prof. F. Cajori.*

While Franklin, not quite convinced, was still hoping for the funds to place his rod at the top of a steeple in Philadelphia, so as to get as high up as possible, the happy idea occurred to him of using a kite for this purpose. Electricity was to be conducted down from the thundercloud by the twine attached to the kite, and a silk ribbon tied to the end of the twine near the hand was to prevent it from going any further. A key was to be tied at the place where the twine and ribbon joined, so as to form a metal conductor.

In June, 1752, Franklin sent up his kite towards the clouds. He put his knuckles near the key, but obtained no sparks. Again and again he tries to draw an electric spark from the key, yet without success. Is his conjecture wrong and the experiment a failure? No, the rain has now wetted the twine and made it a better conductor of electricity. Once more Franklin presents a knuckle to the key, and a strong spark is the result. He obtains a succession of sparks, and uses the electricity from the clouds to produce the same effects as that from man-made machines. He has established the identity of lightning and electricity, and answered Job's question, "Can'st thou send lightnings, that they may go, and say unto thee, 'Here we are'?" Facts were at last available upon which a reasonable theory as to the nature and origin of lightning could be based.

Writers in the popular press, and in technical papers also, frequently indulge in cheap sneers at what they call "scientific theory." In their minds, the man of science lives in a world far removed from the realities of life, and knows little of material things or practical possibilities. Nothing could be more incorrect than this view. With the exception of pure mathematics and metaphysics, every branch of physical and natural science depends for its progress upon practical work in the laboratory or the field. No one appreciates the value of experimental work more than the man of science, and no one is more critical of scientific theory. Whenever a theory is put forward in scientific circles, it is always subjected to severe attack from people most competent to point out its weaknesses; and in any case it only survives until someone brings forward evidence which disproves it.

For example, Newton supported with the weight of his great authority the theory that light is due to the emission of minute particles at a high velocity by a luminous body. When these particles impinge upon the retina of the eye, they produce the sensation of light. According to this view, light ought to travel more quickly in water than in air. Another theory, put forward by Huygens about Newton's time, and developed later, is that light is due to vibration in an imaginary medium called the ether, believed to prevail throughout all space. Luminous bodies set the ether in vibration, and when these undulations reach the eye they give us the sensation of light. On this view, light should travel more slowly in a substance like water than it does in air.

To test the two theories, therefore, an experiment was required by which the relative velocities of light in air and water could be determined. By Newton's emission theory the velocity should be greater in water than in air; while according to Huygens's undulatory theory it should be less. Not until the middle of the nineteenth century was a means found of determining experimentally the velocities of light in water and air in a laboratory. The crucial experiment which would decide which theory was true was performed by a French physicist, Jean Leon Foucault, in 1850; and it showed that light, which travels at the rate of about 186,000 miles a second in air, travels through water at about three-quarters that velocity. The result of this experiment disposed finally of the emission theory, and re-established Huygens's theory that light is due to very rapid vibrations in a hypothetical ether pervading the universe.

Fifty years before the crucial determination was made of the velocities of light in water and air, a genius of the first magnitude—Dr. Thomas Young—had shown that red light is produced by nearly 32,000 ether-waves to the inch, and that the number of such waves in a given length increases progressively in passing from red to violet, until at this end of the colour scale there are about 60,000 undulations to the inch. Young also proved that certain optical effects could be explained only by the principal of interference of ether-waves with one another; but his researches and interpretations, involving as they did the existence of an imponderable ether which, to use his words "pervades the substance of all material bodies, with little or no resistance, as freely, perhaps, as the wind passes through a grove of trees," met with ridicule from leaders in the literary world, and were not given serious attention by his scientific contemporaries. When in 1815 a French investigator, Augustin Jean Fresnel, began experimental work in optics, and was also led to the discovery of interference in light, he knew nothing of the previous work done by Young in the same direction thirteen years earlier. The work of these two investigators revived the undulatory theory and opened a question which may be said not to have been settled decisively until Foucault's crucial experiment had been made.

Here, then, we have an instance of a scientific theory being abandoned when it had been shown to be untenable by decisive experiment. It is possible that, as knowledge increases, the theory which has held its own for three-quarters of a century, may have to be modified; indeed, researches in the domain of radioactivity have proved the existence of minute particles moving with the high velocities demanded by Newton's corpuscular theory of light. It has yet to be shown, however, that such particles can account for optical phenomena as completely as the wave-theory does, though they are probably concerned with radiation of all kinds.

The point on which we wish to insist is that men of science do not regard theories as dogmas to be held at all costs, and in face of all contradictory evidence, but as ways in which phenomena can be explained. Often the theory or the rule is wrong; and it should only be accepted as an approach to truth when it can be put to the test. There must be theories and hypotheses, but it is necessary to distinguish them from the results of careful and accurate observation. The road along which the progress of science has been accomplished is strewn with the remains of hypotheses and theories broken upon the Procrustean bed of facts of observation. A hypothesis is merely a provisional or working explanation of phenomena faithfully observed and recorded, and it must be discarded when further observations prove it to be untenable. In the acceptance of this principle, the scientific type of mind differs from that which is content to accept medieval scholastic philosophy as a final court of appeal for new knowledge.

The poet perceives in Nature resemblances and meanings which are hidden to the ordinary mind. The truly great man of science likewise uses imaginative insight in his theoretical conceptions, and it enables him to project known facts into unknown regions and see the picture produced upon the new mental plane. Many great discoveries have been made by this scientific use of the imagination; but in all cases they have depended upon a basis of fact revealed by observation or experiment. There must be knowledge before any useful hypothesis or assumption can be formed as to what should follow from it. The hypothesis which represents an effort of imaginative power not founded upon a wide range of facts may pass as fiction, but it has no place in science.

Given the results of observation or experiment, the philosopher endeavours to discover a law or principle connecting them. He guesses at their meaning, and invents a hypothesis which will not only explain what is known, but also suggests consequences which may, or may not, be confirmed by future investigations. Prof. A. Senier relates that von Hofmann used to say to him and other research students working in the Berlin laboratory, "I will listen to any suggested hypothesis, but on one condition—that you show me a method by which it can be tested." Without such a condition, the creations of a disordered mind would be as worthy of consideration as the speculations of a scientific genius; and fertile ideas would be sought not in a laboratory but in an asylum. A hypothesis ought, therefore, to be capable of being verified, even though the means may not be available of applying a crucial test to it at the time; it ought also to be sufficiently definite to admit of proof or condemnation.

Imagination as distinguished from fancy is an essential attribute of the scientific mind that makes for progress. "With accurate experiment and observation to work upon," says Tyndall, "imagination becomes the architect of physical theory. Newton's passage from a falling apple to a falling moon was an act of the prepared imagination. Out of the facts of chemistry the constructive imagination of Dalton formed the atomic theory. Davy was richly endowed with the imaginative faculty, while with Faraday its exercise was incessant, preceding, accompanying and guiding all his experiments. His strength and fertility as a discoverer are to be referred in great part to the stimulus of the imagination." Darwin was equal to Faraday in imaginative power; he was continually forming theories, but his fertility in this respect was balanced by the power of severe criticism to which he subjected the products of his imagination. His son says that he was willing to test what would seem to most people not at all worth testing; and that he enjoyed making what he called "fools' experiments" to judge whether a view or hypothesis was false or true.

In science, however, the value of the imagination increases with breadth of knowledge. A child may imagine the stars to be windows in the vault of heaven, and their twinkling the fluttering of angels' wings passing in front of them. His conception of the stellar universe may be beautiful, but it differs widely from that on which the astronomer endeavours to construct a scientific cosmogony.

How easy it is to overlook objects and phenomena when their significance is not understood is illustrated by an incident related by Darwin himself. While a student at Cambridge, he went to Wales with Sedgwick, the professor of geology, and examined the rocks for fossils. This was before Agassiz had shown that at one period of geological history the rocks of the country must have been buried beneath a sheet of ice which left unmistakable marks of its action upon them. "But," says Darwin, "neither of us saw a trace of the wonderful glacial phenomena all round us; we did not notice plainly scored rocks, the perched boulders, the lateral and terminal moraines. Yet these phenomena are so conspicuous that, as I declared in a paper published many years afterwards in the *Philosophical Magazine,* a house burnt down by fire did not tell its story more plainly than did this valley."

Imaginative writers may produce fantastic romances in which future conditions are portrayed, but neither they nor the prophet who bases his prediction upon existing knowledge can forecast with any confidence the character of new discoveries. It is often easy to foretell the development and further application of knowledge already acquired, but this system of extrapolation of curves of existing conditions cannot take into consideration the discovery of new factors which may alter, and frequently do alter, the trend of tendency. Even an author like Mr. H. G. Wells, with wide scientific learning upon which to build his brilliant romances, could not anticipate such discoveries as wireless telegraphy, Röntgen rays or radium, though he could foresee extensions of existing knowledge, and visualise social effects of progressive science and invention.

Science advances by opening completely new fields of knowledge upon which the literary man or investigator may exercise their intellectual activities, and the directions in which these domains are to be found are rarely indicated with success in romantic or in scientific literature. Because it is impossible to know what future work will bring forth, purely imaginative forecasts of things to come are probably as much, or as little, to be depended upon as strictly logical conclusions based upon accomplished fact. True it is that "whether there be prophecies, they shall fail; whether there be tongues, they shall cease; whether there be knowledge, it shall vanish away."

CHAPTER VII

LAW AND PRINCIPLE

The great tragedy of science—the slaying of a beautiful hypothesis by an ugly fact. Huxley.

Consistency in regard to opinions is the slow poison of the intellectual life, the destroyer of its vividness and its energy. Sir Humphry Davy.

Of all monarchs Nature is the most just in enactment of laws, and the most rigorous in punishing the violation of them. Wilkins.

> *Though the mills of God grind slowly,*
> *Yet they grind exceeding small:*
> *Though with patience he stands waiting,*
> *With exactness, grinds he all.* Longfellow.

Nature is so varied in her manifestations and phenomena, and the difficulty of elucidating their causes is so great, that many must unite their knowledge and efforts in order to comprehend her and force her to reveal her laws. Laplace.

For Nature, Time is nothing. It is never a difficulty: she always has it at her disposal: and it is for her the means by which she has accomplished the greatest as well as the least results. Lamarck.

In a scientific sense, a natural law is merely a precise statement of the relationship between certain results of observation. Facts must first be collected by observation or measurement; then they have to be classified and compared with the view of finding any relationship existing between them. When a relation is discovered which shows the dependence of one group of facts upon another, it is called a scientific law, or a law of Nature. Often the law can be expressed in mathematical terms; but it may be only a brief description in words of certain relationships in the field of Nature. In either case, there must be no exception to the law. The laws of civil life can be broken, and sometimes are broken deliberately in order to direct attention to their injustice. But a law of Nature is simply a statement of relationship, and when observations prove the statement to be incorrect, then the law has to be abandoned or modified to take the new facts into consideration.

The method of science, indeed, is the method of the Chancery Court—it involves the collection of all available evidence and the subjection of all such evidence to the most searching examination and cross examination. False evidence may be tendered and for the time being accepted; but sooner or later the perjury is discovered. Our method, in fact, goes beyond that of the courts: we are not only always prepared to reconsider our judgments but always searching for fresh evidence; we dare to be positive only when, time after time, the facts appear to warrant a definite conclusion. *Prof. H. E. Armstrong.*

The broad generalisation which is accepted as a law of Nature by one generation may thus prove to be only an approximation to the truth when fuller knowledge has been acquired. When a formula expressing relationships between facts or phenomena in Nature is so exact and comprehensive that it suffices for whatever new knowledge has been gained by the increase of perceptive powers from one generation to another, it stands out as a great achievement of scientific thought.

The grand, and indeed only, character of truth is its capability of enduring the test of human experience, and coming unchanged out of every possible form of fair discussion. *Sir John Herschel.*

Pre-conceived ideas and traditional beliefs are drags on the chariot of truth. By meditation Plato arrived at the doctrine that the planets move at uniform rates in circles. A circle was conceived to be the most perfect figure, therefore it was concluded to represent the appropriate path of a heavenly body, without any reference to actual observation or experience. For fifteen hundred years Plato's principle of uniform motion in circles was not disputed, and even Copernicus, while constructing his revolutionary system, regarded it as an axiom that "The movement of the heavenly bodies is uniform, circular, perpetual, or else composed of circular movements." The difficulties which this tradition introduced in trying to make observation fit theory were explained in one way or other, but there were always errors or defects which could only be accounted for by complicated reasoning.

When Kepler began his analysis of Tycho Brahe's accurate observations of the positions and motions of heavenly bodies, particularly of the planet Mars, he tried numerous combinations of circles and epicycles with the view of finding a theory to account for them completely. The Copernican theory was sufficient to explain the general aspects of the heavens, but the principle of uniform circular motion postulated by it for the planets was unable to satisfy the standards of precise measurement. Kepler found that when theory was confronted with observation there was always an error of eight or nine minutes of angular measurement, and this amount he believed to be impossible in such careful observations as were made by Tycho Brahe. The amount is about equal to one-fourth the apparent angular diameter of the sun, or to the angle subtended by a halfpenny looked at squarely from a distance of a dozen yards. "Out of these eight minutes," said Kepler, "we will construct a new theory that will explain the motions of all the planets."

All previous theories had assumed the existence of uniform circular movement; and it was only when this doctrine had to be abandoned that Kepler was led to the truths embodied in his three famous laws of planetary motion. In the first of these laws the Platonic principle was disestablished for ever, for it states that the planets do not move in circles but in ellipses, and that the sun is situated at a focus of each ellipse. The second law, announced at the same time, in 1609, defines the rate of movement and shows that a planet moves fastest when nearest the sun and slowest when most distant. The third fundamental truth, which was not discovered until nine years later, is known as the Harmonic law, and gives precisely the relation that exists between periods of revolution and distances from the centre of motion. By means of this law, the distance of a planet from the sun, in comparison with the earth's distance, can be calculated when the period which the planet takes to make a complete revolution round the sun is known. In the work in which he announced this law, the discovery of which had occupied twenty years of his life, Kepler wrote in words of unfeigned delight:

that for which I joined Tycho Brahe, for which I settled in Prague, for which I have devoted the best part of my life to astronomical contemplations, at length I have brought to light, and recognised its truth beyond my most sanguine expectations . . . the die is cast, the book is written, to be read either now or by posterity, I care not which; it may well wait a century for a reader, as God has waited six thousand years for an observer. *Kepler.*

The meaning of Kepler's three laws of planetary motion remained a mystery until Newton's discovery of the principle or law of universal gravitation. By this discovery not only were the facts then known as to celestial forms and movements capable of explanation, but also every case to which the principle has since been applied.

> Nature and Nature's laws lay hid in night.
> God said, "Let Newton be!" and all was light. *Pope.*

There had been many surmises as to the nature of the force which keeps the planets in their courses around the sun and makes the moon describe its path around the earth. It had been shown that the strength of the force of attraction between two bodies does not diminish, as Kepler supposed, in the simple ratio of the distance separating them, that is, is halved when the distance is doubled, but varies as the square of the distance. When the distance is doubled, the force is thus reduced to one-quarter, when trebled, to one-ninth, and so on. The problem was to account for the movements of the planets and their satellites in elliptical orbits upon the assumption of a force varying in this way.

In January, 1684, Sir Christopher Wren offered Hooke and Halley "the present of a book of forty shillings" if either of them could bring him a convincing demonstration within two months that such a force would cause a planet to move in an ellipse. The demonstration had not been given in August of the same year when Halley went to Cambridge to consult Newton on the subject. Without mentioning any of the speculations of Wren, Hooke or himself, he asked at once:

"What will be the curve described by the planets on the supposition that gravity diminishes as the square of the distance?"

Newton answered immediately, "An ellipse."

"How do you know?" asked Halley in amazement.

"Why," replied Newton, "I have calculated it," and he proceeded to search for the calculation, but unsuccessfully.

Halley returned to London with the knowledge that the problem had been solved, but without the demonstration, which, however, reached him in November, and early in the following year was communicated to the Royal Society. Halley was thus the means of bringing Newton's immortal discovery to light; and he used justly to boast that he had been "the Ulysses who produced this Achilles."

Twenty years before this, in 1665, Newton's mind had been directed to the subject of gravity. He had left Cambridge on account of the plague, and was in the garden of his home at Woolsthorpe, Lincolnshire, speculating upon the power of gravity, when an apple fell from a tree and is said to have started a train of thought which led to the discovery of the universal law of gravitation. There is little foundation for this anecdote; and in Newton's case the fall of an apple was certainly not needed to originate a speculation to which several natural philosophers of his day had given attention.

An isolated fact can be observed by all eyes; by those of the ordinary person as well as of the wise. But it is the true physicist alone who may see the bond which unites several facts among which the relationship is important, though obscure. The story of Newton's apple is probably not true, but it is symbolical; so let us think of it as true. Well, we must believe that many before Newton had seen apples fall, but they made no deduction. Facts are sterile until there are minds capable of choosing between them and discerning those which conceal something and recognising that which is concealed; minds which under the bare fact see the soul of the fact. *Henri Poincaré.*

The free fall of an object on the earth made a convenient point of departure for Newton's mental ex-

cursion into space; and the line of reasoning was: a
body falls, or is pulled toward the earth's centre by a
force which is called gravity; does this force extend
beyond the earth to the moon, and if so, will it account
for the motion of our satellite around the earth?

A stone dropped from a height upon the earth's
surface falls 193 inches in a second; how far would it
fall in the same time if it were dropped from the distance of the moon? Assuming that the centre of attraction may be regarded as at the centre of the earth,
the moon is sixty times farther away from this point
than is the earth's surface. The force would, therefore, be not 60 times less but 60×60, or 3,600 times
less, for it diminishes according to the square of the
distance. To make an accurate calculation of the
amount, however, requires a correct knowledge of the
distance from the earth's centre to the surface, that is,
of the earth's radius.

Taking the value accepted in 1666, Newton calculated that the moon would fall towards the earth by 44
thousandths of an inch in a second; in other words,
this is the amount by which the path of the moon
should deviate from a straight line in a second in order
to describe its curved path around the earth in a month.
The amount by which the moon actually swerves from
a rectilinear path in a second is 53 thousandths of an
inch, so Newton saw that the calculated result did not
agree with what was then considered to be fact. The
discrepancy between theory and observation "induced
him to abandon the subject, and pursue other studies
with which he had been previously occupied."

Not until 1684 did he "resume his thoughts concerning the moon." A few years before that time an accurate determination of the size of the earth had been
made by Picard, and this gave a more correct value of

the length of the earth's radius than had previously
been accepted. Using the new value, Newton again
took up the calculation of the moon's deflection from a
straight path, on the assumption of the force controlling it being the same as that which causes bodies to
fall on the earth, but diminished in strength on account
of the distance of the moon from the earth. The result
now obtained showed that the central force should
cause the moon to swerve from a straight line path by
53 thousandths of an inch in a second, which is exactly
the amount that will produce the curved path described
by the moon around the earth. As the calculations
which were thus to extend the domain of gravity from
the earth to the universe were drawing to a close, it is
related that Newton was "so much agitated that he
was obliged to desire a friend to finish them."

It must not be supposed for a moment that the
problem of testing the theory of gravitation by the
motion was so simple as it is here presented. In order
to establish the principle, Newton had to prove that as
regards gravitational attraction, a globe like the sun,
moon, or earth behaves as if the force due to the whole
of the mass resided at the centre alone. This conclusion was only arrived at after infinite labour and by
the employment of a new mathematical method invented by him. By this same method also he was able
to prove that the path of a body under the influence of
attraction depending upon a central force could be an
ellipse or any other related curve. The elliptical paths
of the moon around the earth, the earth and other
planets around the sun, and of all satellites around
their primary planets were explained by this discovery; yet, as we have seen, Newton was content with
having found it, and only through the intervention of
Halley was the world made aware of it.

This is not the place to show that the law of universal gravitation provides a complete explanation of Kepler's three laws of planetary motion, or to discuss its profound significance. There are certain discordances between theory and observation in the motion of the moon which have not been accounted for by gravitational influence; nevertheless, the law of gravitation meets practically all the demands made upon it. It explains the fall of bodies on the earth, and the motions of the planets and their satellites; it enables the paths of comets to be calculated, and the disturbances to which they may be subjected in passing near more massive bodies; it is used to determine the masses of bodies in our solar system, and of stars revolving round one another, and is applied to calculate the tide-raising effects of the sun and moon; while by it tables of the moon's movements are calculated to a high degree of perfection for use in determining longitude at sea.

It has been truly said that "The tendency of the human mind is to exaggerate the possibilities of the unknown." Wherever there is ignorance, Nature is dreaded as much as a child dreads darkness. The appearance of a comet in the sky caused whole nations in earlier days to tremble with fear because nothing was known of the nature and movements of these bodies. From the time that Newton showed that comets travel round the sun in definite paths under the control of gravitational attraction, the feeling of awe and anxiety formerly produced by such celestial visitors has been diminishing. They are now looked upon as interesting spectacles instead of being regarded as heralds of disaster.

Edmund Halley was inspired by Newton's work to calculate the paths of a number of comets. He found that three comets, which appeared in 1531, 1607, and 1682, had practically the same path or orbit, and he concluded that they were really one and the same body travelling around the sun in a period of about seventy-five years. He predicted, therefore, that the comet would appear again in the year 1758, or thereabouts; that is, seventy-six years after 1682. He knew he would not be alive to see if the prediction was fulfilled, but he expressed the hope that, when the comet was seen, posterity would remember the prediction had been made by an Englishman. This was the first prediction of the periodic return of a comet, and Halley's boldness in making it was justified completely. The comet, which was anxiously awaited, appeared in 1758 and again in 1835 and 1910. By examining old records, Halley's comet, as it is properly named, has been traced back in steps of about seventy-five years to the year 240 B.C.

Newton showed that the law of gravitation was sufficient to account for the motion of the comet of 1680 to which he applied it; and since then the paths of hundreds of comets have been calculated on the same principle. Most comets are unannounced visitors to the solar system, called from the depths of space by the attractive influence of the sun, but following paths which carry them away again into the outer darkness. Some, however, like Halley's comet, traverse orbits which are closed curves, and these return after an interval which may be reckoned in years or hundreds of years. But the path of every comet of which sufficient observations are available is calculated upon the basis of the law of gravitation. The apparently adventitious motions of these bodies are thus reducible to perfect law and order; and the decline of the superstitious dread in which they had been held may be said to have begun with Newton's discovery.

A notable example of the prediction of the existence of a body from consideration of its gravitational influence was afforded by the discovery of the planet Neptune. After the planet Uranus had been discovered in 1781 by Sir William Herschel, astronomers calculated the path in which it moved, and predicted the positions it should occupy from time to time. The planet was found, however, to be slightly behind or ahead of its calculated position. If we know a train is moving at a certain rate, we can say where it ought to be on the line at a certain time, and if it is not there we assume that something has happened. So it was with the planet Uranus: the difference between the actual and the calculated positions of the planet was assumed to be due to the disturbing influence of some unknown body beyond it.

There was every confidence that a massive globe somewhere in the darkness of space was making its presence manifest; and though the problem of finding the place of the disturber was very difficult, it was solved by two mathematicians—one an Englishman named Adams and the other a Frenchman named Le Verrier. In September, 1846, Sir John Herschel, son of Sir William Herschel, said: "We see it [the probable new planet] as Columbus saw America from the shores of Spain. Its movements have been felt trembling along the far-reaching line of our analysis with a certainty hardly inferior to that of ocular demonstration." On the twenty-third of the same month a German astronomer, Dr. Galle, found the new body close to the place which calculation had shown it ought to occupy. This is probably the greatest triumph of mathematics applied to the law of gravitation yet achieved.

The law of gravitation has proved to be a universal key which has opened the door of many secret places in Nature, yet what the key itself is—or wherein lies the cause of the attraction of gravitation—is still to seek. Now that the interstellar ether is becoming almost as familiar to us as a household world, and its recondite properties are being unravelled, there is, perhaps, some prospect of the problem being solved. Efforts have been made to discover whether gravitational force is propagated instantaneously through space. If we could suddenly create or destroy a centre of attraction, as we can a beam of light, the answer would be fairly easy. But as it is, we can only watch whether changes of position among the heavenly bodies produce their proper effect upon other bodies at once or after a measurable lapse of time. So far, no evidence of such a lapse of time has been forthcoming, although the most favoured theories demand it.

One of those theories, originally due to Le Sage, supposes that an infinite number of very small "ultramundane" particles is constantly traversing space in all directions. They are partly intercepted by ponderable matter. Hence two bodies will shield each other from the particles on one side, and the bombardment on the outside will drive them together, producing an apparent "attraction" between them. Reasons have been found for the conclusion that at a certain great distance gravitational attraction is intercepted altogether. If this were true, Newton's grand conception of universal gravitation would have to be modified, and we should have to consider the visible universe as held together by beams of light.

Next to the law of gravitation, the greatest generalisation established by science, and the one to which likewise no exception has been found, is the law of the con-

servation of energy, which asserts that though energy
can be converted from one form to another it cannot be
created or destroyed. A related generalisation of much
greater antiquity is the law of the conservation of matter, upon the foundation of which modern chemistry has
been built. Whenever a chemical change takes place,
whether in the burning of a candle, the explosion of
gunpowder, or in any other form, the weight of the substances produced is equal to the sum of the weights of
the constituents involved in the change. Since Lavoisier enunciated this principle, the most accurate investigations have failed to detect a loss or gain of the
minutest particle of matter; and the permanence of the
amount of material in our universe is, therefore, an
axiom of science.

The Sicilian philosopher, Empedocles, born about
494 B.C., seems to have been the first to associate changes
of matter into various forms with force or energy. He
regarded fire and earth and air and water as the four
"elements," and said they were influenced by two dynamic powers or principles—Love and Strife—one
tending to bring them together and the other to separate them. In his universe there was no creation or
absolute destruction of the "elements," but only changing combinations and transformations. "For," he
said, "from what does not exist at all it is impossible
that anything can come into being, and it is neither
possible nor perceivable that being should perish completely." By considering the four material "elements"
as eternal but changing in composition through the
action of forces of attraction and repulsion, Empedocles
approached nearer than any other early philosopher to
the modern doctrines of the conservation of matter and
the relation between matter and energy.

A corollary upon the doctrine of the indestructibility

of matter is that an atom may in its time play many parts. When Shakespeare made Hamlet say:

> Imperial Caesar, dead and turned to clay,
> Might stop a hole to keep the wind away,

he was only expressing the belief in transmigration held by Empedocles. "For in truth I was born a boy and a maiden, and a plant and a bird, and a fish whose course lies in the sea." Our bodies may be buried or burnt, but in either case the elements of which they are composed will merely take other places in a never-ending cycle, while the energy or soul of life will manifest itself in other forms.

The idea of the conservation of mass is easy to understand, but that of the conservation of energy is less obvious and is, perhaps, best explained by a concrete illustration. When a certain amount of energy is caused to actuate a machine, a certain amount of useful work may be obtained from it, but the efficient output is always less than the energy supplied, on account of loss due to friction between various parts of the machine. When the energy thus wasted is accounted for, the total is the same as that of the original supply; hence no machine can be constructed to give out in the form of available work as much energy as is put into it; and, therefore, perpetual motion is impossible. Expressed in other words, we never get something for nothing in Nature. Commission has to be paid whenever energy is exchanged from one form into another; and even with the most efficient engine the charge for the transformation is very high.

The heat produced by the combustion of coal represents energy which is utilised to convert water into steam and thus drive engines. Suppose a certain amount of coal to be capable of generating 100 units of heat when burnt in the furnace of an engine. About 25 per cent. of this quantity of heat is lost from various causes, and 75 per cent. reaches the engine in the steam. Only 6 of these units, however, are convertible into the mechanical work represented by the driving of the engine, and the remaining 69 per cent. is lost. If the 6 units are used to drive a dynamo for the production of electric power, 1 has to be paid as commission for the exchange, thus leaving us with 5 units. Let these 5 units be used to drive an electric motor; the mechanical energy obtained represents about 4½ units, half a unit being lost in the transformation. The final result, therefore, of the transformation of energy from the combustion of coal to the work obtainable from an electric motor is, that of the prime value of 100 units of energy, 95½ per cent. is lost by the various exchanges. In the whole series of these or any other related changes, the items on the two sides of the balance sheet give the same total, the energy supplied being always equal to the sum of the useful and useless energy obtained.

Traces of the idea of the conservation of energy may be found amongst the writings of ancient philosophers, and Descartes held that it was a self-evident truth. To establish the truth, however, precise and detailed investigations were necessary, and these were not made until nearly the middle of the nineteenth century, when interest in the question appears to have been widespread.

Towards the close of the eighteenth century, Count Rumford and Sir Humphry Davy conceived the idea that there was some correspondence between work done and heat produced, but they did not realise completely that mechanical energy and heat were reciprocally convertible. A French philosopher, Sadi Carnot, saw the

connection between the two forms of energy represented by heat and mechanical work, and he announced
in 1824 that the expenditure of a given amount of work
would produce a definite quantity of heat, but his conclusions received no recognition at the time. The
problem was to measure exactly the amount of work
which must be done to obtain a given quantity of heat;
that is, to determine the mechanical equivalent of heat.

Séguin in France calculated this relationship by observing the fall of temperature of steam when expanding against external pressure. From 1842 to 1847 J.
R. Mayer, K. F. Mohr, and H. von Helmholtz, in Germany, and L. A. Colding, in Denmark, all arrived independently, by various lines of reasoning and experiment, at the great generalisation of the conservation of
energy, but the work which established the principle
upon the solid ground of accurate measurement was
done by a scientific amateur, James Prescott Joule, a
brewer at Salford, near Manchester.

By a number of careful experiments Joule showed
that a definite quantity of heat was always produced
by the expenditure of a definite amount of mechanical
work. When a pebble is dropped from a bridge into a
stream flowing beneath, the impact with the water produces a certain quantity of heat, the quantity depending
upon the weight of the pebble and the distance of the
fall. Joule found that the fall of a pound weight
through a distance of 778 feet always generated sufficient heat to raise the temperature of a pound of water
one degree Fahrenheit.

Probably this conclusion does not strike you as very
remarkable; neither did it appear so to the members
of the British Association before whom the experiments were described in 1843, Joule being then a young
man of twenty-five years of age, completely unknown in

the scientific world. Genius dwells with the Gods on Mount Olympus, and only a few daring spirits climb up from the valleys to worship at its shrine. This is as true of science as it is of art, or literature, or music. Commonplace work can be understood by the many, but original conceptions demand effort to comprehend them, and they are, therefore, usually unregarded, or if noticed, condemned.

Undaunted by the chilling reception which his communication received, Joule continued his researches, and in 1845, and also in 1847, he presented accounts of further investigations to two other meetings of the British Association. On the latter occasion he was asked by the chairman of the section to confine himself to a short verbal description of his experiments; and his work would again have gone unheeded but for the presence of another young man, William Thomson, afterwards Lord Kelvin. What happened was described many years afterwards by Joule himself:

Discussion not being invited, the communication would have passed without comment if a young man had not risen in the section, and by his intelligent observations created a lively interest in the new theory. The young man was William Thomson, who had two years previously passed the University of Cambridge with the highest honours, and is now probably the foremost scientific authority of the age.

Joule's discovery of the mechanical equivalent of heat was not a result stumbled upon accidentally, but a consequence of rigorous experiment, precise measurement and philosophic thought. After he had assured himself of the truth of the principle, Joule devoted himself to the elaboration of methods of working, modifying and repeating experiments in various ways in order to determine its numerical value with increased exactness. Many investigators have followed him along the same roads, arriving at much the same value as he did; and the generalisation thus established upon unimpeachable evidence is embodied in the First Law of Thermodynamics, familiar to every mechanical engineer as well as to all physicists, and expressed in the words, "When work is transformed into heat, or heat into work, the quantity of work is mechanically equivalent to the quantity of heat." "Joule's initial work," said Lord Kelvin, when unveiling a statue of him at Manchester in 1893, "was the very foundation of our knowledge of the steam engine and steam power. Taken along with Carnot's work it gave the scientific foundation on which all the great improvements since the year 1850 had been worked out, not in a haphazard way, but on a careful philosophical basis."

Joule's work stands in the esteem of men of science by the side of that of Newton, yet when a movement was started to commemorate it in Westminster Abbey, the Dean of Westminster had to confess he was unacquainted with it, and only after some difficulty was an area about two feet square in a dark corner placed at the disposal of the memorial committee in the English Valhalla.

"And so," says Sir Henry Roscoe, in describing the circumstances which led to the memorial, "a simple tablet is inserted in one of the side walls just below the effigy of Charles Darwin; and thus within a foot or two of one another are placed the simple and unattractive acknowledgments of work done, the like of which hath not been seen, and the importance of which cannot be reckoned. The ridiculous, if it were not the pathetic, position thus accorded to two men who have conferred inestimable benefits not only on our own country but also on the world at large, when compared with the grandiose monuments to political, naval and military nonentities is, it must be confessed, a somewhat humiliating reflection on the lack of appreciation of science shown in the English Temple of Fame. But, after all, this is of little moment, for the names of Darwin and Joule will live for ever in the minds and hearts of all those who appreciate scientific worth.''

The discovery of a law of Nature is always of great advantage to scientific progress. By the warp and woof of experiment, the man of science weaves a pattern from the threads of evidence, and presents the result to the world for anyone to use or improve. A further example of this is afforded by the discovery, in 1826, by George Simon Ohm, the son of a German locksmith, of the law of electricity named after him.

Before Ohm commenced his investigations, many men of science had studied the wonderful and manifold effects of the electric current. Remarkable phenomena were observed, but they formed only a tangled skein until Ohm discovered a simple law stating the relationship between cause and effect in electricity. The law is simply that the rate of flow of an electric current is equal to the electric pressure divided by the resistance offered to the current by the wire or other conductor through which it is flowing. Ohm was working independently and alone when he discovered this law; and even after he had established it beyond question he received little recognition for his work, while from many sides it was sharply criticised. It often happens that a prophet is not without honour except in his own country and among his own people, and this was the case with Ohm, the importance of the work of the unassuming German teacher being recognised in England before it was in his native land.

Ohm's law is of universal application in electrical engineering, and few problems can be worked without making use of it. Except at extremely low temperatures, such as those of liquid air and helium, the law has been proved to be true even when put to the most searching tests. It is one of the most accurately known laws of Nature, and the most important recorded in the whole range of the history of electrical science. The name of the modest student, who never strove for show or glory, is to-day upon the lips of thousands who are busy with the work of electro-technical industries. In 1889, on the hundredth anniversary of his birth, the Royal Bavarian Academy of Sciences, Munich, celebrated his services to posterity by a special meeting, and an address was given, in the course of which the following inspiring passage occurs:

The deeds of a man of science are his scientific investigations. Truth once discovered does not remain shut up in the study or the laboratory. When the moment comes, it bursts its narrow bonds and joins the quick pulse of life. That which has been discovered in solitude, in the unselfish struggle for knowledge, in pure love of science, is often fated to be the mighty lever to advance the culture of our race. When, nearly a hundred years ago, Galvani saw the frog's legs twitch under the influence of two metals touching, who could have suspected that the force of Nature which caused those twitchings would transfer the thoughts of man to far distant lands, with lightning's speed, under the waters of the ocean— would even render audible at a distance the sound of the spoken word? That this force of Nature—after man by ceaseless investigation had learned vastly to increase its strength—would illuminate our nights like the sun! This enormous development of electro-technology could only be accomplished upon the firm foundation of Ohm's law. For only he can govern a force of Nature who has mastered its law. Ohm, by wresting from Nature her long-concealed secret, has placed the sceptre of this dominion in the hands of the present. *Prof. E. von Lommel.*

Natural laws like those of Newton, Joule and Ohm bear any strain to which they may be subjected; they connect cause and consequence so closely that predictions based upon them can be made with complete con-

fidence. Each of these three laws refer to inanimate
or mechanical conditions; the things embraced by them
belong to the regions of dead matter and blind force,
and when we pass to the biological world where organisms possess individuality—call it soul or spirit if
you will—no such perfect truths as are found in physical science can be expected. It is possible, however,
to arrive at broad generalisations, and the greatest of
these is that of organic evolution and its causes.

More than six hundred thousand different species of
animals have been described, while about half that number of species of plants are known, and probably natural science has not yet on its registers one half of the
numbers of animals and plants which actually exist.
Each of these separate species could be, and formerly
was, assumed to have been an object of special creation,
but a more reasonable view is that the various forms
have been evolved as the result of the action of natural
processes.

The idea of evolution goes back to Aristotle and other
early Greek philosophers who attempted to face the
problems of the origin and development of forms of life.
No real advance was, however, made in the use of the
idea in the long period of theologians and natural philosophers which lasted until about the beginning of
the seventeenth century, when Greek traditions were
largely shaken off and the modern method of inductive
observation and reasoning may be said to have begun.
Among the lay writers of that century who suggested
that species of animals and plants might undergo change
in the course of time was Sir Walter Raleigh. In his
History of the World (1621), written during his imprisonment, referring to the days of the Flood, he said,
"But it is manifest, and undoubtedly true, that many
of the *Species,* which now seeme differing, and of sev-

eral kindes, were not then *in rerum natura*"; and he remarked that he could see no difference, except in size, between the cat of Europe and the ounce of India, the dog-fish and the shark, the dog and the wolf.

Buffon, the French naturalist, who is sometimes given the credit of originating modern views of evolution, did not go much farther than this nearly a century and a half later. He surveyed natural history in a series of sumptuous and comprehensive volumes, and inspired interest in it by his animated style and bold speculation, but though he suggested that new species of animals and plants might be produced by progressive change, and that all quadrupeds might have come from a few original forms, he did not indicate how the transformation could have taken place. Other naturalists and philosophers who speculated upon the problems of evolution in the eighteenth century were Goethe, who held that "the more perfect organic natures, from fishes to mammals, and man at their head, were formed on one original type which still daily changes its form by propagation," and Erasmus Darwin, who suggested how successive generations of an organism might by their actions or wants "New powers acquire, and larger limbs assume."

But while these and many other writers had accepted the doctrine of evolution in organic life, none had shown with any force how the development had taken place. The first serious attempt to discover the law governing evolutionary changes was made by Jean de Lamarck, the eminent French zoologist, who devoted many years of his life to studies of the problem of the origin of species. The main points of the principle published by Lamarck in 1801 are that animals may have their structures modified by external conditions or by continued use or disuse, and that the succeeding generation inherits the modification. On this principle, the long neck of the giraffe is explained by the constant strain-ing of generations of the animal to reach the tender shoots at the tops of trees, and the splay foot of the camel by continued walking on desert sands. The two fundamental laws of adaptation and heredity formu-lated by Lamarck to account for the production of new species were stated by him as follows:

1.   In every animal which has not got beyond the period of developing, the frequent and sustained use of any organ grad-ually strengthens it, develops it, enlarges it, and gives it a power proportionate to the duration of the using of it; while the continued disuse of this or that organ imperceptibly weak-ens it; and it deteriorates, loses its power by degrees, and finally disappears.

2.   All that Nature has allowed individuals to gain or lose by the influence of the circumstances to which their race has been exposed for a long time, and consequently, by the effect of predominant use of this organ or continued disuse of that, is conserved in the new individuals who spring from them, and who, therefore, find themselves better adapted than their ancestors, if the conditions of existence have not changed.

Lamarck's principle thus states not only that varia-tions may be produced by the influence of external con-ditions, or by exercise, but also that the new characters thus acquired are inherited by succeeding generations. How far the principle supplies the true cause of natural processes has been a matter of much discussion in re-cent years, but the proof of the inheritance of acquired characteristics postulated by it has yet to be accepted at the bar of scientific opinion.

Lamarck grasped the truth of organic evolution bet-ter than any naturalist who preceded him, and he carried out the principle on a far larger scale and in greater detail than others had done, but his arguments were not convincing. It was reserved for Charles

Darwin and Alfred Russel Wallace to import into the problem an entirely fresh set of considerations, and to establish a new and illuminating theory upon a secure basis of fact.

As naturalist on H.M.S. *Beagle* during a five years' voyage round the world, thrown upon his own mental resources and furnished with many new and interesting facts, Darwin was early confronted with many sides of the process of evolution upon which to exercise his imaginative and reasoning powers. The solitude of the voyage and the almost continuous ill-health afterwards —"For forty years he never knew one day of health" —were contributing causes to the formation of those original and suggestive ideas which were the foundation of his greatness.

Upon returning home in 1836 Darwin began to look for facts in relation to the origin of species, upon which he had reflected long before. A year later, after reading Malthus's *Essay on the Principle of Population,* it occurred to him that in the struggle for existence among animals and plants, individuals which possessed variations favourable to particular circumstances would tend to be preserved, while those having unfavourable variations would be destroyed. The result would be the formation of a new species. Darwin fully understood the possibility of new species being produced by "sports" or "discontinuous variations," but he showed that evolution usually proceeds by taking advantage of slight successive variations. This was the idea upon which he never ceased working for twenty years, and which culminated in the publication of his *Origin of Species,* in 1859.

By collecting all facts which bore in any way on the variation of animals and plants under domestication and nature, some light might perhaps be thrown on the whole subject.

My first note-book was opened in July, 1837. I worked on true Baconian principles, and, without any theory, collected facts on a wholesale scale, more especially with respect to domesticated productions, by printed inquiries, by conversation with skilful breeders and gardeners, and by extensive reading. *Charles Darwin.*

Variation is a common attribute of organic life; no two animals of the same kind are exactly alike in every respect; and the forms best adapted to particular circumstances are the forms which survive longest and carry on their kind. Life is always a struggle, and the fittest for the time being are those which thrive best in their surroundings. The intensity of the struggle for existence, even in so large and open an arena as that of the ocean, is shown by the small number of fish which arrive at maturity in comparison with the immense number of eggs produced. It is estimated that of the five million or more eggs borne by a single codfish, all except two or three meet with untimely deaths at some stage of their career from the egg to the mature adult.

Application of the principles of natural selection can be found throughout the kingdom of animate Nature, but we will mention one only. After a severe storm of snow and sleet in North America, Prof. H. C. Bumpas collected one hundred and thirty-four sparrows which had been rendered insensible by the weather. Of these birds seventy-two survived, while sixty-two perished. On comparing the survivors with the eliminated individuals, very appreciable differences were found between them. Nearly all the birds which were longer than the average were among the dead, and the two shortest birds of the whole number collected also perished. Natural selection was, in fact, found to be most destructive of those birds which departed most from the normal type. The general conclusion drawn from the measurements of the birds which survived or were eliminated was that the next generation of sparrows in the storm-swept area would be shorter in length, weigh less, have longer legs and a greater brain capacity than the former generation.

Of course, many more observations of a similar kind are required before a definite statement could be made of the structural forms favourable or unfavourable to survival. The measurements are valuable so far as they go, but there may have been some characteristics which could not be measured and yet were really the determining causes of survival or death. It is, however, safe to conclude that in general, both with plants and animals, individuals which depart most from the normal type are the first to be eliminated. Even with the human race, we find genius dying early from neglect, while mediocrity treads contentedly along a primrose path. From the point of view of survival, it is just as bad to be in advance of the time as behind it.

Wallace arrived independently at the solution of the problem of evolution by means of the process of natural selection, and, like Darwin, he was led to it by Malthus's essay. It was Darwin's *Journal,* published in 1845, and read by Wallace at the age of twenty-three, which determined him to invite H. W. Bates to accompany him on his journey to the Amazon and Rio Negro, which filled the four years 1848-52. Throughout his whole career as a collector, Wallace had before him the problem of evolution and the cause of the origin of new species in animate nature. Before leaving for South America, in 1848, he wrote:

I begin to feel rather dissatisfied with a mere local collection; little is to be learnt from it. I should like to take some one family to study thoroughly, principally with a view to the theory of the origin of species. By that means I am strongly of opinion that some definite results might be arrived at. *Dr. A. R. Wallace.*

While at Sarawak, in 1855, Wallace was still pondering over the problem, which was rarely absent from his thoughts; and in a paper written at that time he concluded that every species which had come into existence in Nature was closely related to a species which preceded it. This pointed clearly to evolutionary development, and suggested when and where new species would be introduced; but it did not indicate how they could be brought into existence. After the publication of his paper, Wallace was informed by his agent that several naturalists had expressed regret that he was "theorising" when what he was expected to do was to collect facts; nevertheless, he still continued to consider the reason why one species becomes changed either slowly or rapidly into another. Though the cause of the change was unknown, the utilitarian mind considered it more important to increase the size of a collection of birds and insects—of which Wallace himself had gathered nearly nine thousand separate species —than to discover how the various distinct forms had originated.

In February, 1858, during a period of intermittent fever at Ternate, he was pondering over the problem when the conclusions arrived at by Malthus as to the factors affecting increase or decrease of population flashed upon him all the possible effects of the struggle for existence. In two days the entire draft of the paper showing the application of the views to organic species in general was sketched and posted to Darwin, who had been working upon the verification of the same idea for twenty years. Darwin had actually written out a sketch of his theory in 1842; and in 1844 this sketch was enlarged to 230 folio pages, giving a complete presentation of the arguments afterwards set forth in the *Origin of Species*.

When Darwin received Wallace's paper he brought the communication before Sir Charles Lyell and Sir Joseph Hooker, and urged that it should be printed at once. Upon their advice, however, he consented to let an extract from the sketch of 1844 be presented to the Linnean Society with Wallace's paper on July 1st, 1858. "The one great result which I claim for my paper of 1858," said Wallace, "is that it compelled Darwin to write and publish his *Origin of Species* without further delay."

For evolution to proceed in any particular direction, it is necessary for variations in that direction to be encouraged continually, and for the trend of tendency of the parent to be inherited by the offspring. Variation and heredity are thus complementary to each other; and until the laws by which they are determined are understood, no evolutionary theory can be said to be complete. The rule of the road of heredity was discovered in 1866 by Gregor Johann Mendel, an Augustinian monk, Abbot of the old monastery at Brünn, Austria; but the biological world remained unaware of it for thirty years, and Darwin died without knowing of the epoch-making work of his contemporary. "Had Mendel's work," says Prof. W. Bateson, the leading authority upon it, "come into the hands of Darwin, it is not too much to say that the history of the development of evolutionary philosophy would have been very different from that which we have witnessed."

For eight years Mendel carried on experiments on the hybridisation of peas and other plants in the large garden of the cloister of which he was Abbot or Prälat. He described his experiments in the *Proceedings of the Natural History Society of Brünn*, in 1866 and 1869,

Photo. L. Kuhn & Co., Paris.

V. THE THINKER.
Statue by Auguste Rodin, (1840- . . .), Pantheon, Paris.

and they remained unknown outside the circle of that
local society until the year 1900, when attention was
directed to them. He was in the habit of saying *Meine
Zeit wird schon kommen*—my time will no doubt come
—and his confidence has been fully justified. Since the
re-discovery of his two papers, the principles they teach
have been applied to hundreds of different plants and
animals, and Mendel's law has guided most studies of
heredity, while Mendelism has become a clearly-defined
branch of science. The white marble statue erected to
his memory in Brünn, in 1910, represents the esteem
in which scientific men of all nations now hold the
Abbot of the Königskloster in that city.

It would be out of place here to describe in detail the
nature and consequences of Mendel's great biological
discovery, but we may sketch its main principle. Working with garden peas, Mendel found that different
characters, such as wrinkled or smooth seed, colour of
the seed-coats, form of the pods, length of the stem, and
so on, could be used to distinguish them. He observed
that when two plants differing by a given feature were
crossed, the hybrid offspring invariably exhibited one
of the parental characters to the entire or partial ex-
clusion of the other. Thus when tall varieties of peas
were crossed with dwarf varieties, the offspring were
all tall. This character of tallness was called by Mendel
"dominant," while the character of shortness, which
does not appear in the first generation of the hybrid
plants, was described as "recessive."

The tall hybrids were then allowed to fertilise themselves, and it might be supposed that they would breed
true; but that was not the case. After self-fertilisation
each hybrid produced offspring in which the two original parental characters—dominant and recessive—
were exhibited in the ratio, on the average, of three to

one, there being in the case of tall and dwarf peas three tall plants to one short. From the dwarf plants, when self-fertilised, or fertilised from the original short stock, only dwarfs can be obtained henceforth; in other words the recessive minority of the second generation breeds true. Of the three tall plants belonging to the same generation, one possesses the dominant character alone and will produce only pure-bred or tall plants, when self-fertilised; but the two remaining plants are cross-breds and these on self-fertilisation again give the mixed generation of three plants possessing the dominant character of tallness to one plant having the recessive character of shortness.

The same simple rule was found by Mendel to be true when plants differing in several characters instead of one were cultivated; and thousands of experiments made by biologists since 1900 have shown that the results of hybridisation discovered by him hold good for specific characters exhibited by plants and animals of many kinds. The work carried on by Mendel in the seclusion of the cloister at Brünn has, indeed, put the whole subject of heredity upon an entirely new footing, and indicated a mode by which the isolation and per- petuation of definite characters can be assured.

The basal facts of Mendel's rule or principle of in- heritance have been abundantly established, but their interpretation is not so simple, and they cannot be ap- plied to life in general until much more knowledge has been obtained of essential dominant or recessive char- acters in organisms and their physiological meaning. Neither Darwinism nor Mendelism supplies more than a partial interpretation of the operations of animate Nature, and few biologists would now care to proclaim them as impregnable truths. Whatever may be the ultimate decision as to the determining factors of evo-

lution, we can say that Darwin was the first to describe
the significance of variation, and Mendel to show how
the complex threads of heredity could be disentangled.
The names of these two naturalists will be remembered
for all time as those of the two greatest contributors
to the theory of organic evolution.

In looking for the cause of evolution as against
special creation, the central fact which Darwin set himself to explain was that of adaptation to environment,
whereby small differences were accumulated until new
forms were produced. No direct evidence as to this
modifying factor could be obtained from the geological
record, which was also too imperfect to show the tran-
sitions from one species to another demanded by the
theory. The support which evolution was to receive
from the tablets of stone came later.

At the beginning of the nineteenth century it was
well understood by geologists that fossils provide a
means of determining the ages of the sedimentary rocks
of our globe; they were accepted as convenient labels
or signs of relative antiquity, but little was known of
their own lines of development. Gradually, however,
the view was formed that there is no sharp distinction
between organisms existing in our own times and those
represented by fossils; and that in the course of ages
simple forms of life had been modified or developed
into more complicated or more perfect forms, until the
highest animals, and even man, were produced. On
this view, man is heir of all the ages, and in the course
of his life he climbs up his own genealogical tree from
the condition of simple cell to that of lord of creation.
Geoffroy St. Hilaire expressed this important relationship in the words: "The embryological development
of a living creature is a summary of the phases of the
palaeontological development of its species."

We have in this statement a clear recognition of the evolution of animal forms in geological times as opposed to that view that the various groups of fossils represented new creations at different epochs. By the study of living forms Darwin showed that variation provided a key—though not the only key—to the workshop of organic Nature. He was not able to make much use of the record of the rocks in marshalling the arguments for evolution, but the gap was filled by the work of Huxley in England, Albert Gaudry in France, E. D. Cope in America, E. H. Haeckel in Germany, and other naturalists, in the latter half of the nineteenth century.

We happen to live in a world at a certain epoch, and are apt to think this epoch the most important. Of course, it is so for us individually, yet when the whole history of the world is considered, the three score years and ten of man are but an episode. Life upon the earth has been continuous from the amorphous protoplasm of the primeval shore to man in his most perfect form. The animals of the past were the progenitors of those of the present, and there must have been links connecting the fossils and living forms. Palaeontologists have sought the bonds, the relationships, which unite the ancient organisms to one another and to living forms; and they have proved each type to be related by definite characteristics to its ancestors on one side and its descendants on the other, until finally the fossil remains of man appear associated with those of animals, and with the flint implements which represented the first weapons of the human race.

The use of fossils as convenient trade-marks by which geological strata could be identified was established by William Smith, but it was largely left to Gaudry to show the genealogical relations of the different classes of animals and their descent from primeval ancestors, and thus to prove that evolution provides the reason for particular fossils being found in particular geological formations. "The stages of evolution of the fossils which are brought to us for identification," he said, "mark not only the modifications of organisation, but also of the principal divisions of geological time. Taking two different strata, if I find that in one the animals indicate a condition of evolution less advanced than the other, I conclude that the former are of the earlier age."

Much remains to be done before the complete story of the transformations of the animal kingdoms of the past can be told, but it is upon the evolutionary plan that all discoveries of fossil forms are recorded and all modifications of structure interpreted. The history of life is written on the rocks by fossil remains, and the record shows that from the beginning there has been a steady upward tendency. Taken as a whole, the plants and animals of to-day are far more highly organised varied and beautiful than in the past ages of the world, and the future will probably see still higher forms of life. But what of the beginning? Evolution is not creation, and biologists do not pretend to account for the origin of life, but only to trace the changes it has undergone and the conditions which produce them. Increased knowledge of the older rocks has not shown that we are nearer the fulfilment of the biologist's dream, and the secret of Pandora's box remains still undiscovered.

No sane man has ever pretended, since science became a definite body of doctrine, that we know or ever can hope to know or conceive of the possibility of knowing whence the mechanism has come, why it is there, whither it is going, or what may or may not be beyond and beside it which our senses are incapable of appreciating. These things are not "explained" by science and never can be. *Sir Ray Lankester.*

We have not yet reached the beginning of life. Though science can trace and interpret the "footprints on the sands of time," it knows not how life began or what was the first created form. Deeper down than the oldest rocks lies the mystery of creation; deeper also than the development of structural characteristics of organisms may be the origin of mind and intelligence, which do not admit of accurate measurement. The process by which man has become a moral and ethical being with a spiritual life may be different from that by which animals and plants have advanced in perfection of organisation. The history of mankind shows, indeed, as Matthew Arnold said, that there is an "enduring Power, not ourselves, which makes for righteousness" apart from the principle of cosmic evolution and not measurable by its standards.

The principle of the struggle for existence and the survival of the fittest must not, therefore, be understood as a sanction for the exertion of brute force in the service of egotism, but as a struggle towards higher planes and the survival of the race. The road along which the course of evolution has advanced is not that of self-interest, but of self-sacrifice, of the subjugation of the individual to the needs of the type. There is indeed very little evidence of any struggle for existence among animals of the same species. Animals are, as a rule, banded together for tribal protection, and those thrive best which have the best organisation for mutual defence. Evolution thus embodies the idea of social ethics and makes the welfare of the community the essential purpose of the life of the creature. The idea that Darwinism signifies nothing more than striving after personal or national mastery at all costs is a crude misconception of this great principle, which was repudiated alike by its founder and by Huxley, its most powerful exponent, as contrary to the best ends of civilisation.

The practice of that which is ethically best—what we call goodness or virtue—involves a course of conduct which, in all respects, is opposed to that which leads to success in the cosmic struggle for existence. In place of ruthless self-assertion it demands self-restraint; in place of thrusting aside, or treading down, all competitors, it requires that the individual shall not merely respect, but shall help his fellows; its influence is directed, not so much to the survival of the fittest, as to the fitting of as many as possible to survive. It repudiates the gladiatorial theory of existence. It demands that each man who enters into the enjoyment of the advantages of a polity shall be mindful of his debt to those who have laboriously constructed it; and shall take heed that no act of his weakens the fabric in which he has been permitted to live. Laws and moral precepts are directed to the end of curbing the cosmic process and reminding the individual of his duty to the community, to the protection and influence of which he owes, if not existence itself, at least the life of something better than a brutal savage. *Huxley.*

The existence of the spiritual or altruistic side of man's nature cannot be said to be explained adequately by natural selection; as the fittest to survive under certain conditions is often not the best ethically but the worst. "In one aspect," said a leading naturalist, Sir William Thiselton-Dyer, "the religious sentiment is a response to a craving for a supernatural sanction to rules of conduct. Its varied but practically universal manifestation amongst mankind has to be accounted for by evolution just as much as the possession of a vertebral column. It is not practically helpful to dismiss it as irrational."

No philosophic biologist would now insist that the principle of natural selection, or any other plan of organic evolution which leads up to man, is a complete expression of the origin and expansion of human consciousness; but most naturalists are satisfied that the principle truly represents perceptual operations of Nature. Beyond this concept there may be a new and transcendental philosophy, but it belongs to the realm of metaphysics rather than to that of observational science.

CHAPTER VIII

CONQUEST OF DISEASE

Nowadays the serpent that bites man's heel is in nine cases out of ten microscopic. Prof. J. A. Thomson.

Every disease has its own particular mode of production from natural causes. Hippocrates.

Like other natural laws, the laws of health are inexorable . . . Ignorance of the laws is not admitted as an excuse any more than motive; and the sentence for breaches is true now as it was ages ago: "The soul that sinneth it shall die." Sir Lauder Brunton.

Just as the mechanical sciences, when viewed from a broad standpoint, represent man's struggles for the control of the energies available in his environment, so the medical sciences have, as their ultimate aim, the acquisition of control over the functions of man's body. Prof. E. H. Starling.

THOSE who transgress the laws of man sometimes escape punishment; but the laws of Nature can never be broken without paying the penalty. The man who steps over the side of a cliff, consciously or unconsciously, meets the consequences of his action swiftly, whether he be sinner or saint; and the laws of health can no more be broken with impunity than can the law of gravitation. When effects follow quickly upon causes, we learn the relationship between them readily, and from our childhood avoid actions which produce pain, as a burnt child dreads the fire. Science has shown that a disease is just as definitely due to a particular cause, preventible or otherwise, though it may not tread closely upon the heels of action. Ignorance of the law may sometimes be pleaded in a court of justice in palliation of an offence; but Nature accepts no such excuses and decrees a punishment for every crime against her. She never forgives a fault or extenuates it; inexorable is her judgment, and inevitable her sentence, which has often to be suffered not only by the offender but also by his children, even to the second and third generations.

This is a hard saying; yet it is true, and there is no escape from what it implies. As we have to subscribe to Nature's statutes, it is desirable that our knowledge of them should be as complete as possible. "Give me understanding and I shall keep thy law; yea, I shall observe it with my whole heart." Where such understanding does not exist, disease is regarded either as a demon to be exorcised or an "act of God" for which penitence and prayer are remedies. Ignorance made plague the terror of Europe in the Middle Ages; science has proved that the disease is due to a bacillus which is conveyed by flees from rat to rat, and from rats suffering from the disease to mankind. Ignorance ascribed malaria to a miasma or bad air arising from marshy places; science has shown it to be caused by a micro-organism carried from one man to another by a certain species of mosquito. Ignorance of the cause of yellow fever made the regions around the Caribbean Sea the White Man's Grave, where the risk of death for the visitor was greater than in a battle; knowledge that the disease is associated with a parasite which is communicated from an infected to a healthy person by the bite of a particular mosquito, has been the means of converting the same places into tropical health resorts.

When nothing is known of the natural laws of a disease mankind is helpless against it; but when science has discovered the enemy a sound basis can be secured for a plan of campaign to exterminate it. Plague has to be fought by the destruction of rats where it prevails, as well as by better housing and sanitation; malaria and yellow fever have to be kept under control by the continual clearance of breeding-places of mosquitoes in infected areas. Administrative measures based upon the teaching of science have practically abolished plague from the cities of Europe, have cleared Havana, the Isthmus of Panama, the West Indies, and Rio de Janeiro of yellow fever, and have made the Roman Campagna almost free from malaria, though formerly few men who went to the district could hope for more than three years of life in it.

Practical acquaintance with ailments may be obtained by watching the sick and administering drugs, but this clinical experience is not of much use in determining the nature and origin of disease. For centuries, physicians have made their comforting presence felt at the bedside of their patients, but their observations have contributed little to the knowledge of the causes of diseases, the means of conferring immunity, or of providing anti-toxins or chemical antidotes which by their specific action upon the virus of diseases successfully save human beings, as well as the lower animals, from death and incapacitating illness.

In the struggle against diseases and the discovery of means of stamping them out and preventing their development, we must not look for help to the popular physician, but to the bacteriological or the chemical laboratory where scientific research is being carried on, often under harassing conditions and always with inadequate recompense. The ordinary medical practitioner, like the engineer, makes use of scientific results for the benefit of mankind, but originates little for himself. He is able and practical, good at diagnosis and clever in manipulation, but withal an empiric, wanting in scientific ideals and only very occasionally a contributor to scientific knowledge.

Every year an immense amount of time, labour and money is consumed in dealing with the effects of the various diseases to which humanity is liable, and in attempts, more or less successful, to cure these effects, while comparatively little is done toward preventing them by the removal of their chief sources or primary causes. The few brilliant examples which show such striking success in the latter direction only serve to throw into more prominent relief the magnitude of that deplorable amount of loss—in life, health and wealth—which is still waiting to be dealt with.

It is a truism well recognised by medical men that the soldier has much more to fear from the ravages of disease than from the fire of the enemy. During the South African war, the British Army lost nearly twice as many men from preventible diseases, chiefly typhoid fever, as it did from wounds received in battle. In the Spanish-American war, there were twenty thousand men, or one-sixth of the American force, laid by with typhoid. On the other hand, scientific investigation into the cause of beri-beri—which had impaired the efficiency of the Japanese fleet by almost 50 per cent. during previous years—resulted in the complete abolition of this disease from the Japanese ships from 1886 to 1893, and not a single case developed during the war with Russia, amidst the floating force of twenty-five thousand men. In this war, the enlightened and educative measures of the Japanese reduced the deaths due

to disease to one-quarter of those due to battle. Thanks
to the adoption of scientific methods, the incidence of
disease in the British Army during the great European
War has been far lighter than in any previous campaign. The magnificent results achieved by attention
to the essential principles of sanitation and preventive
medicine have disposed—we hope for ever—of the old
saying, "Disease, not battle, digs the soldier's grave."
The health of the British Expeditionary Force is not
only safeguarded by sanitary precautions, but also protected against typhoid fever by a treatment of inoculation instituted by Sir Almroth Wright. The success
of these methods is little short of marvellous. Deaths
of British soldiers from typhoid are much less in proportion than in any preceding war, and men fully protected by two inoculations escape punishment by the
disease almost without exception.

The same principles of preventive medicine are applicable with no less success to civil life. What is true
of typhoid, cholera, dysentery and malaria, is equally
true of smallpox, tuberculosis, yellow fever, scurvy,
rabies, plague and diphtheria, and is true also of
numerous other common illnesses; applicable, therefore, to the poverty and distress which result from
them.

Smallpox was formerly looked upon as practically
unavoidable by members of the human family. People
used to advertise for servants who had got over smallpox in much the same way as we now inquire, before
purchasing a dog, whether it has had distemper. The
difficulty of getting through life without smallpox was
expressed in a popular saying very current in Germany
in the eighteenth century: *von Pocken und Liebe bleiben
nur wenige frei*—from smallpox and love few remain
free. In his *History of England*, Macaulay, referring

to the death of Queen Mary from the disease in 1694 says:

> That disease over which science has since achieved a succession of glorious and beneficial victories was then the most terrible of all the ministers of death. The havoc of the plague had been far more rapid; but plague had visited our shores only once or twice within living memory, and the smallpox was always present, filling the churchyards with corpses, tormenting with constant fears all whom it had not yet stricken, leaving on those whose lives it spared the hideous traces of its power, turning the babe into a changeling at which the mother shuddered, and making the eyes and cheeks of the betrothed maiden objects of horror to the lover. *T. B. Macaulay.*

For the different conditions which exist in civilised countries to-day, and for the fact that the fear of smallpox has become almost as remote as the fear of leprosy, we have chiefly to thank Edward Jenner (1749-1823)—the apostle of vaccination. Others had vaccinated before Jenner, but he was the first to rouse the civilised world to take an active interest in the subject. Among medical men of all nationalities his name is held in the highest reverence. Jenner, Pasteur and Lister form a triumvirate that has given the human race reason to rise up and call it blessed.

The value of vaccination as a protection against smallpox was established by Jenner in 1796; the principle of the method of protective inoculation was used by Pasteur in conferring immunity of animals from anthrax eighty-five years later; and Lister was led to introduce the system of antiseptic surgery by the study of Pasteur's investigations. Jenner opened the door to a new realm of remedies for disease; and we are only now beginning to realise how vast it is and what possibilities it offers for the future.

Jenner was in his teens and in the first stage of his

medical education at Sodbury, Gloucestershire, when his attention was directed to the subject of protection against smallpox. A young girl came there for advice, and on smallpox being mentioned she exclaimed, "I cannot take that disease, for I have had cow-pox." She, like other milkmaids in Gloucestershire and elsewhere, had discovered for themselves that cow-pox was a safeguard against smallpox; but it required the insight and patient labour of Jenner to transform a piece of folklore into a scientific truth, and make the medical profession all over the world receive it as such.

When Jenner went to London, at the age of twenty-one, and was entered as a student at St. George's Hospital, he mentioned this belief to John Hunter, who gave his pupil this excellent piece of advice: "Do not think, but try; be patient, be accurate." On returning to his native town of Berkeley to settle down into country practice as a physician, the belief of the young girl at Sodbury, and Hunter's wise words, were ever constant in his mind. To get at the truth of this opinion was his great object; but it was not until 1780 that he felt sufficient confidence to communicate to a friend his ideas on the subject of propagating the protective cow-pox from one individual to another, and so ultimately staying the plague of smallpox.

"Gardiner," said Jenner, "I have entrusted a most important matter to you, which I firmly believe will prove of essential benefit to the human race. I know you, and should not wish what I have stated to be brought into conversation, for should anything untoward turn up in my experiments, I should be made, particularly by my medical brethren, the subject of ridicule, for I am the mark they all shoot at."

Jenner continued his experiments for another sixteen years before he performed his first inoculation with cow-pox on May 14, 1796, the subject being a boy, about eight years of age. The boy was afterwards inoculated for the smallpox, and as Jenner predicted, no disease followed. A means of protecting the human race against its greatest scourge had been discovered, and Jenner redoubled his efforts to establish its efficacy. He vaccinated all the poor in the neighbourhood of Berkeley gratuitously, and the success of the method of inoculation soon became widely known. He vaccinated his own son on three separate occasions, and prejudice against inoculation with cow-pox began to be overcome when two ladies of title—Lady Ducie and the Countess of Berkeley—submitted their children to it.

If Jenner had kept the secret of his discovery to himself, he could have made an immense fortune from it, but he imparted it to the public, and suffered great loss of time and money in answering inquiries which reached him from all parts of the world. He made known his discovery as soon as he had convinced himself of its value, and never for a moment did he hesitate as to whether he might not be a richer man by keeping his information to himself.

It is scarcely necessary to add that the discovery did not escape the fate which commonly awaits originality. Jenner's views were opposed and misrepresented, the caricaturists of the period drew persons with horns and cows' heads to suggest what might be expected from vaccination, and sermons were preached to show its wickedness. Nothing could, however, prevent the spread of a method which relieved every household of its greatest terror. Marks of distinction soon began to be showered upon the scientific St. George who had rid mankind of the dragon of smallpox that had demanded tens of thousands of victims annually. With the Emperor Napoleon, Jenner was a great favourite. On one occasion Napoleon was about to refuse a petition from Jenner to allow two friends to return to England, when Josephine reminded him that the petition was from the discoverer of vaccination. "Ah," said the Emperor, "Jenner, we can refuse nothing to that man."

In recognition of the national value of vaccination, the House of Commons voted Jenner a grant of £10,000 in 1802, and five years later a further grant of £20,000 was made to him, the intervening time having strengthened the general opinion as to the efficacy of vaccination and as to its great benefit to the nation at large. Competent authorities would not now claim that a single inoculation with vaccine lymph is a perfect antidote against smallpox throughout life, but only that it confers a high degree of protection against the disease. Absolute immunity cannot be ensured in all cases because of individual differences of the blood and tissues of the human body; yet with this reservation the practice of vaccination has been completely justified. We owe our deliverance from the fear of smallpox not so much to improved sanitation, or to a natural decline of the disease or acquired immunity from it, as to the protective principle introduced by Jenner. The progress of preventive medicine depends largely upon the application of this principle, which has proved to be of even greater biological value than was anticipated by Jenner of the physicians of his day.

Many diseases of animals, as well as those of man, are now controlled or conquered by the application of scientific principles. Before science showed the nature of anthrax, and provided the remedy, many thousands of cattle and sheep died annually from the disease. A formidable yearly tribute had to be paid to this mysterious scourge until enlightenment came through the labours of Robert Koch and Louis Pasteur.

Koch cultivated a microbe from the blood of an

animal that died from anthrax, and he found that when this microbe was inoculated into guinea-pigs, rabbits and mice, they inevitably took the disease. Pasteur proved that the power of conveying anthrax was due to the bacillus, and to it alone; and, later, he suggested that, by vaccination of animals with the virus, it would be possible to give them the disease in a mild form, and so secure their immunity from fatal attacks. His conclusions met with the usual reception of ridicule from the practical man concerned with the care of cattle; and the veterinary profession proposed an experiment to test them. Pasteur accepted the challenge, and the conditions of the battle between knowledge and incredulity were drawn up. Sixty sheep were put at his disposal; twenty-five were vaccinated, by two inoculations, with the attenuated virus of anthrax. Some days later these, and twenty-five others, were inoculated with some very virulent cultures of the anthrax bacillus. Ten sheep underwent no treatment at all.

"The twenty-five unvaccinated sheep will all perish," wrote Pasteur; "the twenty-five vaccinated sheep will survive." The result turned out exactly as he had predicted. The sheep which had been vaccinated with a mild form of anthrax, in order to make them more capable of resisting the later inoculation, survived, while those which had not thus been rendered immune, perished. The conclusion of the experiment is one of the most dramatic incidents in the history of science. It was arranged that believers and unbelievers in Pasteur's views should meet on June 2, 1881, at the farmyard where the sheep had been placed, there to celebrate a victory or proclaim a failure.

When Pasteur arrived at two o'clock in the afternoon, at the farmyard of Pouilly le Fort, accompanied by his young collaborators, a murmur of applause arose, which soon became loud acclamation, bursting from all lips. Delegates from the Agricultural Society of Melun, from medical societies, veterinary societies, from the Central Council of Hygiene of Seine et Marne, journalists, small farmers, who had been divided in their minds by laudatory or injurious newspaper articles—all were there. The carcasses of twenty-two unvaccinated sheep were lying side by side; two others were breathing their last; the last survivors of the sacrificed lot showed all the characteristic symptoms of splenic fever (anthrax). All the vaccinated sheep were in perfect health. . . . The one remaining unvaccinated sheep died that same night. *R. Vallery-Radot.*

Pasteur was an exact experimenter, and when the effect of any treatment was under investigation always had untreated or "control" cases side by side with the others for the purpose of distinguishing the difference between the two sets. Lady Priestley relates that on one occasion she told Pasteur of apparently successful experiments made by inoculating sporting dogs with vaccine lymph against distemper. "Ah," said Pasteur, "and the control experiments?" This control or proof of the efficacy of the inoculation had not been used, and without it the results fall to the ground in the estimation of the great experimenter.

The method followed by Pasteur in the control and treatment of anthrax were extended by him to that terrifying disease—rabies. By his discoveries in this field alone, he earned the eternal gratitude of humanity. He sought first for the specific microbe of the disease, but unsuccessfully. The prevailing view was that the rabic virus was contained in the saliva of the mad animal. Pasteur wished to test this, and inoculated rabbits with saliva from mad dogs, but the results were inconclusive. It was then suggested that the symptoms shown by an animal or human being suffering from hydrophobia indicated a connection with the nervous system. Pasteur was thus led to use for his inoculations an emulsion of the brain or spinal cord of a rabid animal, instead of the saliva; and in every case hydrophobia occurred after inoculation. By attenuating the virus and inoculating dogs with it in increasing strengths, he was able to secure for them immunity against the bites of rabid companions, and to find the period of incubation.

This was his first step in making dogs refractory to rabies by preventive inoculation; the second was to prevent the onset of rabies in dogs bitten or subjected to inoculation. The period varies from about a fortnight to seven or eight months, but the average length is six weeks. A person bitten by a mad dog was thus haunted for a long period by the anguish of uncertainty as to whether the virus was developing in his system or not. Pasteur believed that if such a person was inoculated with increasing strengths of the rabic virus during this period, beginning within a few hours or days of the bite, the system would be able to resist the onset of the disease at a later stage. He could not test his conviction deliberately by successive inoculations of a human being, but an opportunity of treating an actual case of hydrophobia by this principle occurred in 1885.

A young Alsatian boy, Joseph Meister, who had been badly bitten only two days before by a mad dog, was brought to his laboratory. After careful consideration and consultation with several leading physiologists and physicians, Pasteur decided to apply anti-rabic inoculation to little Meister. The treatment lasted ten days, during which the boy was inoculated twelve times. It was completely successful; and an infallible remedy had been found for a dread disease against which all previous measures had failed. The results of the treatment of rabies on this principle are now well known, but for several years strong opposition was offered to it by certain people in Great Britain, while at the same time terrified British sufferers from the disease were continually sent to Pasteur for salvation. In scientific circles Pasteur's great advance in the treatment of disease was understood and fully appreciated, but as it had been obtained by means of experiments on animals, it was misrepresented and vilified by opponents of such experiments until its beneficial effects overwhelmed them.

Experiments made with the noble object of not only increasing human knowledge but also diminishing human suffering are deserving of the highest praise; yet those who carry on such researches are often assumed to be among the most callous of mankind. Pasteur was one of the most tender-hearted of men. An instance of disinclination to inflict pain was given by Lord Lister in a speech some years ago, in a reference to his work on rabies. It had been established that the introduction of the portion of the brain of a mad dog under the skin of a healthy animal was liable to cause rabies, and, as has been explained, Pasteur had reason to believe that it was principally in the nervous centres that the poison accumulated. He felt a very strong desire to introduce some of the poison into the brain of an animal; but he was a peculiarly humane man. He never could shoot an animal for sport. He was more humane than the majority of human beings; and for a long time he could not bring himself to make the experiment of trephining an animal's skull, and introducing some of the poison of rabies into the brain. He was exceedingly desirous of doing this, to establish the pathology of the disease, but he shrank from it. On one occasion, when he was absent from home, one of his assistants did the experiment, and when Pasteur came back he told him he had done so. "Oh," said Pasteur, "the poor beast! His brain is doubtless injured. I am afraid he will be paralysed."

The assistant went into a neighbouring room and brought in the animal, which was a dog. It came in frisking about, and investigating everything in a perfectly natural manner; Pasteur was exceedingly pleased, and though he did not like dogs, yet he lavished his affection upon this particular animal, and petted it, and from that time forth his scruples no longer existed. The pain inflicted by the process of trephining is, in fact, very slight; yet the operation is sometimes described as hideously painful.

Although Pasteur may be considered to be the founder of modern methods of scientific investigation of disease, he was one of the most modest of men. At the International Medical Congress held in London in 1882, he was desired by the Government of the Republic to represent France. Before the Congress, everyone was inquiring whether he had arrived, but no one had seen him until he entered St. James's Hall to attend the opening meeting. The hall was filled to overflowing, but as Pasteur entered he was recognised by one of the stewards, who was leading him to the place reserved for him on the platform, when there was a great outburst of cheers. Perfectly unconscious that the applause was meant for him, Pasteur turned to his two companions, his son and son-in-law, and said, with a little uneasiness: "It is no doubt the Prince of Wales arriving; I ought to have come sooner." "But it is you that they are all cheering," explained the president of the Congress, and the applause was so great that he had to rise and bow to the great assembly.

Pasteur had not studied medicine, yet he was able to

determine the true cause of disease and to discover secrets hidden to physicians throughout the world's history. When in 1860 he was awarded the prize for experimental physiology by the French Academy of Sciences, he wrote to his father: "God grant that by my persevering labours I may bring a little stone to the frail and ill-assured edifice of our knowledge of those deep mysteries of life and death, where all our intellects have so lamentably failed."

Pasteur's remains rest in a mausoleum at the Institute which bears his name in Paris. Upon the occasion of their interment, the French Minister of Education eloquently remarked:

As at the tombs of saints where people saw prodigies accomplished, so that of Pasteur will be enriched by a halo of miracles. At every discovery beneficial to mankind, at every ray of scientific glory which will be added to the aureole of France, the gratitude of the country and of the world will flow to this building, henceforth august in the annals of science, as to the source of ulterior progress.

The French people honour him above all other men; and when on one occasion they were asked to name their greatest countrymen, they put Pasteur first, Napoleon second and Victor Hugo third.

A few years ago diphtheria was one of the most dreaded of the infectious diseases which afflict the human race; to-day, thanks to scientific research, it is the disease which can be treated with the greatest confidence of success. Formerly the medical man standing at the bedside of a child struggling for breath was almost helpless to relieve its anguish except by a dangerous operation; now he has at his disposal a remedy which, if used quickly enough, extinguishes the disease as surely as water does a raging fire. He used to fight in the dark against an unknown foe, but he now knows the nature of the forces against him, and has a weapon which will vanquish them completely.

It is scarcely too much to say that of all the infective diseases which trouble mankind, diphtheria stands foremost as the one concerning which our knowledge is the most complete; and in this knowledge lies the physician's power. The isolation of the specific microbe which causes the disease was accomplished by Loeffler in 1884. When this virulent bacillus is grown in broth, it produces a quantity of a toxin which can be obtained in the form of a clear liquid. Upon injecting the liquid into a horse several times over a period of two or three months, the horse's blood acquires a quality which counteracts its effects; and the serum obtained from the blood of such an inoculated animal is the basis of the anti-toxin of diphtheria upon which every doctor now depends for the treatment of the disease. It was Behring who first enunciated the principles of toxin and anti-toxin in diseases, and to the studies of Roux we owe the preparation of anti-diphtherial serum.

The result of the use of the serum has been marvellous. In pre-anti-toxin days, one child of every three infected by the disease ended its sufferings in death; now only one diphtheria case in ten proves fatal, and when the anti-toxin is used on the first day of the disease not more than two or three cases in a hundred succumb to its effects. If there were reason for boasting in the sphere of medical science, the array of brilliant discoveries which has brought about this result might be quoted with pride as conquests for humanity, won by much toil in the face of great difficulties.

Pasteur was the first to realise the significance of micro-organisms in the economy of Nature; and it was his work which directly inspired Lord Lister to introduce those antiseptic methods in surgery which have made thousands of sufferers bless his name. By his researches on brewing, Pasteur showed that living organisms—yeasts—unseen to the naked eye, convert the brewer's wort into ale, and that the germs which may afterwards be introduced cause the beverage to become sour or bad. Lister saw that germs introduced into wounds in human flesh might be similarly responsible for the fevers and death which usually followed surgical operations in his early days; and he took measures to prevent their entrance, and thus permit Nature to do her work of healing under favourable conditions. The brewer may himself introduce the cause of souring into the beverage he desires to keep pure; and the surgeon may likewise infect the patient while endeavouring to relieve him.

Recognition of the application to surgery of Pasteur's investigations on fermentation and putrefaction induced Lister, in 1865, to make use of antiseptics in the treatment of compound fractures—an operation previously attended with the gravest risk, but now, thanks to Pasteur and Lister, performed without any danger of introducing the germs which caused the complications that were the despair of surgeons. Well has it been said that Pasteur and Lister "formed a brotherhood of science labouring to diminish the sorrows of humanity"; yet the principles taught by both met at first with nothing but opposition or indifference.

Fifty years ago the slightest surgical operation was attended with great danger, on account of mortification of the wound and blood-poisoning due to the introduction of putrid matter into the body. By a long and systematic investigation of the causes of the inflammation which followed injuries to living tissues,

Lister was able to show that the danger which formerly existed could be avoided, and by so doing he founded modern surgery. When he commenced his experiments, the healing of injuries or wounds after an operation could not by any means be confidently expected as it can at the present time. It was almost impossible to avoid inflammation and festering of the parts affected, and the wound-fevers which usually followed were the despair of surgeons.

Lister came to the conclusion that all the putrefactive changes to which wounds were subject, and which send to the grave so many patient sufferers, were due to the presence of bacteria. To prevent this action, he developed a system of careful disinfection of everything which came into direct or indirect contact with a wound. He invented also an antiseptic dressing which excluded bacteria from the wound and assisted the natural tendency of tissues to heal themselves. The results obtained since Lister's methods were introduced in the seventies of the nineteenth century are astounding in their success. To-day, thanks to his careful scientific work, surgeons are able to carry out the most difficult operations without any fear of the terrible mortality which troubled those of a past generation. Thousands of people alive and happy at the present time owe their lives and their relief from suffering not so much to the skill of a surgeon as to the knowledge of the means of preventing inflammation by methods indicated by Lister's work.

At the present time there is scarcely a hospital in the civilised world where the principles of aseptic surgery are not carried out, not a household which has not in some measure benefited by it, not a medical man who is unaware of its meaning. The amount of prevention of suffering and the prolongation of life due to it are altogether incalculable.

At the International Medical Congress at Amsterdam in 1879, Lister's appearance called forth the greatest ovation ever witnessed at one of these assemblies. As the applause subsided, the president of the Congress stepped forth and said: "Professor Lister, it is not only our admiration which we offer you; it is our gratitude, and that of the nations to which we belong."

At the close of the nineteenth century it was asserted that "Listerism" had saved more human lives than all the wars of the expiring century had sacrificed. "My Lord," said the American Ambassador, in proposing his health at a Royal Society banquet, "it is not a profession, it is not a nation, it is humanity itself which, with uncovered head, salutes you."

Of Lister's tender-hearted nature and love of children, one of his Glasgow students relates the following story:

One day when Lister was visiting his wards in the Glasgow Royal Infirmary, there was a little girl whose elbow-joint had been excised, and this had to be dressed daily. Lister undertook this dressing himself. The little creature bore the pain without complaint, and when finished she suddenly produced from under the clothes a dilapidated doll, one leg of which had burst, allowing the sawdust to escape. She handed the doll to Lister, who gravely examined it, then, asking for a needle and thread, he sat down and stitched the rent, and then returned the dolly to its gratified owner.

Lister died in February, 1912, and by his wish he was laid to rest by the side of his wife in West Hampstead Cemetery. An impressive funeral service was, however, held at Westminster Abbey; and at it an anthem was sung composed for the funeral of Queen

Caroline, in 1737, and chosen for the special appro-
priateness of the words, which were:

When the ear heard him, then it blessed him; and when the
eye saw him, it gave witness of him. He delivered the poor
that cried; the fatherless and him that had none to help him.
Kindness, meekness, and comfort were in his tongue. If there
was any virtue, and if there was any praise, he thought on
those things. His body is buried in peace, but his name liveth
evermore.

Pasteur's experiments on dogs, which led to the discovery of a remedy for rabies, and most of the operations performed by Lister and his successors, would
not have been possible without the use of chloroform.
Anæsthesia is the handmaid of surgery; it permitted
many new departures and rendered operations feasible
which had been undreamed of before. Pasteur had a
great horror of useless suffering, and always insisted
upon anæsthesia before undertaking the trephinings
which his experiments involved. It is essential that
conscious pain should be avoided in all such operations,
whether on animals or man. The anguish endured by
patients undergoing operations before the days of
anæsthetics has been vividly described by Dr. George
Wilson. Dr. Wilson had to undergo the protracted
and painful experience of having one foot removed by
surgeons.

"During the operation," he says, "in spite of the pain it
occasioned, my senses were preternaturally acute. I watched
all that the surgeons did with a fascinated intensity. Of the
agony it occasioned, I will say nothing. Suffering so great as
I underwent cannot be expressed in words, and thus fortunately cannot be recalled. The particular pangs are now
forgotten; but the black whirlwind of emotion, the horror of
great darkness, and the sense of desertion by God and man,
bordering close upon despair, which swept through my mind

and overwhelmed my heart, I can never forget, however gladly
I would do so.''

Now, in the words of Oliver Wendell Holmes: ''The
fierce extremity of suffering has been steeped in the
waters of forgetfulness, and the deepest furrow in the
knotted brow of agony has been smoothed for ever.''

The bust of Sir James Young Simpson in Westminster Abbey bears the inscription: ''To whose Genius
and Benevolence the world owes the Blessings derived
from the Use of Chloroform for the Relief of Suffering.'' When a young medical student, Simpson was
so greatly distressed by the groans of a woman under
an operation that he thought of relinquishing his career
for work in which he would not meet so much suffering. After reflection, however, he decided to continue
his studies with the problem ever on his heart and
mind how the pains to which humanity is subject could
be relieved. When lecturing to his students in later
years, he never wearied in insisting that ''the proud
mission of the physician is distinctly twofold—viz.,
to alleviate human suffering as well as to preserve
human life.'' It was this noble motive which made
him eager to adopt any method of surgical anæsthesia
and to carry on systematic experiments and inquiries
with the object of finding an aid to painless surgery.

Before Simpson proved the power of chloroform to
put man into a deep sleep, several anæsthetics had been
used for this purpose. While working at the Pneu-
matic Institution in Bristol near the end of the eighteenth century, Sir Humphry Davy discovered the
intoxicating and stupefying action of nitrous oxide,
and suggested its use in surgical operations. Nearly
half a century later Dr. Horace Wells, an American
dentist, had one of his upper teeth extracted without

any pain after deeply breathing this gas. A later experiment at the Boston Medical School and Hospital
was, however, unsuccessful owing to an insufficient
quantity of the gas being used, and the failure appears
to have discouraged Dr. Wells. His former pupil and
partner, Dr. W. T. G. Morton, of Boston, then took up
the subject, and was led to the use of sulphuric ether
as an anæsthetic. In September, 1846, he extracted
a tooth without pain while the patient was breathing
sulphuric ether, and in the following month a severe
operation was performed painlessly under the gas at
the Boston Hospital.

More than four years earlier, in March, 1842, Dr.
C. W. Long, then of Jefferson, Jackson County,
U.S.A., had used sulphuric ether as an anæsthetic dur-
minor operations, but he took no steps to make his discovery known, and the new era in anæsthetics and in
surgery opened with Dr. Morton's work. Within a
few weeks the vapour of sulphuric ether had been used
successfully in several other cases of surgical operation in Boston. So soon as the news reached Edin-
burgh, Simpson was eager to prove the virtue of the
new anodyne to relieve the agonising pains of women
in travail. He entered the field immediately, and,
selecting a difficult case for experiment, proved in January, 1847, that the sufferings of the mother during
childbirth could be alleviated by the inhalation of
ether-vapour, and that the use of the anaesthetic was
not injurious to the child.

Simpson was not satisfied, however, that sulphuric
ether was the best agent for producing anæsthesia.
He obtained a number of other volatile liquids, and
tested them systematically with the object of finding
an anodyne as potent as ether but less irritating and
disagreeable to the patient. With his two assistants,

Dr. Keith and Dr. Duncan, he tried the effects of various liquids night after night, though the tests were not without great risk to the experimenters. The discovery of the power of chloroform has been told dramatically by Prof. Miller:

Late one evening—it was the 4th of November, 1847—on returning home after a weary day's labour, Dr. Simpson, with his two friends and assistants, Drs. Keith and J. M. Duncan, sat down to their somewhat hazardous work in Dr. Simpson's dining-room. Having inhaled several substances, but without much effect, it occurred to Dr. Simpson to try a ponderous material, which he had formerly set aside on a lumber-table, and which, on account of its great weight, he had hitherto regarded as of no likelihood whatever. This happened to be a small bottle of chloroform. It was searched for and recovered from beneath a heap of waste paper. And, with each tumbler newly charged, the inhalers resumed their vocation. Immediately an unwonted hilarity seized the party, they became bright-eyed, very happy and very loquacious—expatiating on the delicious aroma of the new fluid. . . . But suddenly there was a talk of sounds being heard like those of a cotton-mill, louder and louder; a moment more, then all was quiet, and then—a crash. On awakening, Dr. Simpson's first perception was mental—"This is far stronger and better than ether," said he to himself. His second was, to note that he was prostrate on the floor, and that among the friends about him there was both confusion and alarm.

The inhalation of chloroform was repeated many times that night, and ten days later, Simpson was able to announce that he had administered the anæsthetic to about fifty individuals "without the slightest bad result of any kind." Much opposition was at first offered to the use of chloroform in childbirth, largely upon the grounds of the penalty pronounced upon Eve for her transgression in the Garden of Eden—"in sorrow shalt thou bring forth children,"—but it was met with the apt reply by Simpson that "the Lord God caused a deep sleep to fall upon Adam" before taking a rib from him to make a woman for his mate. It was not, however, until Queen Victoria had herself taken chloroform during a confinement that the clamour of a section of the clergy began to give way before the voice of wisdom and experience.

It is difficult to understand the mind that seeks for Biblical justification of scientific achievement or application. People who manifest it are like those of the Middle Ages who attributed all disease to some special outpourings of divine wrath on account of human iniquities, and looked for relief from it to prayer instead of works. In this way was the Black Death, or plague, regarded in medieval times, and only in 1894 was its cause discovered by two Japanese doctors, Yersin and Kitasato, to be a particular parasite which grows in bodies of rats and like animals. The disease is conveyed from rats to human beings by the bites of fleas which have fed upon the blood of rats containing the parasite. For three thousand years "the pestilence that walketh in darkness" took its toll of human beings without being discovered, but now that its true nature is known the human race has in its own hands the means of emancipation from the disease. The chain which connects microbe and man in the plague-stricken has been revealed, and by breaking it humanity can be delivered from a thraldom under which it has groaned for unknown ages.

A few years ago mosquitoes, flies, ticks, fleas and related biting and blood-sucking insects, were considered by most people to be unworthy objects of serious study, but it is now known that they are most important factors in the spread of various diseases, especially in tropical countries. It has been established by many investigators that these creatures are the sole

VI. SCIENCE.

Statue by Giovanni da Bologna, (1524-1608),
in the Palazzo dell' Università, Genoa.

agents of inoculation into man of the germs of malaria, yellow fever, sleeping sickness, plague, East-coast fever, Kala-azar, typhus fever, recurrent fever and other maladies which have brought suffering and death to millions of people. In most cases they are not merely mechanical bearers of disease germs from one victim to another, for if that were so the problem of discovering the part they play would be relatively simple. Usually their bodies are breeding-places of microscopic organisms which they suck from the blood of one victim—beast or man—and these parasites, after undergoing profound transformations within their hosts, are afterwards injected into other victims. Insects have thus been shown to be intimately related to the life of man; and a branch of study which was formerly considered to be of purely zoological interest has proved to be closely connected with practical problems of European colonisation in tropical regions.

If it is better to save life than to destroy it, then laud and honour should be given to those patient scientific investigators whose studies have shown how to lessen human suffering and prevent the spread of fatal diseases. Before a disease can be prevented it must be understood; there must be a knowledge of its nature and mode of transmission if a sure remedy is to be found, and that knowledge is obtained by the man of science, whose work meets with little encouragement either officially or publicly, and is usually without reward.

No better examples could be found of the benefits of such work to the human race than are afforded by the studies of tropical and other diseases carried on in recent years. Perhaps the most important of these diseases is malarial fever, which causes the death of more than a million people yearly in India alone. When

Sir Ronald Ross was carrying out at Bangalore the intricate and minute researches required to determine the cause of malaria and its remedy, he wrote the pleading lines:

In this, O Nature, yield, I pray, to me.
    I pace and pace, and think and think, and take
The fever'd hands, and note down all I see,
    That some dim distant light may haply break.

The painful faces ask, can we not cure?
    We answer, No, not yet; we seek the laws.
O God, reveal thro' all this thing obscure
    The unseen, small, but million-murdering cause.

At that time it was believed by most people that malaria was caused by some kind of vapour or "miasma" which rose from swampy or marshy land. It is now known to be transmitted by a certain kind of mosquito which can harbour the germs of the disease and convey them from one person to another.

This conclusion seems simple enough, but it was only proved to be true by slow steps and persistent work. The theory that mosquitoes are carriers of disease, and that malaria is transmitted by them or flies, was put forward fourteen centuries ago, and was revived in more modern times, but systematic practical study was necessary to establish it. The links of evidence by which the mosquito has been convicted of causing many millions of deaths from malaria were not forged together until recent years.

First, Dr. C. L. A. Laveran, a French army surgeon, studying malaria in a military hospital in Algiers, discovered that the blood of a person suffering from malaria always contains a peculiar parasite or organism. Sir Patrick Manson then suggested that these parasites pass a part of their existence in the bodies of mosquitoes, which carry them from one person to another. When in the blood of a human being the parasites are in a certain stage of development, but they can only complete their life-cycle in the body of their insect host.

To Sir Ronald Ross belongs the honour of tracing the various stages of the existence of the parasite in the body of the mosquito until it was ripe for injection into a human being by the bite of the insect. He proved by numerous experiments that the only means by which a healthy person can acquire malaria is by the bite of a mosquito which has previously bitten someone whose blood contains the particular organisms associated with the disease. In other words, if there were no mosquitoes of the kind required by the malarial parasites to complete their life-cycle, there could be no malarial fever. On the eve of this remarkable discovery, Ross offered up a prayer of thanks which makes a beautiful supplement to the lines written several years before:

> This day relenting God
>   Hath placed within my hand
> A wondrous thing; and God
>   Be praised. At His command,
>
> Seeking His secret deeds,
>   With tears and toiling breath,
> I find thy cunning seeds,
>   O million-murdering Death.
>
> I know this little thing
>   A myriad men will save.
> O Death, where is thy sting?
>   Thy victory, O Grave?

The cause of the disease having been found, the remedy was evidently to stamp out the mosquito, so far as possible, by searching out its breeding-places and destroying the larvae in them. This is not so difficult as it may appear at first sight, because the larvae can easily be distinguished in the puddles and other collections of stagnant water in which they occur. By carrying on a vigorous campaign against mosquitoes, many very malarious places on the earth have been made habitable, and prosperous townships are growing up in districts which formerly sustained only a few sickly and miserable inhabitants.

Where the teachings of science have been followed, our race has triumphed over its enemies; where ignorance or apathy prevails, the toll is being paid in human lives. This is exemplified not only by malaria, but also by many other diseases which have been studied by scientific methods. During the Spanish-American war the American troops suffered great losses from yellow fever. Inspired by Ross's work, an investigation of the cause of the disease was undertaken, with the result that, like malaria, it was found to be transmitted by a mosquito, though a different kind from that which conveys malaria.

In the year 1900, the president of the United States appointed a commission of five, with Dr. Walter Reed at its head, to carry out investigations in the Island of Cuba, with the object of discovering the cause of yellow fever. Believing that the mosquito theory could only be tested by actual experiment upon a human subject, one of the members of the commission, Dr. Lazear, permitted himself to be bitten by a mosquito which had previously bitten a person suffering from yellow fever; with the result that he contracted the disease and died in a few days. He gave up his life for others, and the plain record of his sacrifice upon a tablet erected to his memory reads: "With more than the courage and devotion of the soldier, he risked and lost his life to show how a fearful pestilence is communicated and how its ravages may be prevented."

Two private soldiers volunteered their services for experimental purposes, though they were warned of the danger and suffering probably involved. When both made it a stipulation that they should receive no pecuniary reward, Dr. Reed touched his cap and said respectfully, "Gentlemen, I salute you." For one of the first experiments, three brave men slept for twenty nights in a small ill-ventilated room screened from mosquitoes but containing furniture and clothing which had been in close contact with yellow-fever patients, some of whom had died from the disease. None of the men contracted yellow fever, thus indicating the disease was not of a contagious nature. The next experiment was to divide a similar building by a wire screen, and to admit mosquitoes which had bitten yellow-fever patients into the section on one side only of the screen. One of the soldiers, John J. Moran, entered this section a few minutes later and allowed these mosquitoes to bite him. He had a sharp attack of yellow fever, while three soldiers on the other side of the screen, being protected from mosquito bites, remained in perfect health; it had been demonstrated that the scourge of the tropics was conveyed by the agency of the mosquito.

In the same year the Liverpool School of Tropical Medicine sent Dr. H. E. Durham and Dr. Walter Myers to Para to study yellow fever there. Both fully understood the dangers to which they would be exposed and the risks they ran, but they decided to take the risks and do the work that came to their hand. Both contracted the disease, and Myers died from it—a victim to his love of science and humanity—on January 20, 1901. His death added another name to the roll of martyrs to scientific investigation. High courage and an unselfish spirit led him to accept the invitation to take part in a most dangerous expedition; and he died that others might live.

One practical result of the discovery of the cause of yellow fever was that it made possible the construction of the Panama Canal, which had been abandoned as hopeless. It was not a hostile army or political difficulties that obstructed the progress of the work, not mountain chain or desert waste, but an insect which raised a barrier of disease and death between endeavour and accomplishment.

For four centuries the narrow Isthmus of Panama was regarded as the white man's grave. "Yellow Jack," or yellow fever, prevented Spaniards, French, or English from founding colonies there, and it was abandoned to negroes and half-breeds, who were immune to the disease. When Ferdinand de Lesseps, the constructor of the Suez Canal, commenced to cut the canal through the Isthmus of Panama, the chief obstacles in his way were yellow and malarial fevers. His men died like flies. It has been stated that before the work was finally abandoned by the French, a human life had been sacrificed for every cubic yard of earth excavated. Out of every hundred men employed upon the work, at least eighteen were sacrificed to a disease which is now known to be preventable, and many more were rendered helpless.

When the United States took over the control of the canal, the Government set to work to exterminate the mosquitoes responsible for the transmission of yellow fever and malaria. An army of sanitary officers, organised by Colonel W. C. Gorgas, was employed in a vigorous fight against the death-dealing mosquito, with the result that yellow fever has been practically

stamped out. Death from yellow fever on the Isth‑
mus of Panama since 1905, when the canal zone came
under the complete control of the United States, is
almost unknown. By the destruction of a little grey
gnat, a great engineering enterprise was made pos‑
sible of realisation.

Wherever steady war has been waged upon the mos‑
quito, yellow fever and malaria have practically dis‑
appeared. Formerly, yellow fever was the constant
scourge of the West Indian Islands. One writer
says: "The churchyards of Barbadoes and the other
islands are full of the bones of the victims; and it is
said of the slopes of the Morne, in St. Lucia, that there
is not a square yard without the remains of a soldier
under it, more being there from the results of yellow
fever than from the bullets of the enemy." Now what
do we find? The scourge which terrified the inhabi‑
tants of the West Indies every year in the old days
has entirely vanished as the result of establishing reg‑
ulations dealing with the breeding-places of mosqui‑
toes. Action founded upon the word of science has
converted into health resorts districts in which for‑
merly a European could scarcely hope to survive.

Malaria and yellow fever have thus been formidable
barriers to colonisation; and to have discovered their
cause and their remedy is of the highest importance to
the human race. Let us give one more instance of a
similar kind. In certain districts of Central and South‑
ern Africa thousands of cattle and animals die yearly
of what is known as fly disease. This disease is car‑
ried from a sick to a healthy animal by the bite of a
tsetse-fly—an insect only slightly larger than the ordi‑
nary house-fly. Domestic animals which enter fly‑
districts are seized in the course of a few days with
fever and wasting, and they almost invariably die.

Books of African travel are full of records of horses, teams of oxen, and herds of native cattle having been destroyed by the tsetse-fly disease; and on one occasion a native army, proceeding to the attack of an enemy, was effectually routed by having incautiously crossed fly-country.

Scientific investigations, carried on chiefly by Sir David and Lady Bruce have shown that sleeping-sickness, which has destroyed millions of human beings in Central Africa, is probably spread by the bite of a tsetse-fly closely related to that which causes the fly-disease in cattle. Though the suffering caused by sleeping-sickness has been known for many years, it was not until toward the end of the nineteenth century that a systematic study of its cause was undertaken. It was soon found that the tsetse-fly does not possess a venom of its own, but is the carrier of poison matter. When the fly bites a sick person or animal, it sucks up some of the parasites of the disease. These multiply and persist within the body of the insect, and may be transmitted to every person on whom it feeds during several weeks, and perhaps months. Sleeping-sickness was long supposed to be fatal to black races only, but the immunity of the white man from it was disproved by the death in 1907 of Lieutenant Tulloch, who contracted the disease while engaged in investigating it in Uganda, and whose name must be added to the same honourable roll as that upon which the names of Lazear and Myers are inscribed.

In the case of sleeping-sickness, then, we have a particular insect as the agent for the spread of a particular disease. People who devote attention to the study of insects are usually considered to be concerning themselves with subjects far removed from the ordinary affairs of life; they may be tolerated, but they are not to be encouraged. But now that biting flies have been shown to be responsible for the transmission of a number of terrible diseases, knowledge which was considered quite useless has proved to be of the greatest importance. There could not be a better illustration of the ultimate value of faithful scientific work. Take this lesson to heart; whatever is worth doing is worth doing well. Every addition to knowledge is a stepping-stone by which the human race can pass to new regions of discovery. Science asks not for words, but work; for the patient study of the things before us rather than for dreams and vague speculations. Listen to the trumpet-call of a naturalist and philosopher, whose labours for many years "to search out the secrets of nature by the way of experiment" have made life happier and surer in many parts of the world:

We must not accept any speculations merely because they now appear pleasant, flattering, or ennobling to us. We must be content to creep upwards step by step, planting each foot on the firmest finding of the moment, using the compass and such other instruments as we have, observing without either despair or contempt the clouds and precipices above and beneath us. Especially our duty at present is to better our present foothold; to investigate; to comprehend the forces of nature; to set our State rationally in order; to stamp down disease in body, mind, and government; to lighten the monstrous misery of our fellows, not by windy dogmas, but by calm science. *Sir Ronald Ross.*

CHAPTER IX

SCIENTIFIC MOTIVE

No man ever had genius who did not aim to execute more than he was able. Sir Humphry Davy.

The pleasure of life is according to the man who lives it, not according to the work or place. Emerson.

It is no paradox to say that in our most theoretical moods we may be nearest to our most practical applications. Prof. A. N. Whitehead.

Scientific subjects do not progress necessarily on the lines of direct usefulness. Very many applications of the theories of pure mathematics have come many years, sometimes centuries, after the actual discoveries themselves. Prof. A. R. Forsyth.

In all cases, the structure, habits, instincts, and faculties of living things, from the upward growth of the plumule of the sprouting seed to the moral sense of man, are primarily for the good of other beings than those which manifest them. Prof. W. K. Brooks.

SCIENTIFIC research may be conveniently divided into two classes—one in which the motive is solely the desire to extend the boundaries of knowledge, while in the other the special purpose is to obtain results which have a direct bearing upon problems of manufacture and construction. Explorers on the ship of science go out to discover new lands; and their spirit is not the same as that which actuates the prospectors who follow them with the intention of making the lands profitable to themselves and others. Both these classes of pioneers have their proper places in the

234

scheme of progress, but they live in different atmospheres. The scientific investigator must have freedom to follow his own course wherever it may lead, whereas technical research can be organised and definite problems presented for which solutions of direct service to man are sought. The standard of value in one case is that of knowledge only, while in the other it is that of profit or use. The scientific mind seeks to understand Nature; the engineering mind to control her for material purposes.

Some time ago the votes of the readers of an American periodical—*Popular Mechanics*—were taken as to what inventions were considered to be the "seven wonders of the modern world." From a list of numerous inventions, seven had to be selected; and those which received the highest number of votes were: wireless telegraphy, the telephone, the aeroplane, radium, anaesthetics and antitoxins, spectrum analysis, and X-rays. Each one of these things had its foundations in purely scientific work and was not the result of deliberate intention to make something of service to humanity.

Wireless telegraphy has its origin in the work of Clerk Maxwell and Hertz; the telephone depends upon the principles of magneto-electric induction discovered by Faraday; Langley's investigations of the resistance of the air to moving bodies led him to construct the first working model of an aeroplane; radium was isolated by the Curies solely on account of its scientific interest and without any view of its practical value; Chloroform was discovered by Liebig and Soubeiran; nitrous oxide or "laughing gas" by Davy, and sulphuric ether by Valerius Cordus; the principle of antitoxin treatment was established by Pasteur, Roux and Yersin, and the application of it to diphtheria by Behring and Kitasato; spectrum analysis began with Newton's observations of the decomposition of light by a glass prism, and became a means of discovering the constitutions of the sun and stars by the work of Fraunhofer, Wollaston, Kirchhoff, Lockyer and Huggins; and X-rays were discovered by Röntgen as a natural consequence of previous investigations of Crookes, Hertz and Lenard.

We are aware, of course, that Marconi made wireless telegraphy a commercial undertaking, that Graham Bell, Edison and others perfected the telephone, and the Wright Brothers constructed the first man-carrying flying machine; but these developments represent applications or extensions of new knowledge and not the creation of it. A scientific investigator working in a laboratory was in every case the originator of the fact or principle utilised in the production of what a consensus of opinion considers to be the seven greatest achievements of modern times.

The history of science shows that the greatest advances have always been made by men who undertook their inquiries into Nature without thought of proximate or ultimate practical application or pecuniary reward. The best kind of scientific research cannot be carried on in an atmosphere of commercialism, or where personal profit is the end in view. Few people outside purely scientific circles have any clear idea as to the meaning and object of research.

The object may be purely visionary, as was the object of the early chemists and alchemists, whose operations, extending through the dark centuries of the Middle Ages, left behind practically nothing but an extensive, though barren, literature, the witness of the credulity and ignorance of those times. The lesson to be derived from the whole of this strange history is one which needs to be continually revived and set in the new light of modern discovery and invention. The lesson is simply that until men began to observe and interrogate Nature for the sake of learning her ways, and without concentrating their attention on the expectation of useful applications of such knowledge, little or no progress was made. In other words, until a sufficient foundation of pure science has been successfully laid there can be no applied science. Real progress comes from the pursuit of knowledge for its own sake. *Sir William Tilden.*

Whether the world recognises it or no, all its material advance has been achieved by men of science. In the arts of sculpture and architecture, in literature, in philosophy, the position gained by Greece two thousand years ago remains the standard of excellence for the moderns, whereas the last fifty years or so have seen more additions to natural knowledge than all the ages before them; and the result has been not only advance in material welfare and comfort but also in intellectual outlook. The present era will not be remembered in future history for its art, its literature, or its drama, but for its science, by which it is placed in a pre-eminent position. The names of the men who have made this the golden age of scientific discovery do not loom so large to-day in the public eye as those of successful military commanders or popular orators and authors, but future generations will cherish them when the warrior, the politician and the scribe have passed into the limbo of forgotten things.

Many of the intellectual giants to which the human race will do homage came from the most unexpected places, and the great discoveries they made—often in poverty or in the face of other obstacles—went unregarded by a world which believes that the business of science is to find out useful things. Poisson, one of a brilliant array of mathematicians whom France produced a century ago, spent his early life in a hovel.

Fourier, Ampère, Arago and Fresnel were other great Frenchmen who gave glory of the highest kind to their native land, as did their contemporaries, Faraday in England, and Gauss in Germany. Nearly every one of these men was poor and was descended from the "common people."

This generation of great men was not students of the past so much as pioneers of the future. They only used traditional machinery when it served their purpose, and were constantly devising new methods of attacking problems relating both to the heavens and the earth. In mathematical works which excite wonder and admiration they discussed the motions of the masses forming our planetary system; they developed the mathematical theory of heat transmission and of light waves; they led the way into the vast field of electrical industries in which tens of millions of pounds are now invested; they made it possible for the engineers of our day to do what has been done.

Such men have always been the ones to open up new fields of industry, and new lines of human thought. Their work must precede the work of the engineer and the inventor. And when any nation has reached such a stage in its existence that scientific discovery is put in the background, and the entire current of work is expended in engineering and business enterprise, that nation is on the way to the civilisation of China. For the new problems before us are greater than they ever were before. If the pioneers do not appear, all advance will come to an end. *Prof. F. E. Nipher.*

National well-being can be secured only when the close relation between it and scientific progress is understood. Discoveries which lead directly to developments of industry and manufacture may almost be left to take care of themselves, and the search for them is not likely to be neglected, but it is not the case with

those for which no immediate use can be seen, yet
almost all scientific research comes within that category. This is the kind of research which needs encouragement more than any other, and demands the
greatest amount of originality, inspiration and enthusiasm to produce apparently insignificant results. The
man who has zeal for work of this kind, who is a born
researcher, should be cherished by his country above
all others.

We have any number of practical men, but *brain-craft* is the
master of *hand-craft*. England needs brain-craft. We want
men who cultivate chemistry for its own sake without sub-
stratum of utilitarianism. Men whose discoveries, like that of
phosphorus by Brandt, of the electric oxidation of nitrogen
by Priestley, of potassium and sodium by Davy, of aniline by
Unverdorben, of benzene by Faraday, and of chloroform by
Soubeiran, seemed at the time never likely to be of the slightest use to anybody. *Sir William Crookes.*

"La Rèpublique n'a pas besoin de savants"—the
Republic has no use for men of science—coldly remarked the president of the tribunal of French Revo-
lutionists which condemned to death the great chemist
Lavoisier in 1793. The founder of modern chemistry
met his death calmly and with dignity, and his body
was placed in an unmarked grave. It was not long,
however, before the French people realised that the
execution of Lavoisier was a crime against the whole
intellectual world. Two years after his life had been
sacrificed to the terrorists of the Revolution, the nation
took part in a solemn funeral ceremony; and orations
in his honour were publicly pronounced not only by
friends who mourned his death, but also by politicians
responsible for it. "Compared with the growth of
science," said Prof. C. S. Minot, "the shiftings of
Governments are minor events. Until it is clearly
realised that the gravest crime of the French Revolu-

tion was not the execution of the King, but the execution of Lavoisier, there is no right measure of values; for Lavoisier was one of the three or four greatest men France has produced."

Lavoisier lived for his fellow men; and he died because he was the champion of the French Academy of Sciences against the National Convention which desired to suppress it and all the other learned societies of France. Even when the Convention had decreed the destruction of the Academy, he urged the claims of men of science to national consideration.

"There is not," he said, "an academician who, if he had applied his intelligence and means to other objects, would not have been able to secure a livelihood and a position in society. It is on the public faith that they have followed a career, honourable without doubt, but hardly lucrative . . . if you allow the men of science who composed the defunct Academy to retire to the country, to take other positions in society, and to devote themselves to lucrative occupations, the organisation of the sciences will be destroyed, and half a century will not suffice to regenerate the order. For the sake of the national honour, in the interests of society, as you regard the good opinion of foreign nations, I beseech you to make some provision against the destruction of the arts which would be the necessary consequence of the annihilation of the sciences." *Sir T. E. Thorpe.*

Scientific discoveries of direct and immediate application to human affairs rarely spring forth full-grown and clothed, like the goddess Minerva from the head of Jupiter. Their beginnings are usually inconspicuous, and their development slow. As the acorn gives birth to the giant oak, so what seems to be a trivial experiment or observation is often the seed of a great industry.

Electric telegraphy of every type depends upon the work of men of science of many nations. Volta, an

Italian, discovered in 1800 his voltaic pile by means of which a continuous current of electricity can be produced. In 1819 Hans Christian Oersted, a professor at the University of Copenhagen, observed that when a wire conveying an electric current was placed lengthways over a compass needle, the needle turned aside from it. The discovery was made accidentally in the course of a lecture, but, as in many other instances in the history of science, "such accidents only meet persons who deserve them." The principle of the relationship thus disclosed between electricity and magnetism was worked out in detail by Ampère, the leading French investigator of electricity; and he suggested that the effect of the current might be used for signalling at a distance. Two German men of science—Gauss and Weber—established this means of communication upon a short line in Göttingen in 1833, and the first magneto-electric telegraph thus came into being out of laboratory experiment and mathematical analysis.

When Oersted published the results of his observations of the influence of an electric current upon a magnet, no one supposed that they could have an important practical value, yet upon his simple experiment the system of electric telegraphy was based. By sending an electric current through a wire, a compass needle can be deflected to one side or the other at the distant end, and the signals thus received can be translated into messages.

Oersted would never have made his great discovery of the action of galvanic currents on magnets had he stopped in his researches to consider in what manner they could possibly be turned to practical account; and so we should not now be able to boast of the wonders done by the electric telegraphs. Indeed, no great law in Natural Philosophy has ever been discovered *for* its practical application, but the instances are *innumerable* of investigations apparently quite *useless* in this narrow sense of the word which have led to the most valuable results. *Lord Kelvin.*

There have been many improvements since the early days of electric telegraphy, but they all depend upon magnetic effects produced by electric currents. In electricity, a far fleeter messenger has been found than Puck, who boasted in *Midsummer Night's Dream:* "I'll put a girdle about the earth in forty minutes." The land wires and submarine cables now devoted to telegraphic service would girdle the earth 250 times, and with the telephone lines the total length is about thirty-three million miles—one-third of the distance from the earth to the sun.

Fourier's work—which has been described as a "mathematical poem"—on the analytical theory of heat, was published in 1822—long before electric cables were dreamt of—but it enabled Kelvin thirty years later to attack a problem, the successful solution of which created submarine telegraphy.

Prof. Joseph Henry in the United States, Ampère in France, and Faraday in England, gave particular attention to Oersted's experiment and its consequences; and to their work we owe the construction of the electric dynamo by which the current for lighting, traction, and other purposes is now produced. They reasoned that since electricity in motion could disturb a magnet, the reverse should hold good, and a magnet in motion should be able to produce an electric current in a conductor near it. Both Henry and Faraday commenced experimenting with the view of creating a current by the action of a magnet, and both eventually succeeded. In 1831 Faraday wrote to a friend: "I am busy just now again on electro-magnetism, and think I have got hold of a good thing, but can't say. It may be a weed instead of a fish that, after all my labour, I may at last pull up."

A little later Faraday was able to show that when a magnet is brought rapidly near a coil of wire, a slight electric current is induced in the coil. Upon quickly removing the magnet, a momentary current in the opposite direction is created. Here, then, was a means of producing electric current by the expenditure of mechanical energy. All that was required was to set a magnet in rapid motion near a coil of wire properly arranged, and a supply of electricity could be obtained. This was not fully realised, however, until many years after Faraday performed the experiment to which the electric dynamo owes its origin, though scientific men understood the significance of the experiment. "This discovery of magneto-electricity," wrote Tyndall, "is the greatest result ever obtained. It is the Mont Blanc of Faraday's own achievements. He always worked at great elevations, but higher than this he never attained."

Nearly fifty years elapsed before the discovery was used with commercial success in the construction of the dynamo; and now as we travel at high speed upon electric railways, and illuminate our streets and homes with electric light, let us remember that we owe these advantages to persistent and purely scientific experiments made by Faraday at the Royal Institution between the years 1824 and 1831. The new era of electrical invention did not have its origin in the engineering workshop but in the scientific laboratory.

Necessity is not the mother of invention; knowledge and experiment are its parents. This is clearly seen in the case of many industrial discoveries; high-speed cutting tools were not a necessity which preceded, but an application which followed, the discovery of the properties of tungsten-chromium-iron alloys; so, too, the use of titanium in arc lamps and of vanadium in steel were sequels to the industrial preparation of these metals, and not discoveries made by sheer force of necessity. *Prof. W. R. Whitney.*

It would be easy to give many further instances of the foundation of great industries upon results obtained in scientific investigation. Credit is, of course, due to engineers who convert laboratory experiments into commercial undertakings, and to inventors for making use of scientific results in the production of instruments and devices for the convenience and comfort of man; but in both cases they are adapters of new knowledge rather than creators of it. The new field is opened by the man of science, but he is usually forgotten by those who afterwards take possession of it.

Facts which seem trivial in themselves may be rich in suggestion to the thoughtful mind. From observing the structure of wasps' nests, which are constructed of a papery-like material produced by the insects by the mastication of bits of stick and other vegetable substances, the naturalist, Réaumur, in the early part of the eighteenth century, was led to suggest that wood-fibre should be used for making paper. Out of that observation has arisen the great industry of paper manufacture from wood-pulp, the demand for which is now so immense that it threatens to exhaust the forest resources of the world.

So long ago as 1755 Priestley observed that when electric sparks pass through air, the nitrogen and oxygen are caused to combine together and form certain compounds of these two elements. Not long after, Cavendish showed that when air treated in this way was absorbed by a solution of caustic potash, the resulting product was saltpetre, or nitrate of potash. This was not an accidental discovery, but a result which was anticipated from the knowledge that saltpetre is made up of certain definite proportions of potassium, nitrogen and oxygen.

The practical application of Cavendish's experiment did not come until the beginning of the twentieth century, when the demand for saltpetre or similar substances containing nitrogen in a particular form as one of its constituents had reached such a high value that the artificial production of the salt offered prospects of commercial profit. Nitrogen is part of the constitution of every explosive used until the middle of the nineteenth century for military purposes, and "villainous saltpetre," which is chemically known as nitrate of potash, was the only source from which it was obtained. Nitrate of soda is a similar substance, but it was known only as a laboratory product until the discovery of great deposits of the salt in the arid region of the Andes in 1821. This Chile saltpetre can be converted into nitrate of potash by a chemical process, and thus provides the true saltpetre required for the manufacture of sporting and military powders.

But the demand for nitrates proceeds from arts of peace as well as from those of war. Nitrogen in some form or other is an essential fertiliser in agriculture, and nitrate of soda has proved to be a most valuable means of increasing the productiveness of the soil. Sir William Crookes pointed out in 1898 that while the average yield of wheat is but 12.7 bushels per acre, the yield could be increased to 20 bushels by the use of 1½ cwt. of nitrate of soda upon each acre each year.

As about two million tons of nitrate of soda are shipped from South American ports annually, there is a prospect of the ultimate exhaustion of the supply. In the earth's atmosphere, however, there is practically an inexhaustible store of nitrogen, and by methods based upon the experiments of Priestley and Cavendish the nitrogen of the air is now being used in the manufacture of nitrates or other compounds which can take the place of the natural saltpetre.

In 1828, a Swedish chemist, J. J. Berzelius, whose investigations have been a lamp unto the path of succeeding generations, discovered a rare element to which the name Thorium was given; he also carried out noteworthy researches on another rare earth—Cerium—discovered by a German chemist, M. H. Klaproth, some years earlier. Until recent years these substances were rarely mentioned even in text-books of chemistry, and their existence was only regarded as of academic interest, yet, by their use in the manufacture of the incandescent mantle in 1885, they saved coal-gas from being superseded by electricity.

The German chemist, Auer von Welsbach, while investigating the rare metals of the thorium group, found that certain compounds became luminous when held in the flame of a Bunsen burner. He dipped a piece of fabric in a solution of thorium compound and then held it in the Bunsen flame, with the result that the fabric was consumed and a coherent residue of thoria, which gave a bright light, remained. This was the beginning of the incandescent mantle now in common use everywhere. To increase the luminosity of the mantle, a small quantity of some other substance has to be added to the thorium compound; and by experiment von Welsbach found that the best result is obtained by the addition of one per cent. of a compound of cerium. The whole industry of the manufacture of incandescent mantles, of which many millions are produced annually, has thus arisen from purely scientific studies of the rare elements thorium and cerium.

Even the air-gas burner which gives a non-luminous flame suitable alike for rendering an incandescent mantle luminous or for heating purposes, was devised and used for scientific work, and was later adapted to everyday use. The inventor was R. W. von Bunsen, the famous Heidelberg professor to whom chemistry is indebted for important researches in every branch of the science. Sir Henry Roscoe relates how he took to the Heidelberg laboratory in 1853 a sample of the gas-lamp which was used for heating purposes in the chemistry department of University College, London. The lamp consisted of an ordinary argand burner, above which was a cylindrical copper chimney, on the top of which was a disc of wire gauze. By this arrangement a non-luminous flame was obtained, but the temperature was often low, and in other respects the device was unsatisfactory. Bunsen was not satisfied with this lamp, and he said: "Roscoe, I am going to make a lamp in which the mixture of air and gas shall burn without any wire gauze." After making a large number of experiments on the relative size of the openings for gas and air, the Bunsen burner was produced in 1855. The principle of this burner is used in every gas-fire and every incandescent gas-lamp, as well as in numerous forms of air-gas burners employed in various arts and manufactures.

Calcium carbide has become a common substance on account of its use in the production of acetylene for house lighting and for motor and cycle lamps, and in oxy-acetylene welding. It provides another example of a substance discovered by scientific experiment before it became an important commercial product. When it was discovered by Frederich Wöhler in 1862, and acetylene gas was produced from it, little importance was attached to the fact, partly, perhaps, on account of the great expense of its preparation. During the past few years, however, acetylene has assumed commercial importance owing to the development of the electric furnace constructed by Prof. Moissan in 1892, in which calcium carbide can be produced readily and cheaply from lime and carbon in the form of coke. The discovery was made independently by an American chemist, Willson, who was trying to produce metallic calcium by heating a mixture of coke and lime in an electric furnace. By the addition of water, the grey mass thus obtained is rapidly decomposed into acetylene and lime; and as by various mechanical devices the flow of water upon the carbide can be regulated, a convenient means of producing any quantity of the gas for illuminating purposes is obtained.

In 1895, M. Le Chatelier found that when acetylene was burnt with an equal volume of oxygen gas, a temperature was obtained nearly two thousand degrees Fahr. higher than that of the oxy-hydrogen flame; and it was suggested that the use of acetylene in blow-pipes would be of great value in the production of high temperatures in the laboratory. A few years later such blowpipes were applied industrially for oxy-acetylene welding of metals, and they are now used in thousands of workshops for this purpose. There is not a stage in this story of the application of a substance to the service of man but is directly dependent upon laboratory studies in chemistry.

Wöhler, whose discovery of calcium carbide, though forgotten for a generation, laid the foundation of a great industry, was the first chemist to prepare from inorganic materials in the laboratory a substance— Carbamide—previously known only as a product of vital action. All the complicated chemical bodies which occur in animal and vegetable life consist mainly of the elements carbon, hydrogen, oxygen and nitrogen. About one hundred and fifty thousand organic compounds are now known, and have mostly been produced artificially by chemists.

This vast development of organic synthesis is due chiefly to the discovery by Prof. August Kekulé in 1858 of the characteristics of atomic structure of organic compounds. His laws did for organic chemistry what Kepler's laws and Newton's theory of gravitation did for astronomy; they revealed the system upon which the immense number of natural substances may be built up from a few elements, and enabled chemists to predict the consequences of different arrangements of these elements. As an architect may produce different edifices by the use of a few building stones, so the chemist is able to construct almost numberless compounds from three or four elementary constituents.

To one untrained in experimental science, nothing can be more uninteresting than a laboratory of organic chemistry. To stand over furnaces on a hot day, it may be, burning minute quantities of white or brown powders in long tubes; to watch uninviting liquids for crystals which are very slow to appear; to separate liquids from coloured solids—an operation which often interferes with the beauty of the fingers; to inhale odours which may be of the violet or the meadow-sweet, but usually are not—all this must be dreary enough to the untrained mind, the mind incapable of responding to the chemist's idea. How different to the chemist. He is trying to unravel the mysteries of the architecture of some molecule. He has an idea which he hopes may do this. He is testing its validity. In the light of this idea, labour otherwise unpleasant seems pleasure, days seem minutes. To succeed is his greatest joy. He may not succeed, but, as it is with sport, he does not know final defeat, but modifies his idea and tries again. *Prof. A. Senier.*

During his Easter vacation in 1856, a lad only seventeen years of age set himself the task of trying to prepare quinine artificially. His name was William Henry Perkin; and the problem which he faced still remains unsolved, but his experiments led to the discovery of the first aniline dye, and from it has arisen a great industry. In the course of his attempts to make quinine, Perkin obtained a black mass, which would have been left by most students as the final result of the inquiry. But Perkin had the true scientific spirit, and proceeded to investigate this uninviting substance. He obtained from it finally the violet dye known as mauvine or aniline purple. Aniline, from which this dye was derived, is one of the substances found in the tar obtained during the manufacture of coal-gas. In the early days of gas-making, coal-tar was regarded as a waste product of no use to anyone, and often a great nuisance to the manufacturer. It is now known to be a rich mine from which many useful substances can be obtained by chemists, in addition to hundreds of dye stuffs.

After Perkin's discovery of mauve, numerous other dye-stuffs were produced in quick succession from coal-tar by variations of the process discovered by him; and there are now several hundreds of similar dyes on the market, all of which owe their origin to his work. Here, then, we have a striking example of a vast industrial development being founded upon a result obtained during a purely scientific investigation. Referring to this, a great chemist once remarked:

Whenever one of your chemical friends, full of enthusiasm, exhibits and explains to you his newly-discovered compound, you will not cool his noble ardour by asking him that most

terrible of all questions, "What is its use? Will your compound bleach or dye? Will it shave? May it be used as a
substitute for leather?" Let him quietly go on with his work.
The dye, the leather, will make their appearance in due time.
Let him, I repeat, perform his task. Let him indulge in the
pursuit of truth—of truth pure and simple—of truth not for
the sake of Mauve—let him pursue truth for the sake of truth.
Prof. A. W. von Hofmann.

The discovery of oxygen gas by a poor Swedish
apothecary, Scheele, and independently by the Englishman, Joseph Priestley, son of a humble cloth-dresser,
was one of the most important ever made in chemistry,
but more than a century elapsed before practical value
was given to it by the use of oxygen with hydrogen
in the oxy-hydric process of cutting metals, and in
many other arts. Chlorine—another gas discovered
by Scheele—not only influenced the progress of pure
chemistry but also now plays an important part in
practical affairs. It is used for bleaching straw, paper
and other materials, and is essential to the manufacture
of chloroform, which could never have been discovered
but for Scheele's work. It is used extensively in the
chlorination process for the extraction of gold from its
ores; and the noxious green gas first produced with
simple apparatus in a little room of an apothecary's
shop has thus become a valuable servant of a great
industry as well as a diabolical weapon of warfare. One
of the deadliest poisons known to chemistry, potassium
cyanide, when in dilute solution, will dissolve natural
gold; and here again a laboratory observation has given
rise to an important practical process. The chief
method now used for the extraction of gold from its
ore is the cyanide process, and it enables large quantities of the precious metal to be obtained from resi-

dues which in the absence of this process would be waste tailings.

The first gas ever liquefied was chlorine, and when Faraday succeeded in transforming it by pressure into the liquid state he opened a new era of benefit to man. Liquid air, liquid oxygen, and liquid hydrogen are all now commercial articles and not scientific curiosities. Large quantities of sulphur dioxide and ammonia in the liquefied form are now used for the artificial production of ice, and for the refrigerating machinery which enables fruit, meat and other articles of food to be transported from their place of origin to distant parts of the earth in a fresh condition.

Sir James Dewar, working at the Royal Institution, where Faraday made his pioneer experiments on the liquefaction of gases, worthily carried on the work there, and succeeded in reducing the most intractable gases to the solid as well as the liquid form. A device adopted by him for retaining liquid air and other liquefied gases became later an article of commerce in the form of the Thermos or vacuum flask. An instrument devised originally for a scientific purpose has thus been converted into an everyday commodity by which liquids can be kept at a constant temperature for many hours. Before it was generally realised that the vacuum flask had not been patented, certain manufacturers made small fortunes out of it by charging a guinea for what had cost about a shilling to produce; but neither then nor later has the actual inventor of this scientific device reaped any pecuniary reward for his ingenuity.

Saccharin, which has an intensely sweet taste, and is of great value in cases of diabetes and other disorders in which ordinary cane-sugar has to be avoided in a patient's diet, was discovered in 1879 while an investigation was being carried on in Prof. Ira Remsen's laboratory that seemed as little likely to lead to practical results as any that could well be imagined.

Any practical man would unhesitatingly have condemned the work as being utterly useless, and I may add that some did condemn it.   There was no hope, no thought entertained by us that anything practical would come of it.   But lo! one day it appeared that one of the substances discovered in the course of the investigation is the sweetest thing on earth; and then it was shown that it can be taken into the system without injury; and finally that it can be manufactured at such a price as to furnish sweetness at a cheaper rate than it is furnished by the sugar cane or the beet.   And soon a great demand for it was created, and to-day it is manufactured in surprising quantities and used extensively in all corners of the globe. *Prof. Ira Remsen.*

Early in the nineteenth century Sir Humphry Davy succeeded in decomposing caustic potash and caustic soda by means of the electric current, and in obtaining from them the metals potassium and sodium.   The experiment was made to settle a disputed question in pure chemistry, but it was the starting-point of an immense industry.   At the present time, the only process of commercial importance for making sodium is that of electrolysis of caustic soda, all chemical methods of manufacturing the metal being superseded by it.   Caustic soda itself, together with chlorine for bleaching purposes, is obtained from common salt by electrolytic methods on a large scale; and its manufacture is an important industry.

In 1833, Faraday obtained the metal magnesium from a compound of the element by means of electrolysis; and now the magnesium ribbon and powder used for flash-light and other purposes are almost entirely made by the same method. But the most important application of electricity to industrial chemistry is the electrolytic production of that most useful metal, aluminum, which is destined to compete with iron and steel in its importance. Aluminum is now manufactured exclusively by electrolysis of a fused mineral containing it, though a few years ago it was obtained wholly by purely chemical methods. Unlike the examples already mentioned, the actual process of producing aluminum by electrolysis was not derived directly from a scientific laboratory, yet it and all other electrolytic methods would never have come into being but for the discovery by men of science of the chemical effects of the electric current.

Industrial chemistry has, in fact, been revolutionised by the application of electrical methods; and the foundation of the new branch was laid chiefly by the genius and research of Davy and Faraday, being practically based on the laws enunciated by the latter. Metals, such as copper and iron, are obtained in the highest state of purity by electrolysis; in the United States alone, more than twenty million pounds' worth of copper are electrically refined every year. Silver, gold and lead are also refined on a large scale by electrical methods. Electro-plating with gold, silver, nickel and other metals; electrotyping, which is used in every printing works to obtain copies of type and engravers' blocks; the electrolytic reproduction of medals and similar articles, and a hundred other commercial uses have been found for methods which when first discovered were considered to be of interest only to the world of science. It was the remembrance of such facts as these as to the influence of scientific work upon industrial progress that induced Huxley to remark, so long ago as 1877, in urging the value of technical education:

I weigh my words when I say that if the nation could purchase a potential Watt, or Davy, or Faraday, at the cost of a hundred thousand pounds down, he would be dirt-cheap at the money. It is a mere commonplace and everyday piece of knowledge that what these men did has produced untold millions of wealth, in the narrowest economical sense of the word. *Huxley.*

CHAPTER X

PRACTICAL PURPOSE

Purpose directs energy, and purpose makes energy. C. H. Parkhurst.

A life without a purpose is a languid, drifting thing. Marcus Aurelius.

Still o'er the earth hastes opportunity
Seeking the hardy soul that seeks for her. J. R. Lowell.

The Time is great
(What times are little? To the sentinel
That hour is regal when he mounts on guard.)
George Eliot.

There are two distinct classes of men: first, those who work at enlarging the boundaries of knowledge, and secondly, those who apply that knowledge to useful ends. Prof. R. W. von Bunsen.

Scientific investigations carried on with the single motive of acquiring new knowledge often lead, as we have seen, to results of great practical value. Such applications are, however, only incidental, and in the world of science they provide no test of the importance of the work done. The practical man judges scientific research from the point of view of its direct service to humanity, or that of money-making capacity; and he considers that people who devote their lives to studies having neither of these profitable objects in mind are wasting their time and abusing their intellectual faculties.

It comes as a surprise to most men to be told that in

VII. SCIENCE REVEALING THE TREASURES OF THE EARTH.

Painted by Edwin Austin Abbey, R.A. (1852-1911), in the Harrisburg Capitol, Pennsylvania.

scientific circles usefulness is never adopted as the standard of value; and that even if not a single practical result is reached by an investigation, the work is worth doing if it enlarges knowledge or increases our outlook upon the universe. This proposition, of course, leaves the practical man cold; yet it is all that science desires to offer in justification of its activities. While the discovery of truth remains its single aim, science is free to pursue inquiries in whatever direction it pleases; but when it permits itself to be dominated by the spirit of productive application it becomes merely the galley-slave of short-sighted commerce. Almost all the investigations upon which modern industry has been built would have been crushed at the outset if immediate practical value had determined what work should be undertaken. Science brings back new seeds from the regions it explores, and they seem to be nothing but trivial curiosities to the people who look for profit from research, yet from these seeds come the mighty trees under which civilised man has his tent, while from the fruit he gains comfort and riches.

Industrial research is concerned not with the discovery of truth but with the production of something which will be of direct service to man and from which pecuniary profit may be secured. It is the province of the inventor rather than that of the man of science. Such research and that carried on with no ulterior motive are complementary to one another. Science has done its part when it has made a new discovery; constructive engineering renders good service when it shows how the discovery may be chained to the chariot of industrial advance. To foresee the possibilities of a discovery, to transform a laboratory experiment into the mechanical plant of a large works, or to apply it to the needs of ordinary life, require aptitudes not commonly possessed by the scientific investigator. The engineer usually has such practical purposes in mind; discoveries are to him things to be used and not ends in themselves, as they are to the man of science. He seeks not so much to know Nature as to circumvent her; and the research which he undertakes or organises has for its object the artificial preparation of substances which are naturally rare, the production of a new process or the improvement of an old, the design of machines which will increase his power over her, and of instruments which will enable him to laugh at limitations of time and space.

Research is necessary for these advances, but the spirit in which it is carried on is essentially different from that of the scientific worker. The engineer or the inventor first of all perceives a need and then endeavours to devise a means of meeting it. If he is of a scientific type of mind he will make an accurate analysis of the conditions to be fulfilled, and then design his machine or instrument to fulfil them; but the usual way is to find practically what will perform the required functions, and to leave experience or scientific knowledge to indicate how improvements may be effected.

The two methods may be illustrated by the discovery of the safety-lamp for miners. With no access to scientific works, or intercourse with scientific men, George Stephenson constructed a safety-lamp which, like Davy's, depended upon the principle that the flame would not pass through tubes of small diameter and ignite explosive gases outside. Stephenson first made a lamp with a long chimney and a tube at the bottom to admit air for the flame. As this was found to give an unsteady flame, he corrected the defect by using several tubes of reduced diameter instead of a single tube, to supply the air. This lamp was found to burn better than the first lamp, and was used with safety in a dangerous mine early in November, 1815. A few weeks later he had a third lamp constructed in which small holes in metal plates took the place of the tubes, but in this device he was forestalled by Davy, who presented to the public on November 9, 1815, his safety-lamp having wire gauze surrounding the flame.

It is not our intention, however, to revive the angry controversy which arose over the respective claims of Stephenson and Davy as the discoverer of the miner's safety-lamp; all we wish to do is to use the invention to illustrate the different methods by which the same end may be reached. Stephenson made a lamp and then proceeded to test and perfect it; Davy, when he took up the problem of the cause and possible prevention of explosions in mines, first inquired into the nature of the explosive gases and of flame, and was soon able to announce his discovery "that explosive mixtures of mine-damp will not pass through small apertures or tubes; and that if a lamp or lanthorn be made air-tight at the sides, and furnished with apertures to admit the air, it will not communicate flame to the outward atmosphere." Davy discovered a principle and then constructed a lamp based upon it. Stephenson made a lamp and was led by it to a principle. Though there may be differences of opinion as to who was the inventor of the safety-lamp, the establishment of the principle of its construction was undoubtedly discovered by Davy, and was a notable advance of scientific knowledge. It was, however, left to practical men to devise the improvements which removed some of the defects of the lamp in its original form, and made it an efficient protection against the dangers of fire-damp in mines.

The combination of mechanical ingenuity with scientific genius is rare; two men in whom it was notably manifest were James Watt and Lord Kelvin. Watt was of an inquiring turn of mind from his boyhood. The story is told that, sitting one evening with his aunt, Mrs. Muirhead, the latter said: "James Watt, I never saw such an idle boy; take a book or employ yourself usefully; for the last hour you have not spoken one word, but taken the lid off that kettle and put it on again, holding now a cup and now a silver spoon over the steam, watching how it rises from the spout, and catching and connecting the drops of hot water. Are you not ashamed of spending your time in this way?" Whilst thus blamed for his idleness, his active mind was busy in investigating the properties of steam, and he was then only fifteen years old! He also busied himself with chemical experiments, repeating them till satisfied of their accuracy from his own observations. As an instance of his versatility in all kinds of instrumental work, he was asked, amongst other things, to make an organ for a Masonic Lodge in Glasgow. A lecturer at Glasgow University wrote to a friend:

We imagine that Mr. Watt could do anything; and though we all knew that he did not know one musical note from another, he was asked if he could build this organ. He said, "Yes," but he began by building a very small one for his friend, Dr. Black. . . . In doing this a thousand things occurred to him which no organ builder ever dreamed of— nice indicators of the strength of the blast, regulators of it, etc. . . .

Steam had been used to drive engines long before the time when Watt devoted attention to the subject. More than two thousand years ago, Heron of Alexandria, who with Archimedes stands out from the Greek philosophers of his day because of his mechanical ingenuity, invented a kind of steam-engine in which the reactive force of steam escaping from jets on a hollow metal ball caused the ball to spin round. The principle of this engine was similar to that of the steam-turbine which has been developed so remarkably by Dr. de Laval and the Hon. Sir Charles A. Parsons since 1880. Heron's machine, however, was only a toy, and the first successful engine put to practical use was invented by Captain Savery in 1698. This engine was employed for pumping water; and the principle of its action is the same as that of the modern pulsometer pumps now extensively used.

The beginning of the steam-engine as we now know it, containing a cylinder into which steam enters, and a piston moving in the cylinder, was the atmospheric engine devised in 1705 by Thomas Newcomen, a black-smith of Dartmouth, England. An overhead beam capable of swinging up and down, like a see-saw, was connected with a piston on one side and with a pump-rod on the other. The piston could move up and down in a cylinder connected to a boiler by a steampipe furnished with a valve. When the piston was at the top of the cylinder, steam was admitted, the valve was closed, and a jet of water was caused to play into the cylinder. The steam was thus condensed, leaving a partial vacuum in the cylinder, with the result that the piston was forced down by the pressure of the atmosphere above it; and as it pulled down one arm of the overhanging beam, the other arm connected with the pump-rod was pulled up. The weight of the pump-rod would then pull down its end of the beam and the piston would thus be brought to the top of the cylinder again, ready for another stroke.

Watt's constructive work on the steam-engine began

after 1757, when he was given a workshop as a mathematical instrument maker within the walls of the University of Glasgow. He first tried some experiments on a Papin's digester, which is merely a small sealed iron vessel having a safety-valve, so that water can be boiled in it under a pressure much greater than that of the atmosphere. Watt made a form of steam-engine by fixing upon the digester a syringe one-third of an inch in diameter with a solid piston, and furnished also with a tap to admit the steam from the digester or shut it off at pleasure, as well as to open a communication from the inside of the syringe to the open air, by which the steam contained in the syringe might escape. The steam from the digester forced the piston up, and was allowed to escape; the pressure of the atmosphere then pushed back the piston to its original position, and the action could be repeated. This single-acting high-pressure syringe engine was made and experimented upon by Watt about 1761; and, with certain additions, still constitutes one of the best forms for road motors.

In 1763-64, Watt had to repair a model of Newcomen's engine belonging to the Natural Philosophy Department of the University of Glasgow. He saw that the alternate heating of the cylinder by steam and cooling it by water involved great loss of heat; and he set to work to devise a means of remedying this and other defects of the engine. The solution of the chief difficulty occurred to him while taking a walk on a fine Sunday afternoon in 1765. He tells us:

I was thinking upon the engine at the time, and had gone as far as the herd's house, when the idea came into my mind that, as steam was an elastic body, it would rush into a vacuum, and if a communication were made between the cylinder and an exhausted vessel, it would rush into it, and might be there condensed without cooling the cylinder. *James Watt.*

It must not be supposed, however, that Watt's improvements of Newcomen's engine were due only to a happy thought put into action. He approached the question of perfecting the steam-engine as a scientific problem, and under the inspiration of the principle of "latent heat" discovered by Joseph Black, his friend and guide in the many researches. Black, who was a professor in the University of Glasgow, measured the amount of heat required to transform ice into water and water into steam, and found that a great quantity of heat was used up in each case without producing any rise of temperature. Conversely, when steam is condensed into water, or water is frozen into ice, the change of state involves the liberation of heat. A pound of steam, for example, contains enough latent heat to raise five pounds of ice-cold water to the boiling point.

Watt discovered, by numerous experiments, that the quantity of heat thus contained in steam was nearly constant for different pressures within the ranges used in steam-engines—a conclusion which showed that decided advantage could be gained by using steam at high pressure. He proved also by experiment that, with the Newcomen engine, three-quarters of the heat of the steam was lost in making the cylinder hot at each stroke, and he aimed at lessening this waste of steam and consequently of fuel, with the result that he gave to the world an engine which consumed per horse-power only one-quarter of the fuel previously used by any engine. Though now the consumption of coal per horse-power is only from one-third to one-quarter what it was in Watt's time, yet the advance he made was a most remarkable engineering achievement.

The principles Watt followed in effecting his improvements of the steam-engine were that the cylinder should be kept as hot as the steam that enters it, that steam should be condensed in a vessel distinct from the cylinder, and that the steam itself should move the piston, instead of the pressure of the atmosphere doing it, as was the case with Newcomen's engine.

Watt's earliest commercial engine (1769) represented the realisation of these principles. The cylinder was clothed with non-conducting materials, and fitted with a steam-jacket in order to keep it hot; condensation of the steam was effected in a separate condenser, and the piston was pushed down the cylinder by admitting steam above it, the force of the steam thus taking the place of the pressure of the atmosphere in the Newcomen engine. A further improvement was made in 1782, when Watt introduced for the first time the principle of making the steam act alternately on the top and bottom of the piston. The Watt engine, with its many ingenious details of construction, was the prime mover in most general use for eighty years, until the middle of the nineteenth century, when the compound engine and other highly developed forms began to be introduced.

Watt transformed a rude and imperfect steam-engine into an efficient and powerful working instrument, and by so doing accomplished the greatest work performed by any engineer of modern times. He combined the qualities of the practical mechanic with those of the patient investigator, and the perfection to which he brought the steam-engine was due even more to scientific experiment than to mechanical skill. "Nature can always be conquered," he used to say, "if we can but find out her weak side"; and this thought encouraged him to persevere in his questioning and attack until the secret he desired to discover was revealed to him. Even after the brilliant idea of separate condensation had occurred to him, he had to work for more than twenty years before he could see that his steam-engine would bring him anything but disappointment and loss, yet he endured unto the end, and saw his engines used in increasing numbers in mines and manufactures. No invention has had a greater influence upon material progress than Watt's engine, and none has been brought to perfection by a closer combination of genius, scientific study and mechanical ingenuity, all of which were blended in one man—James Watt, mathematical instrument maker to the University of Glasgow.

Thomas A. Edison is the embodiment of the method of specialised research with a practical purpose. By quickness of perception, fertility of resource, and persistent trial of everything until the best means of achieving his end has been found, he has become the leading inventor in the world. When he was endeavouring to find the best material to use for the filament of the incandescent electric lamp, he dispatched agents to search through China and Japan, to explore the American continent from the Atlantic to the Pacific, and to seek in India, Ceylon and the neighbouring countries for a vegetable fibre which could be carbonised most efficiently; and he finally used a strip of carbonised bamboo for the filament. He invented the phonograph in 1877, and from the rough instrument then devised developed the perfect means of recording and reproducing sound represented in the modern form of talking machines. He constructed new forms of transmitter and receiver of telephones, and from his fertile brain have come a system of multiple telegraphy, new methods of treating ores and many other agents for the service and pleasure of man.

The phonograph and the kinematograph are, perhaps, the greatest of Mr. Edison's achievements, both in a scientific and in a popular sense. He was not the first to photograph and combine a series of moving pictures, but he was the inventor of the instrument by which this is now accomplished. So long ago as 1870, Dr. E. J. Marey in France, and a little later Mr. E. Muybridge in the United States, began the analysis of animal movements by means of photographs taken at very short intervals. A few years afterward, Mr. Muybridge arranged successive pictures on glass discs, and by rotating them in front of an optical lantern he was able to produce the visual impression of motion.

The invention of the celluloid ribbon enabled pictures to be taken on a continuous strip of film, instead of being arranged on a glass disc, and after careful attention Mr. Edison succeeded in doing this in 1893. The modern kinematograph pictures may be said to date from this development of the work of Marey and Muybridge.

In his first fantastic romance, Mr. H. G. Wells created a time-machine by means of which time could be accelerated or retarded, and a journey could thus be made into the past or the future. The kinematograph is a veritable time-machine, so far as the past is concerned. It can show the life of an insect or the life of a man in a period which is but a fraction of the true duration, and the period of projection may be the same in each case. If the insect be imagined to be endowed with a mind, its life, though but a day, will seem as long as the three score years and ten of man, for the ultimate conception of time is in terms of duration of life. A thousand years may be but an hour to the time-machine which Mr. Edison has produced to delight and instruct the modern world.

To the engineer the fascination of experimental research lies, as Cap'n Cuttle would observe, "in the application thereof." He seeks to know; not from the pleasure to be derived from the acquisition of knowledge, but in order to bring that knowledge to bear upon everyday problems of life, labour and economy. It must not be supposed that this spirit is necessarily foreign to the man of science. Robert Boyle, one of the most active originators of the Royal Society, refers particularly to practical use of the researches undertaken by himself and other pioneers of the experimental method of investigation in England. Writing in 1646, he alludes to his studies in "natural philosophy, the mechanics and husbandry, according to the principles of our new philosophical college that values no knowledge, but as it hath a tendency to use."

A Chinese proverb states that he who holds the iron of the world will rule the world. This, however, is only a half truth; for China itself has probably as large deposits of iron ore as any part of the world, but it has not the scientific knowledge required to make the best use of them. The talents which that country possesses have been buried in the ground instead of being used to gain other talents. The masters of the world of iron must be those who understand best the properties of the metal, whether now or in the future. As the result of a systematic study of the effects of adding to iron a special element other than carbon, Sir Robert Hadfield produced his famous manganese-steel, which is used extensively for all purposes where toughness as well as hardness is required, whether for arts of peace or purposes of war. Ten years' persistent research upon the influence which different percentages of manganese exert upon the properties of steel were required before that remarkable metal, manganese-steel, was discovered, and showed the way to the production of dozens of other alloys possessing qualities required in arts and industries.

It is much easier to accept things as they are than it is to inquire into them and decide whether they are capable of improvement. Throughout the world's history, progress has been accomplished by the men who were not content to do as their forefathers did, but were continually asking, "Why?", "Wherefore?", "Is that the best way?", "Is this the best possible thing?". Lord Kelvin was a brilliant example of this type of scientific mind, ever critical of defects, alert as to practical needs, and fertile with possible improvements. His views as to the practical value of science were definite and unmistakable.

The life and soul of science is its practical application; and just as the great advances in mathematics have been made through the desire of discovering the solution of problems which were of a highly practical kind in mathematical science, so in physical science many of the greatest advances that have been made from the beginning of the world to the present time have been made in the earnest desire to turn the knowledge of the properties of matter to some purpose useful to mankind. *Lord Kelvin.*

When Lord Kelvin turned his attention to the mariner's compass, about 1870, that instrument had been in use in much the same form by European navigators for about six hundred years, and by the Chinese long before. The compass in the simple form in which it was used for many centuries was in many respects unsatisfactory. In the Navy it was found to be useless during gun-fire, and to be affected so much by the rolling of the ships during stormy weather that little dependence could be placed upon it. These defects came directly under the notice of Lord Kelvin after he had undertaken to write an article for a magazine. "When

I tried," he said in the article, "to write on the mariner's compass, I found I did not know nearly enough about it. So I had to learn my subject. I *have* been learning it these five years." He not only noted the defects of the existing instrument, but also set himself to devise a means of remedying them; and in the end he produced the compass which has made his name famous to every nautical man. The existing compasses were made with needles ten, twelve, or even fifteen inches in length, in order that, when shaken, their period of vibration or swing should be long. The card also was made large, with the view of keeping the compass steady; but the result was that, on account of the weight of the needles and card upon the pivot, the compass was apt to stick, and was always sluggish in its action.

Lord Kelvin first showed in a mathematical paper that steadiness of the compass at sea in stormy weather could be obtained by small needles and a light compass card instead of large needles and a heavy card, if certain conditions of construction were fulfilled. He took out the first patent for his improvements in 1876, but he had to wait thirteen years before the instrument was adopted as the standard compass for the Navy. The compass is now being supplemented by a new form in which the magnets and card are immersed in a liquid which fills the compass-bowl, and by the gyro-compass, which is independent of magnetic conditions, but it was Lord Kelvin who made the first departure from the crude instruments which had been in daily use by thousands of practical men from early times without one of them suggesting any substantial improvement.

All sailors are grateful to Lord Kelvin for his inventions for the preservation of life at sea, notably by means of his compass and sounding machine. With these two aids to navigation a safe course can be fol-

lowed with confidence in fog or darkness; and every
sailorman can tell of disasters from which he was
saved by them. A characteristic tribute to Kelvin from
a sailor's point of view has been given by Admiral Sir
W. R. Kennedy.

"Some years ago," he says, "I left a port on the coast of
Patagonia in the *Ruby*. We shaped a course for Golfo Nuevo
for the night. At 8 p.m. the navigating officer came into my
cabin and showed me the position of the ship, well clear of the
land, and 100 fathoms no bottom, marked on the chart.
'All right,' I said. 'Get a cast of the lead.' 'Throw Thomson overboard,' was the way I put it. The navigator looked
at me to see if I was joking. 'Why, there's no bottom at 100
fathoms, sir.' 'Well, heave Thomson over.' He left the
cabin, and presently I heard the whirr of the wire suddenly
stop. I rushed on deck. Fifteen fathoms! Stop her, hard-
a-port, leadsmen in both chains! Sure enough, 15 fathoms.
I hove to all night, head off shore, and next morning steered
for the gulf, which we reached without further adventure,
but had we continued our course we should have been ashore
before daylight. The navigating officer was not at fault, but
the coast-line was not correctly charted. No wonder that we
sailors bless the name of Lord Kelvin."

By his improvements of the two oldest aids to navigation — the compass and the sounding line — Lord
Kelvin earned profound gratitude from all who go to
sea. He has been called the best friend the sailor ever
had; and it is said that a blue-jacket was once over-
heard to remark, "I don't know who this Thomson
may be, but every sailor ought to pray for him every
night."

Lord Kelvin's work for submarine telegraphy is another example of a practical problem solved by scientific knowledge. The first Atlantic cable was laid in
1858, but scarcely had the enthusiasm awakened by it
begun to subside when the signals grew more and more

feeble and in a few weeks the cable altogether ceased to transmit messages. This failure was sufficient to discourage most people, but Lord Kelvin encouraged a fresh attempt. "What has been done," he said, "will be done again. The loss of a position gained is an event unknown in the history of man's struggle with the forces of inanimate Nature." Faith and courage were both required to attack the problem again. A new type of cable was designed, better adapted than previous kinds to bear the strain of laying, and in 1865 this cable had established telegraphic communication between England and America. The appliance, known as the siphon-recorder, invented by Lord Kelvin to register the electric impulses transmitted by the cable, still remains in universal use as the standard instrument in submarine telegraphy. It was scientific knowledge, and the spirit of converting difficulties into opportunities, that make Trans-Atlantic telegraphy possible.

When the first iron ships were built, it was found that the compasses were so greatly affected by the magnetism of the ships that accurate navigation was impossible. Long before Kelvin devised his instrument, a method of determining a ship's permanent and temporary magnetic conditions had been worked out, and a means of counteracting them had been found. No magnetic compass would be of any practical use if the effect upon it of the fixed and movable iron of a ship could not be compensated effectively.

The problem presented by the use of iron in ships was definite but complicated; and it could be solved only by scientific investigation. Mr. Archibald Smith, a Chancery barrister who devoted all his leisure hours to the application of mathematics to navigation, had this practical purpose in mind; and his work was recognised by the award to him, in 1872, of a gift of £2,000 "for the long and valuable services which he had gratuitously rendered to naval science in connection with the magnetism of iron ships, and the deviation of their compasses." The chief credit must, however, be given to Sir George Airy, the Astronomer Royal, who, in 1838, was asked to undertake experiments on a ship —the *Rainbow*—for the purpose of discovering a correction for the deviation of the compass produced by the iron of which it was constructed. The deviation was so great that the compass of the ship was as much as fifty degrees out of the magnetic north and south direction.

Airy investigated the subject theoretically as well as practically, and calculated the strength of the magnetic action required to counteract the disturbance. In a month he had completed his inquiry. He took the necessary compensating magnets and iron correctors to Deptford, where the ship was lying, mounted them in their proper places, tried the ship, and the compass was then found to be sensibly correct. In the same year, another iron ship—the *Ironsides*—built at Liverpool, had her compass similarly corrected by Airy; and in this case, as in the *Rainbow*, the disturbance was so great as to make the vessel worthless without a mechanical means of correcting the effect due to the iron.

The success of the methods employed for the correction soon became widely known, and led immediately to extensive building of iron ships. Though some acknowledgment of an important service thus rendered to navigation might have been expected, the Admiralty refused to sanction any reward for it; possibly because the Government did not then possess a single iron vessel and was not disposed to urge the inquiry into the effect of a ship's magnetism upon the compasses.

When Airy commenced the investigation, the whole subject was in darkness, yet by the application of a mechanical theory he brought it under control. Lord Kelvin made a great advance later by the use of short needles for the compass cards, but the method of correcting the compasses in iron ships, now adopted not only in the merchant service but also in the navies of all countries, is that worked out by Sir George Airy in 1839. Airy—mathematician and astronomer—has thus been justly called the father of the mode of mechanical compensation of the compass now followed throughout the civilised world.

Neither Airy nor Kelvin had any special knowledge of ships' compasses when they took up the problems which they solved with such complete success, but they knew that the best way to attain a practical purpose is to submit the conditions to scientific analysis before devising arrangements to meet them. This method may be tedious, but it is always the best in the end. No matter to what branch of human activity the subject belongs, the preliminary scientific investigation undertaken with the view of understanding it fully makes the surest foundation of advance. All work which has not this basis is of the empirical, trial and error, rule of thumb, kind; it is a shot in the dark, and though the target may hit the chances are very much against it. When science is brought to bear upon a practical problem, it first discovers exactly what has to be done, and then seeks the most efficient way of doing it.

In 1865, Pasteur was urged by Dumas to undertake the investigation of a disease of silkworms, called pebrine, which had for several years been ruinously prevalent in the south of France. The loss was estimated at four millions sterling; and the disease had spread to many other countries from which silkworms' eggs had been brought to France. Pasteur had no intimate knowledge of silkworms, and he hesitated to take up the study of the causes of the epidemic. Writing to Dumas he said:

Your proposition throws me into a great perplexity; it is indeed most flattering, and the object is a high one; but it troubles and embarrasses me! Remember, if you please, that I have never even touched a silkworm. If I had some of your knowledge on the subject I should not hesitate; it may even come within the range of my present studies. However, the recollection of your many kindnesses to me would leave me bitter regrets if I were to decline your pressing invitation. Do as you like with me. *Pasteur*.

Many silkworm cultivators expressed regret that the Government should choose a "mere chemist" for the investigation of the disease instead of a zoologist or silkworm cultivator. Pasteur only said, "Have patience"; and he began his attack of the problem with the precision and acuteness of observation characteristic of him. He suspected that certain "corpuscles" found in the bodies of diseased silkworms and in the moths and their eggs were disease-producing organisms, and directed his chief studies to them, while making also a careful investigation of the whole disease. He proved that the disease was not only contagious, but hereditary—diseased moths laying diseased eggs from which came diseased silkworms which died young or were useless for the production of silk. Thus the disease passed on by inheritance from year to year. The germs in eggs laid by diseased moths survived; but those left on leaves, or in the dust, or in the bodies of dead moths, soon perished. Only in the diseased and living eggs was the contagion maintained.

These things were proved by repeated experiments, and by observations by Pasteur in his own breeding-chamber; and they made him believe that the disease might be put an end to by the destruction of all diseased eggs. To this end he invented the plan which has been universally adopted, and has restored a source of wealth to the silk districts. Each female moth, when ready to lay eggs, is placed on a separate piece of linen on which it may lay them all. After it has laid them, and has died, it is dried and then pounded in water, and the water is examined microscopically. If "corpuscles" are found in it, the whole of the eggs of this moth, and the linen on which they were laid, are burnt; if no "corpuscles" are found, the eggs are kept, to be, in due time, hatched, and they yield healthy silkworms. *Sir James Paget.*

By the adoption of these methods, arrived at by scientific investigation, a national industry was restored, and the bread of hundreds of poor families was again assured. No wonder that his name is now blessed in the land which profits by the fruit of his splendid discoveries; yet throughout the whole period of his researches he met with unbelief from practical cultivators of silkworms, and opposition from merchants of eggs and chimerical remedies for the disease.

The successful production of Smyrna figs in California is a remarkable example of the application of scientific knowledge of fertilisation of plants to the establishment of a new industry. The green fig which grows in our gardens usually has no true seeds, and does not retain the flavour when dried. In the latter part of the nineteenth century, an endeavour was made to produce seed-bearing figs in California. A number of cuttings of Smyrna fig-trees was obtained and planted, but with no success. The failure was due to the fact that the dried Smyrna fig owes its peculiar flavour to the number of ripe seeds which it contains; and these seeds are only formed when the flowers of the cultivated fig are fertilised with pollen derived from the wild fig, or caprifig.

Since time immemorial it has been the custom of natives in Oriental regions to break off the fruits of the wild fig, bring the branches to the edible fig-trees, and tie them to the limbs. From the wild fig thus brought to the plantations, or from a caprifig which may be planted with the other trees, a species of minute wasp emerges at the right season covered with pollen; it crawls into the flower-receptacles of the edible fig, fertilises them, and thus produces a crop of seeds, as well as assists in the ripening of the fruit.

Herodotus knew that an insect passed from the wild fig to the cultivated tree, and Pliny the Elder, in the beginning of our era, described the relation of the insect to the two kinds of fig-tree, but he knew nothing of the process of fertilisation, and supposed that the seeds of the wild fig were themselves transformed into insects. For a couple of thousand years the fig-tree was culti-vated in the Mediterranean regions without anyone troubling to examine the details of the natural proc-esses upon which the production of the seeds depended. This knowledge, combined with persistent endeavour extending over nineteen years, has enabled the United States to transplant to the new world a distinctive product of the old, and to base a new industry upon it.

When the practical man—particularly he who is engaged in rural pursuits — reaps any profit from science, he does so against his own convictions. The motto of the Royal Agricultural Society of England is "Practice with Science," yet how rarely do farmers show by word or deed that they realise the intimate connection between scientific investigations and agri-cultural arts. To the husbandman in general, science means theory, and his own experience fact; and he is as contemptuous of the one as he is confident of the other. He will pay a fancy price for a patent fertiliser,

when a little scientific knowledge would show him that
the same stimulating constituents could be obtained
at one-third the cost, or less. He will lose hundreds
of pounds on his crops or stock, by pests and diseases, without knowing anything of the nature of
his enemies, against which he has to fight. He prides
himself upon being a "practical man," and regards
all scientific work as unpractical, though every fly that
troubles him, and every fungus that infests his plants,
has to be studied laboriously by biologists before any
accurate knowledge of its life-history can be obtained.
Whatever is known of the exact relation between cause
and effect in all branches of agriculture, and whenever
fact can be placed against opinion as regards diseases
of animals and plants, the credit belongs to the scientific investigator, and not to the actual cultivator of
the soil.

Swift, with severe satire, made the King of Brob-
dingnag express to Gulliver the opinion "That whoever could make two ears of corn, or two blades of
grass, to grow upon a spot of ground where only one
grew before, would deserve better of mankind, and do
more essential service to his country, than the whole
race of politicians put together." The increase has
been effected, but the men whose scientific work has
led to it are mostly unknown to the politicians and
other people who benefit by it.

Before the knowledge of chemistry had sufficiently
advanced to provide a basis for a theory of nutrition of
the plant, all observation of the good effect of this
or that substance on the crop was merely empiric and
possessed no value beyond the particular case to which
it referred. The science of agricultural chemistry
may be said to have been founded early in the nineteenth century when Davy was appointed professor of

chemical agriculture to the Board of Agriculture. In the latter part of the previous century, Priestley had shown that green plants, when exposed to bright sunlight, decompose the carbonic acid in the atmosphere into its elements carbon and oxygen, keeping the carbon for themselves and setting free the oxygen; but this fact, and De Saussure's work on plant chemistry, may be said to represent the state of scientific knowledge of the subject at the time.

Davy did not make any very substantial contributions to the science of agriculture, but he rendered valuable service by insisting upon the value of studying agriculture problems by scientific methods. He knew that the farm and not the laboratory provided the final test of the principles he expounded; and he carried out some field experiments himself. "Nothing is more wanting in agriculture," he wrote, "than experiments in which all the circumstances are minutely and scientifically detailed. This art will advance with rapidity in proportion as it becomes exact in its method."

Twenty-five years after Davy's lectures, the great French agricultural chemist, Boussingault, published the results of detailed investigations of what may be termed the balance-sheet of plant growth; and his conclusions were adopted by the renowned German chemist, Liebig, about 1840. Liebig took up the complicated problems of soil constitution and fertility with the practical purpose in mind of increasing its productiveness. He traced clearly the relations between the nutrition of plants and the composition of the soil; and he was the first to study carefully the mineral constituents of plants, and to recognise the importance of certain substances, especially potash and phosphates.

The principle of replacing artificially the substances removed from the soil by crops was given a scientific foundation by Liebig's work, and is now followed by every progressive farmer. Knowing the nature of a soil and the needs of a plant, suitable artificial fertilisers can be applied to make up any deficiency in the main constituents required for vigorous and profitable growth. For example, a soil may be rich in humus, and in compounds of nitrogen and phosphorus, and yet be almost barren land because of deficiency in another essential constituent—potassium. Dr. Cyril Hopkins tells an impressive story of the result of applying potassic fertilisers to such land in Illinois. A man who had been farming soil of this kind came to see a demonstration field of the Illinois Agricultural Experiment Station, and brought with him his wife and children.

As he stood looking first on the corn on the treated and untreated land, and then at his wife and children, he broke down and cried like a child. Later he explained to the superintendent who was showing him the experiments that he had put the best of his life into that kind of land. "The land looked rich," he said, "as rich as any land I ever saw. I bought it and drained it and built my house on a sandy knoll. The first crops were fairly good, and we hoped for better crops, but instead they grew worse and worse. We raised what we could on a small patch of sandy land, and kept trying to find out what we could grow on this black bogus land. Sometimes I helped the neighbours and got a little money, but my wife and I and my older children have wasted twenty years on this land. Poverty, poverty, always! How was I to know that this single substance which you call potassium was all we needed to make this land productive and valuable?"

Without the artificial supply of nitrogen to the soil, it would be practically impossible to grow sufficient wheat to supply the needs of the present inhabitants of the earth who use it for food. The nitrogen is obtained chiefly from nitrate of soda mined in Chile, but these deposits are by no means inexhaustible. Fortunately, science has come to the rescue; and nitrogenous fertilisers are now produced on a large scale from the nitrogen of the atmosphere. The chief source of potash, which greatly increases the fertility of certain soils, is immense saline deposits in the Stassfurt district of Germany. The deposits were discovered about the middle of the nineteenth century, and were at first regarded as useless, but now nearly all the potash required in the arts as well as in agriculture is obtained from them.

In addition to nitrogen and potash, most plants require compounds of phosphorus, such as phosphates, to stimulate their development and quicken the ripening. It was an English country gentleman, Sir John Bennet Lawes, who, in 1834, guided by the researches of De Saussure on vegetation, showed by experiments the value of this constituent when added to the soil, and discovered a means of producing any quantity of it. Mineral phosphates, such as apatite, are usually too insoluble to have any practical value in agriculture, but Lawes found that if they were previously treated with sulphuric acid (oil of vitriol), a "superphosphate" was produced in which the phosphates are almost entirely soluble in water, and which has a most beneficial influence upon growth upon heavy soils, as well as upon light. This production of this fertiliser was the result of deliberate intention and practical purpose, and it has proved of the highest importance in agriculture.

About six million tons of superphosphate are now manufactured annually, and the influence of this compound on the productiveness of the soil in civilised countries is incalculable. The farmer is no longer dependent, as he was formerly, upon bone or guano for a supply of phosphates, for the vast deposits of phosphatic rocks and minerals can be converted into a powder which enables him to restore or increase the fertility of his land in the most effective and economical manner. A dressing so small as half a hundredweight cast over an acre has been found to double the yield of cereals in soil of Southern Australia; and the effect has been found equally marvellous in other places.

Lawes was thus the actual benefactor of mankind to whom Swift gave so high a place in *Gulliver's Travels.* For more than fifty years he carried on agricultural experiments at Rothamsted, in Harpenden, Hertfordshire, with Sir J. H. Gilbert, who had been a pupil of Liebig's; and the work of these two men has made the Rothamsted Experiment Station renowned throughout the world. A memorial tablet in Harpenden Parish Church bears the appropriate inscription: "In affectionate memory of Sir John Bennet Lawes, Bart., F.R.S., born at Rothamsted, Dec. 28, 1814, died at Rothamsted, Aug. 31, 1900. He used his long life and his great knowledge and experience as an agricultural chemist and as a practical and scientific farmer, in the pursuit of truth, and for the benefit of his fellow men in his own country and in all parts of the world.

Agricultural Experiment Stations similar to that at Rothamsted now exist in all civilised countries; they are laboratories of industrial or technical research in which problems are attacked with the object of ensuring the supply of man's daily bread by fighting the natural agents and forces which would deprive him of it. Thousands of chemists are engaged in researches

which have as their aims the definite practical purposes of increasing man's comforts or pleasures, or
strengthening his power over Nature. They have by
their intensive investigations produced hundreds of
dyes from coal-tar; they have produced an artificial
indigo which has taken the place of the natural dyestuff even in the home of the indigo plant, Asia, and
a dyestuff, alizarin, which has similarly displaced the
natural dye obtained from the madder root. Numerous other natural products have been built up from
their elements by chemical technologists, mostly by
systematic purposeful research having profitable commercial ends in view. We have as the result, cabinets
of synthetic drugs to alleviate pain and fight disease,
and artificial essences which cannot be distinguished
in their fragrant qualities from the scents of flowers
—lilac, lily of the valley, violet and the rose.

The intention of technical research is not so much
to contribute to scientific knowledge as to create new
industries or develop old into higher or more productive forms. The country which neglects this pioneer
branch of its industrial army cannot maintain an important position in the struggle for existence or su-
premacy in commercial life. Lord Beaconsfield once
said that the condition of the chemical trade of a
country is a barometer of its prosperity, and King
George the Fifth accentuated this remark in a speech
made at the opening of a Congress of Applied Chemistry in London in 1909. His Majesty said:

I fully appreciate the important part which chemistry plays
in almost every branch of our modern industry. We all
recognise that without a scientific foundation no permanent
superstructure can be raised. Does not experience warn us
that the rule of thumb is dead, and that the rule of science has
taken its place, that to-day we cannot be satisfied with the

crude methods which were sufficient for our forefathers, and that those great industries which do not keep abreast of the advance of science must surely and rapidly decline?

It would be easy to give many examples of the beneficial effects of the co-operation of scientific theory with practical methods. One of the most striking illustrations is afforded by the optical trade. About 1863, the firm of Carl Zeiss, of Jena, asked Ernst Abbe to assist them in the development of the microscope by investigating the optical theory of the instrument. Abbe proved mathematically that with the glass then at the optician's disposal no great improvement in the optical parts of the microscope could be expected. Progress in the art of glass-making was necessary before any substantial advance could be made in microscopic or photographic lenses. Abbe himself, with Otto Schott, began, therefore, in 1881, to investigate the relation between the optical properties and the chemical composition of glasses. When they began their work, about six chemical elements were the constituents of glasses; and they tested by experiment the effect of adding definite quantities of other substances, as had been done previously in a small way by the Canon W. V. Harcourt in England.

What had been a rule-of-thumb industry was thus re-constructed on a scientific basis. Glasses could be produced having particular properties for microscope lenses, for photographic lenses, for thermometers, or any other special purpose. Works were established at Jena, and they soon became the chief centre of optical glass manufacture in the world. On account of the indifference shown to scientific theory by its manufacturers and State officials, England lost an industry in which it was once pre-eminent.

This has not only been the case with glass manufacture, but also is largely true of the construction of photographic lenses. The principles of the design of such lenses were worked out by Sir John Herschel, Sir William Hamilton and Sir George Airy, but their significance was not appreciated by practical opticians in the country of their origin, and it was left to optical experts of another nation to apply them to practical needs. Empirical methods followed by British opticians have achieved some notable successes in optical instruments, but the guidance of theory is essential for steady advance, and scientific knowledge is necessary to see any close relation between theory and practice. In originality and inventiveness, the English mind will compare favourably with that of any race, but its attitude to scientific theory is supercilious, and the nation suffers loss by it. If England does not lead in industrial development, it is not because of lack of new ideas, but on account of want of scientific insight among her manufacturers, and want of faith in the ultimate value of organised industrial research. We commend to the men who have the nation's future in their keeping the words of a president of the Royal Society:

Sciencia vinces—whether it be on the field of battle, on the waves of the ocean, amid the din and smoke of the workshop, or on the broad acres under the light of heaven; and assuredly, in the future, even more than in the past, not only the prosperity, but even the existence of the Empire will be found to depend upon the "improvement of Natural Knowledge"— that is, upon the more complete application of scientific knowledge and methods to every department of industrial and national activity. *Sir William Huggins.*

It is commonly supposed that the marvellous development of aviation within recent years owes nothing to scientific work; indeed, the assertion is often made —unjustly so—that men of science declared the flight

of an aeroplane to be a mathematical impossibility.
Aviation engineers have certainly had few scientific
principles to guide them in the design of their machines, and the improvements which have been effected
have been by trial-and-error methods; but the error
has unfortunately involved the sacrifice of many
promising lives. Artificial flight has been achieved
chiefly by these empirical methods; and in the absence
of exact knowledge they are the only methods available, though they are expensive and wasteful.

As in other cases mentioned already, the problem of
flight with heavier-than-air machines was approached
by two separate roads of invention and science. Early
in the nineteenth century, Sir George Cayley designed
an aeroplane driven by an engine which used the
explosive force of gunpowder; and the machine appears to have lifted itself from the earth. Nearly
forty years later, W. S. Henson projected, and his
friend J. Stringfellow constructed, model aeroplanes
from Cayley's designs, driven by a light steam-engine
of about one-third horse-power; and the models are
said to have been capable of free flight. About 1875
Alphonse Pénaud, a French mechanic, constructed the
well-known toy aeroplane with a propeller in the rear
and driven by a rubber band, the machine thus utilis-
ing motive energy which it carried with it.

Experiments with man-carrying machines were made
about 1889 by Otto Lilienthal in Germany, Percy
Pilcher in Scotland, and Octave Chanute in the United
States. These machines were, however, only gliders,
by means of which the experimenters could soar in the
air for a hundred yards or so, after taking a short run
against the wind, along the top of a hill or mound. In
none of these cases was a motor used successfully to
drive the wings of the aeroplane against the air and

thus maintain it from falling. Sir Hiram Maxim built in 1894 a huge machine driven by a steam engine, and proved by it that the whole weight could be lifted slightly off the rails on which the machine ran by driving the planes against the air with sufficient velocity. A little later M. Ader, in France, traversed a distance of about fifty yards in his "Avion" aeroplane.

All these machines may be not inappropriately classified as devices of engineers to achieve flight by invention—call it practical experiment if you will—before the principles of dynamic motion had been studied. The practical man makes his machine first and lets experience decide whether its design is sound or not; the scientific man begins by investigating the principles involved in the problem, and then suggests how they may be met. The only satisfactory way to determine such principles is by experiment and calculations based upon the results. The possibilities of artificial flight were studied experimentally by a man of science at a time when anyone who gave attention to the subject received nothing but derision for his pains. Modern aviation was based upon the results he obtained, for he himself first showed that a system of planes could be sustained in the air if made to advance through it fast enough.

Until a few years ago, very little was known of the resistance offered to air by a body advancing through it. Sir Isaac Newton considered the subject, and came to the conclusion that the resistance opposed to a thing in rapid motion would be so great that enormous mechanical power would be required if artificial flight were to be accomplished. It was not a practical engineer or an aviator who undertook experiments to test the rule which Newton gave to calculate this power, but an American man of science—Samuel Pierpont

Langley, secretary of the Smithsonian Institution of Washington.

Prof. Langley commenced his experiments in 1887, and his work gave, for the first time, some accurate knowledge as to the resistance offered to planes moving through air at different speeds and inclinations. He proved that what had been called the Newtonian Law was wrong; and that it takes less power to support a plane moving through air at high speed than at low. By simply moving a given weight fast enough in a horizontal plane, Langley found that it was possible to sustain the weight with less than one-twentieth the power demanded by Newton's rule. His conclusion as to the relation of speed to power for a body in motion in air was as follows:

These new experiments (and theory also when viewed in their light) show that if in such aerial motion there be given a plane of fixed size and weight inclined at such an angle and moved forward at such a speed that it shall be sustained in horizontal flight, then the more rapid the motion is, the less will be the power required to support and advance it. *Prof. S. P. Langley.*

This rule, now known as Langley's Law, represented a definite advance of knowledge secured by the methods of exact science. The practical men who, in these days of rapid locomotion, might have been expected to investigate the laws of air resistance, left it to a man of science to prove that a rule which had been accepted for two hundred years was incorrect. His experiments demonstrated that relatively little power was required to sustain a given weight if the horizonal velocity reached a certain rate. All that was needed in order to make mechanical flight possible was a light motor capable of forcing a plane or set of planes through the air with sufficient velocity.

Guided by his results, Langley had a model aeroplane constructed, weighing about 25 lb.; and successful flights, each about half a mile in length, were made with it in 1896. His experiments were regarded, however, as the trivial amusements of a scientific man; and when, in 1903, his man-carrying aeroplane was wrecked, owing to an accident in launching it, so much ridicule was thrown upon the trials that he abandoned the subject and devoted himself to other things. Eleven years later, in 1914, the same machine was used for flights with a pilot. Langley did not live to see this success, but he never lost faith or confidence in the ultimate possibility of aerial flight with heavier-than-air machines. Concluding an account of his experiments in 1897, he said:

I have brought to a close the portion of the work which seemed to be specially mine—the demonstration of the practicability of mechanical flight—and for the next stage, which is the commercial and practical development of the idea, it is probable that the world may look to others. The world, indeed, will be supine if it does not realise that a new possibility has come to it, and that the great universal highway overhead is now soon to be opened. *Prof. S. P. Langley.*

How completely Langley's belief in flight by aeroplanes has been justified is known now to everyone, though his experiments are rarely mentioned. Faraday once said, referring to the electric dynamo, "I gave you this machine as an infant; you bring it back as a giant." Had Langley lived, the same remark could have been applied appropriately by him to the development of flying machines from his models. Purely scientific investigations gave the world the dynamo, and with the construction of this means of producing electricity there commenced a new era in engineering. In like manner, the work of a man of science opened a new epoch in the history of aerial navigation.

When, in May, 1896, Langley's power-driven model aeroplane flew over the Potomac River for a minute and a half (for which time only it was provided with fuel and water), and accomplished a flight of little over half a mile before it settled down upon the water with a gentle descent, the possibility of free dynamic flight was established. It was Langley, and no one else, who was the father of modern aeroplaning, both on account of his investigations of the scientific principles of air resistance and the work of the wind, and because he put the principles into practice by constructing a self-balancing heavier-than-air machine which would sustain itself in the air so long as the power driving it lasted. No one before Langley had succeeded in building an aeroplane capable of sustained free flight with a man as pilot.

When Wilbur and Orville Wright commenced their experiments in artificial flight, the only exact experiments they could find as to the resistance of the air to machines driven at different velocities were those made by the man of science, S. P. Langley. They were the pioneers of sustained flight with man-carrying aeroplanes, and they have acknowledged that their confidence in the practical solution of the problem was derived from Langley and his work.

The knowledge that the head of the most prominent scientific institution of America believed in the possibility of human flight was one of the influences that led to undertake the preliminary investigations that preceded our active work. He recommended to us the books which enabled us to form sane ideas at the outset. It was a helping hand at a critical time, and we shall always be grateful. *Wilbur and Orville Wright.*

In December, 1903, the Brothers Wright made the

first actual flight with an aeroplane driven by a petrol motor. It is constantly stated that artificial flight would have been accomplished long before if engines light enough to drive them had been available, but that is not the case. Flights with two, three, or more passengers show that lightness of the motor is not the only consideration, and motors with equivalent weights were available ten years before the Wrights designed their man-carrying aeroplanes. It was by following the scientific guidance of Langley, and using machanical ingenuity to extend it, that they were able to give practical effect to the desire of man to rise above the clouds.

Though the Wrights were the first aviators to make successful flights with a heavier-than-air machine driven by its own power, little was known of their work for about two years after 1903. During this period they were engaged in perfecting their aeroplane until, in 1905, they were able to remain in the air for half an hour and cover a distance of about twenty-four miles. They did not give a public demonstration of their achievements until 1908—two years after a young Brazilian, M. Santos Dumont, had made a short public flight in France, using an aeroplane designed by him without any definite knowledge of what the Wrights had done. Since that period, the advance of dynamic flight has been rapid and marvellous, culminating in a flight in stages from Newfoundland to Plymouth, via the Azores and Lisbon, by an American seaplane, N.C. 4, piloted by Lieut.-Commr. Read, and directly from Newfoundland to Clifden, Ireland, on June 14-15, 1919, by Capt. J. Alcock and Lieut. A. W. Brown, in a British aeroplane; and aeroplanes of various types are now in everyday use for civil and military purposes.

The performances of the earlier machines depended very largely upon the pilots, who had to give close attention to different controls in order to keep the planes in a condition of stability in the air. The problem of producing a machine which is automatically steady in free flight is largely mathematical; and it involves the theory of small oscillations about a state of steady motion developed by Lagrange, Kelvin, Routh and other men of science. Definite attention has been given to the mathematical conditions which have to be satisfied, in order to solve the problem of inherent stability, by G. H. Bryan and F. W. Lanchester; and their conclusions, with the results of experimental research on models at the National Physical Laboratory, largely by L. Bairstow, led to the construction of the B.E. biplane, which is almost independent of the pilot except when near the ground, where personal control must be exercised.

Work in the laboratory and calculation in the study have determined the lines upon which a flying machine can be designed that may be launched into the air with as much confidence in its safety and inherent stability as a vessel can be trusted to leave the slips of the dockyard in which it has been built.

CHAPTER XI

ACROSS THE BORDER

Nature does not allow us to explore her sanctuaries all at once. We think we are initiated, but we are still only on the threshold. Seneca.

The seemingly useless or trivial observation made by one worker leads on to a useful observation by another: and so science advances, "creeping on from point to point." Prof. Sylvanus P. Thompson.

One day telleth another: and one night certifieth another. There is neither speech nor language but their voices are heard among them. Their sound is gone out unto all lands: and their words into the ends of the world. Psalm xix, 2, 3, 4.

We find ourselves, in consequence of the progress of physical science, at the pinnacle of one ascent of civilisation, taking the first step upwards out on to the lowest plane of the next. Above us still rises indefinitely the ascent of physical power—far beyond the dreams of mortals in any previous system of philosophy. Prof. Frederick Soddy.

SCIENCE advances by bringing into view facts and phenomena previously unknown. Galileo turns his simple telescope towards the heavens, and lo! thousands of stars beyond the grasp of unaided vision are revealed; the microscope is invented, and by its aid an unseen universe, the inhabitants of which are far more numerous than the stars in heaven, is made known. In neither case were new worlds or organisms created, the extension of knowledge being but a consequence of the improved powers of seeing. The limits of visible light-waves have now been extended so that in wireless telegraphy we produce and detect electric waves which do not affect the organ of vision; and from darkness we derive by X-ray tubes and radium new radiations which light up a land of promise across the border.

Of all the achievements of science, that which creates the deepest impression upon the minds of most people is wireless telegraphy, the triumphs of which can be traced back to researches carried on in laboratory and study. Its development is due even more to theory than to practical work. When the effects of currents upon magnets, and upon one another, had been determined, science demanded an explanation of them. The effects can be produced in a vacuum, or through glass, wood, or similar substances; so evidently what seems to be empty space or material bodies must really be filled with something capable of transmitting the electric and magnetic forces. Ampère suggested that the observed facts could be explained by the presence of a universal medium which could convey these forces from one point to another. Henry and Faraday also held this view, and it was developed in detail by a mathematical physicist, James Clerk Maxwell, about the middle of the nineteenth century.

What Maxwell did was to extend by brilliant mathematical analysis the conception formed by Faraday as to the propagation of electro-magnetic action by an intervening medium. The theory of "action at a distance" assumed that no medium was actively concerned with the transmission of electric or magnetic forces, whereas Faraday, by experimental researches and reasoning, showed that the action took place along curved lines, which he termed "lines of force."

Faraday in his mind's eye saw lines of force traversing all space, whereas the mathematicians saw centres of force attracting at a distance; Faraday saw a medium where they saw nothing but distance; Faraday sought the seat of the phenomena in real actions going on in the medium; they were satisfied that they had found it in a power of action at a distance impressed on the electric fluids. *Clerk Maxwell.*

As the result of his analysis of Faraday's experimental results, and the lines of force which he invoked to explain them, Maxwell was able to prove that electro-magnetic disturbances, and waves of light, are transmitted by one and the same medium, and with the same velocity. Thus, electro-magnetic and optical phenomena are identical in kind, and differ only in the rapidity of vibration of the medium — the universal ether—which transmits them. Sunlight comes to us across ninety-three millions of miles of so-called empty space, and starlight from distances hundreds of thousands of times greater; and they both reach us as waves which can be measured, and their interference effects observed, more easily than can those seen on the disturbed surface of a lake or other sheet of water. A medium had to be invented to account for the transmission of these waves; and this medium is appropriately termed the "ether," signifying the sky—the home of the gods. No one can see the ether, or weigh it, or isolate any part of it, yet it apparently pervades all space and permeates all material things, as water does a wet sponge; and through it electro-magnetic waves, as well as waves of light and heat, are propagated.

In 1842, Joseph Henry arrived at the conclusion that when an electric spark is produced by the sudden discharge of a Leyden jar or other form of electric condenser, the spark is not due to a single splash of electricity from one point to another, but to many rapid

oscillations of electric action between the two points.
The total duration of the discharge is far too short to
be analysed by the eye, but if it could be extended over
a sufficiently long interval the spark would be seen
swinging like a pendulum from one point to the other
until the surging disturbance which produced it had
settled down again. Both Lord Kelvin and von Helmholtz independently reached the conclusion expressed
by Henry before them as to the oscillatory character
of the electric discharge; and Clerk Maxwell showed
that such a discharge must give rise to etheric disturbances which would travel through space with the
velocity of light.

When a theory can be stated in mathematical terms
it is possible to predict effects before they are actually
observed. The consequences of Maxwell's theory were
clearly understood by physicists, two of whom, Prof.
Heinrich Rudolf Hertz in Germany, and Sir Oliver
Lodge in England, devoted themselves to the task of
detecting the ether waves which must be created by an
oscillatory electric discharge. About 1888 Maxwell's
prophetic conclusions were brought within the range of
demonstration by Hertz, who discovered a means of
increasing the amplitude of the electric waves radiated
from the discharge circuit, and devised a sensitive
detector of these periodic disturbances of the ether.
It was Hertz, therefore, who provided the experimental proof for which science had waited twenty
years.

The difference between light waves and electric
waves—now called Hertzian waves in honour of their
discoverer—is a difference in length, or of rate of
vibration of the ether. The shortest waves which affect
our sight are those of violet light, produced by about
seven hundred millions of millions of vibrations in the

ether per second. This frequency of oscillation de-creases as we pass down the scale of colour through blue, green, yellow and orange to red light, which is caused by about four hundred millions of millions of etheric vibrations in a second. Hertzian waves are due to much slower vibrations in the ether—a few millions per second—and though they do not affect our visual sense directly, they have precisely the same other properties as waves of light. Light and electricity are, in fact, merely different manifestations of waves in a universal medium, the undulations in the case of visible light being from about one thirty-thousandth to one sixty-thousandth of an inch in length, while the waves used in wireless telegraphy may be from 6 to 20 thousand feet long, from crest to crest.

Soon after Hertz had described his remarkable re-searches on the production and detection of electro-magnetic waves, the scientific world realised their importance. It was pointed out that as Hertzian waves possess the property of passing through fog or material obstacles they could be used for a system of wireless telegraphy. Among the men of science who saw clearly the possibilities of the application of the waves for this purpose was Sir William Crookes, who, writing on Hertz's work in *The Fortnightly Review* of February, 1892, said:

Here is unfolded to us a new and astonishing world—one which it is hard to conceive should contain no possibilities of transmitting and receiving intelligence. Rays of light will not pierce through a wall, nor, as we know only too well, through a London fog. But the electrical vibrations of a yard or more in wave length will easily pierce such medium, which to them will be transparent. Here, then, is revealed the bewildering possibility of telegraphy without wires, posts, cables, or any of our present costly appliances. Granted a few reasonable postulates, the whole thing comes well within the realms of possible fulfilment. *Sir William Crookes.*

The receiver used by Hertz was not suitable for telegraphic work, but a more practicable form was soon found, and was used in lectures delivered by Sir Oliver Lodge before the Royal Institution, and at Oxford, in 1894, when signals were transmitted up to a distance of sixty yards and the suggestion was made that the limit attainable with the apparatus was probably more like half a mile. Two years later Mr. Marconi filed a provisional specification of apparatus for signalling by means of electric waves.

Mr. Marconi not only saw that the laboratory experiments of Hertz might be put to practical use, but also proceeded to adapt them to a system of telegraphy through the ether. As the radiator of electric waves he introduced a long vertical wire, broken by a spark gap, so that the pulses could surge up the wire and down into the earth, sending waves out into the ether in all directions as they did so. He constructed a more sensitive and trustworthy instrument to detect the waves, and ascertained what energy was required to make it possible to signal over any distance. To his knowledge, confidence and daring must be ascribed the commercial development of wireless telegraphy. By experiments carried out on Salisbury Plain, he first succeeded in transmitting messages over a distance of two miles; in 1898 he sent messages from Poole to Alum Bay, Isle of Wight—a distance of eighteen miles; and by 1910 he was able to produce electric waves so powerful that their influence could be detected, and signals read, at a distance of six thousand miles. This remarkable performance, which suggests marvellous possibilities for the future, was achieved as the direct outcome of the scientific work of Hertz, Maxwell, Fara-

day and Henry.   As Mr. Marconi himself acknowledged
in 1900:

The experimental proof of Hertz, thirteen years ago, of the
identity of light and electricity, and the knowledge of how to
produce, and how to detect, these ether-waves, the existence
of which had been so far unknown, made possible wireless
telegraphy. *G. Marconi.*

Wireless telegraphy has become part of our everyday life.   The waves conceived by a mathematician
and demonstrated in a physical laboratory are now
continually carrying messages across the sea and land.
From the Admiralty Offices at Whitehall the ether—
invisible, intangible, immaterial—is set vibrating, and
its tremors awaken sympathetic response in instruments on warships hundreds of miles away.   Ships
in distress, if equipped with the means of producing
Hertzian waves, can send their call for help into the
darkness.   Their throbbing plea goes out in ever-wid-
ening circles, like the waves formed when a stone is
dropped into a placid lake, so that any vessel with
wireless telegraphy apparatus which comes within
their sphere of influence will respond to it and hasten
to the rescue.

The first notable instance of the use of this wireless
message in saving life at sea occurred in January, 1909,
when the ocean liner *Republic* collided with the *Florida*
in a dense fog.   The *Republic's* operator, Mr. Jack
Binns, was in his cabin at the time of the collision, and
immediately sounded the wireless signal of distress.
The sides of the cabin were shattered by the shock, and
the ship was plunged in darkness, but the wireless
apparatus remained intact, and he remained at the instruments flashing into the fog the cry, "Am in distress and need assistance," and when it had been an-

swered, notifying the position in which the sinking
ship would be found. He was first able to communicate with the wireless station at Siasconsett, Massa-
chusetts, which in turn sent the news of the distress
of the *Republic* to the *Baltic,* the *Lorraine* and other
vessels equipped with the Marconi apparatus. The
dense fog hindered the speedy approach of the relieving vessels, but at last the *Baltic* came within reach,
and succeeded in rescuing the whole of the imperilled
passengers and crew of the sinking ship.

A few months after the wreck of the *Republic,* all
the passengers and crew of another ocean liner, the
Slavonia, which had been stranded on the South-west
of Flores Island, were rescued by a vessel which had
heard the call for help when at a distance of 180
miles, and turned back at once to give assistance. But
the most dramatic use of wireless telegraphy at sea
occurred in April, 1912, when the *Titanic,* the largest
vessel in the world, struck an iceberg on her maiden
voyage from Southampton to New York. She was in-
stalled with Marconi instruments having a sphere of
influence of about five hundred miles by day and treble
that distance at night. Several vessels heard the wireless appeal for help, but none was able to reach her
before she foundered, four hours after collision with
the iceberg. When the relieving vessels reached the
scene of the disaster they were able to rescue nearly
nine hundred survivors, who had taken to the boats,
but the remainder of the human freight of more than
two thousand souls had found a grave with the *Titanic*
in the waters of the Atlantic. The only bright spot
in this sorrowful history is that the passengers and
crew in the crowded boats owe their lives to wireless
telegraphy, which summoned the vessels that saved
them.

One further impressive instance of the aid rendered by this development of science is that of the steamship *Volturno,* which was destroyed by fire in mid-Atlantic in October, 1913, during a heavy gale. The wireless telegraphic call for help was first received by the *Carmania,* which immediately made use of her wireless installation to spread it far and wide, with the result that ten steamships hurried to the burning vessel and were able to save all the people—more than five hundred—who had remained on board.

The maximum distance at which a light can be seen depends upon the brightness of the light and the sensitiveness of the eye. A light of twelve candle-power is visible at a distance of five miles, and for it to be seen at a distance of 100 miles it would have to be nearly five thousand candle-power. In wireless telegraphy the transmitting station sends out electric waves precisely similar to the waves which produce the sensation of sight, but they are invisible and have to be detected by sensitive receiving instruments instead of the eye. These detectors have reached such a degree of perfection that they are of the same order of sensitiveness as the human eye.

Expressed in terms of energy, we may say that the light which can just be seen by the eye, the sound which can just be heard by the ear, and the electric wave which will just affect a receiver, are all of the same intensity. If, therefore, energy could be radiated at the same rate, either as waves of sound in the air, or as waves of light, or as the longer electric waves, we should be able to detect them at approximately the same distance by means of our ears, or our eyes, or a wireless telegraphy receiver. When we speak, our voice is heard and understood by those who listen to us; and if we could speak with the same energy as that of the transmitting apparatus of a wireless telegraphy station, the ear would be able to detect the sound at about the same distance as that at which a wireless receiver is affected. The energy of the vibrating air acting upon the drum of the ear in the case of the faintest audible sound is about the same as that falling upon the retina of the eye from the faintest visible star. The energy of the loudest sound which can be distinguished (at the point when the ear cannot decide which of two tones is the louder) has been estimated to be about as much as that involved in the growth of a single blade of grass in June.

"Communication by wireless telegraphy is very wonderful," once remarked a lady to Mr. Marconi. "It is not half so wonderful as our conversing together now," modestly replied the inventor; and he was right. The production of sounds by the organs of speech, their transmission by waves in the air, and their appreciation by the organs of hearing, involve infinitely more complicated actions than are concerned in producing electric waves at one station and detecting them hundreds or thousands of miles away.

It is not possible here to refer to the further developments of wireless telegraphy. Already the messages sent out from the Eiffel Tower and other high-power stations can be read with instruments which can be carried in the pocket and connected with an iron railing or gate; and human speech has been conveyed by wireless telephony from Arlington (Virginia) to Mare Island (California)—a distance of 2500 miles! With such remarkable achievements to command our admiration, who will have the temerity to assign limits to what will be accomplished by science in the future.

Next to wireless telegraphy, the discoveries of science which seem the most wonderful to most people are those of Röntgen rays and radium. When in 1895 the announcement was made that Prof. Röntgen, then of Marburg University, had discovered rays which would pass through opaque substances, such as wood or the human body, more easily than through a glass, it was scarcely believed. The observation was, however, only a natural consequence of scientific work done by earlier investigators.

It has been known for many years previously that when an electric discharge is caused to take place through a sealed glass tube or bulb containing only extremely rarefied air, the tube becomes filled with a beautiful luminosity. Sir William Crookes made a number of experiments with vacuum-tubes of this kind after reducing the air in them to the highest degree of rarefaction. He found that electrified particles seemed to be shot out from one of the two slips of metal sealed into the tube for connection with the machine which produced the electricity. Diamonds, rubies and other substances, when placed in the tube so that these particles or rays fell upon them, became phosphorescent, and emitted a shimmering light. When a pattern was cut out of a sheet of mica and placed in the path of the rays, it stopped them, the result being that a dark shadow of the pattern was seen at the end of the tube opposite that from which they were projected, while all round the shadow was phosphorescent light.

Hertz, who first demonstrated the existence of electric waves, showed that the rays would pass through thin sheets of certain metals; hence, a pattern made of one of these metals, and placed in a vacuum-tube in the same way as the mica pattern, produced no shadow, for, though opaque to light, they were transparent to Crookes's rays. This was a decided step in advance, and the next was taken by Prof. Lenard, in 1894, who, by using a vacuum-tube having an aluminium end or window, was able to pass the rays out into the air, without reducing their properties of producing phosphorescence. He further showed that the Crookes's rays, or kathode rays, thus set free from the tube, were capable of recording their existence upon a photographic plate. In 1895 Prof. Röntgen began to investigate these Lenard rays, which will not pass through glass, and are extinguished by even a small thickness of air. He soon observed that rays capable of exciting luminescence were emitted by the Crookes's tube itself and were produced whenever the kathode rays struck an obstacle—whether glass or a metal target—placed in their path. These are the X-rays.

A vacuum-tube rendered luminous by the electric discharge, was surrounded by Prof. Röntgen with a shield of black paper in a completely darkened room. A piece of paper, having one side covered with a phosphorescent substance, was brought into the neighbourhood of the tube, and found to become brilliantly luminous, in spite of the fact that the light of the vacuum-tube was covered up. This proved beyond doubt that certain rays can pass through paper, and still possess the ability to produce fluorescence. A book of 1,000 pages did not prevent this action, nor did two packs of cards, thick blocks of wood, or ebonite, while a sheet of aluminium nearly an inch thick only reduced the effect. Plates of copper, silver, lead, gold and platinum permitted the rays to pass, but only when they were thin. When the hand was held between the vacuum-tube and the fluorescent screen, the shadow showed the bones darkly, with only faint outlines of the surrounding flesh, the reason being that the bones are almost opaque to the active rays, while the flesh is transparent to them. By substituting a sensitive plate for the fluorescent screen, a photograph could, therefore, be obtained, showing the internal structure of the hand or other parts of the human body.

These properties of X-rays seemed very wonderful when they were first made known; but, as we have seen, their discovery was only a natural consequence of earlier scientific work. Without Sir William Crookes's investigations on the electric discharge in high vacua, there would have been no Crookes's tube and no X-rays. Röntgen suspected that an excited Crookes's tube would cause fluorescence, that is, make certain substances shine faintly; and he noticed that paper covered with a certain substance did show a faint shimmer when the tube was in action, although the tube was covered so that no light could be seen from it. Many other people had used the tubes for lectures and experiments, and the effects visible in them are so beautiful that it is not strange that attention was concentrated upon them. It would have seemed strange at that time to cover up a luminous tube and look not at its own brilliant colours, but at something else, yet that is what Röntgen did, and he found that the unseen rays emitted by the tube were of far greater interest than those which affected the human retina.

Most of the tubes now used for the production of X-rays are modifications of the "focus tube" devised by Sir Herbert Jackson, of King's College, London, for the study of phosphorescence, before Röntgen's discovery was announced. Sir Herbert Jackson might have made a fortune by patenting his invention, but he decided deliberately not to do so, and for the sake of scientific knowledge left his device unprotected. In thus sacrificing personal profit to scientific needs, he manifested a spirit which the commercial world may appreciate but cannot understand.

After the discovery of Röntgen rays, their application to medicine was soon seen; and now there is scarcely a hospital but makes use of the rays, not only for the examination of inner parts of the body, but also for treatment of certain diseases. The use of the rays to show the position of embedded needles or other foreign objects in the body, or to reveal fractures or dislocations of bones, is obvious, but the extension of this method of diagnosis has been even more valuable to the physician than to the surgeon. Improvements in apparatus and methods have made it possible to show, not only the outlines of the bones, but also minute details of their structure; and more than this, a considerable amount of detail of the internal soft parts of the human body can now be examined by means of the rays. It is quite easy to estimate in this way the size, shape and position of the heart, to detect the earliest stages of congestion of the lungs due to phthisis, to prove beyond doubt and with perfect safety, whether a calculus (stone) is present in either kidney, and to study the digestive canal throughout its length.

For this last purpose, the patient sits upright and drinks a harmless dose of carbonate of bismuth. This fluid is opaque to Röntgen rays, so that the shadow thrown by it can be seen upon a fluorescent screen. The passage of the fluid from the mouth to the stomach can, therefore, be observed upon the screen; and any obstruction in the food-pipe or deviation from the normal course at once becomes apparent. The regular contractions of the stomach by means of which the food is expelled into the small intestine may be observed, and a few hours later the course can be traced through the large intestine. Before this development of diagnostic methods, irregularities and obstructions in the digestive system were largely a matter of conjecture; and an operation was necessary to discover the exact origin of the disorder. Röntgen rays enable almost the whole of the internal anatomy to be scrutinised and photographed, so that no operation need be undertaken until its necessity has been demonstrated by ocular evidence.

The beneficial use of X-rays are alone sufficient to make the discovery of the highest significance in the history of humanity; but advance has not been limited to them. The discovery directed renewed attention to the subject of phosphorescence and fluorescence, and the field thus opened up has proved to be the richest ever explored.

Certain substances, such as salts of uranium, phosphoresce, or continue to shine, after Röntgen rays have been permitted to fall upon them. In 1896 Henri Becquerel found that uranium salts which had been made phosphorescent by exposure to sunlight gave out rays having similar properties to those discovered by Röntgen; that is, they could pass through materials opaque to ordinary light, would affect a photographic plate, and so on. Further investigations showed that these functions are inherent in uranium and its compounds, which are thus independent of the exciting influence of Röntgen rays or sunlight. Similar properties were shortly afterwards found by Schmidt to be possessed by thorium; and then Prof. and Madame Curie, by infinite labour, succeeded in isolating from pitchblende two new substances, radium and polonium, which were far more active in their radiations than any others. The discovery of actinium by Debierne quickly followed, and, said Sir J. J. Thomson, in 1909: "Now the researches of Rutherford and others have

led to the discovery of so many new radioactive substances that any attempt at christening them seems
to have been abandoned, and they are denoted, like
policemen, by the letters of the alphabet.''

It is an axiom of scientific theory that you cannot
create energy any more than you can add or destroy a
single atom of matter in the universe. If light or heat
are being given out in any way, energy is being expended to produce it, and the same is true of other effects. Radium, however, is a spontaneous producer
of light, heat and electricity; in other words, it continually produces luminous, thermal and electrical
effects without using up energy capable of being
measured. Unlike ordinary prosphorescent substances,
which only shine after exposure to light, radium is
luminous over its whole mass, and the luminosity does
not diminish at any time. Moreover, radium salts
give off heat continuously, without any chemical
change such as occurs in ordinary combustion; and the
amount of heat is sufficient to keep the temperature of
the radium salts nearly three degrees Fahr. above that
of their surroundings.

It is believed that the rays emitted by a radioactive
substance represent the results of the breaking-up of
atoms of the substance, and mark, therefore, stages of
atomic disruption. Radium, for example, gives off a
gas—called ''radium emanation'' by the first observers, Sir Ernest Rutherford and Prof. F. Soddy—which
represents the product of the disruption of radium
atoms. On this view, which is based upon substantial
experimental investigation, there must be a limit to
the life of a radioactive element. In the case of
radium, one grain would be reduced to half a grain in
1760 years; but the emanation has a much shorter span
of life, for its activity is reduced by one-half in four
days.

When first collected, radium emanation is more energetic than radium itself, and will produce precisely the same effects; but it runs through its stock of energy in a few weeks, whereas the activity of radium remains practically unaltered for hundreds of years. Suppose a ton of coal could be kept burning in a furnace continuously for about two thousand years, then it would produce approximately the same energy as would be given out by one gram (15 grains) of radium in the same period. If the rate of atomic disruption could be increased, and the life of radium therefore reduced, the rate of output of energy would be proportionately greater.

An illustration of the magnitude of the energy which might thus be obtained has been given by Sir William Ramsay. "Suppose," he said, "that the energy in a ton of radium could be utilised in thirty years, instead of being evolved at its invariable slow rate of 1760 years for half-disintegration, it would suffice to propel a ship of 15,000 tons, with engines of 15,000 horse-power, at the rate of 15 knots for thirty years—practically the life of the ship. To do this actually requires a million and a half tons of coal."

When radium from which the emanation has been collected by suitable means is left to itself for about a month, it recovers completely its original condition, and a fresh supply of emanation can be obtained from it. In cases, therefore, where radium is required for any purpose, but cannot be procured on account of its high price, radium emanation provides a cheap substitute possessing all the properties of its parent. Like the widow's barrel of meal and cruse of oil, radium wasteth not, neither does it fail, though a supply of emanation is taken from it every few weeks. It may be likened also to Draupnir, the ring of Odin, which, after being placed by him upon the pile of his son Baldur, acquired the power of dropping every ninth night eight rings of equal weight with itself.

Whatever may be the atomic changes by which the energy manifested by radioactive substances can be explained, we have the fact that radium salts continually produce sufficient light to be observed readily in' semi-darkness, heat enough to be appreciably warmer than other objects near them, rays which have an energetic action upon photographic plates and by which radiographs can be taken, and emissions which blister the skin and produce other remarkable physiological effects. It is, perhaps, fortunate that the new element is probably the rarest in the universe. Pitchblende, from which radium is obtained, is comparatively rare, and only about one and a half grains of radium salt can be extracted from a ton of pitchblende ore.

Röntgen rays, radium and radium emanation are all now largely used by physicians, not merely as a means of diagnosis, but for curative purposes. Early experimenters with Röntgen rays did not realise the extraordinary powers of the rays to produce virulent effects upon the skin long exposed to them. The X-ray burns thus caused are most intractable, and usually the hand or arm badly affected by them has to be removed to prevent further extension or death. Odin bought for himself wisdom at the price of his right eye, but it was Tyr who, among all the Aesir, was held by the Norns or Fates of northern myths to be worthy of the highest honour, for he sacrificed his strong right hand not for himself but for others. This is what was cheerfully done by several early workers with X-rays, notably Dr. Blacker, of St. Thomas's Hospital, and Mr. Harry W. Cox, who were the first martyrs of the rays, and Dr. Hall Edwards, whose left arm had to be removed.

Mankind should not forget the names of these and other experimenters by whose sufferings increased knowledge has been attained.

Operators with X-rays now protect themselves from injury by using screens which shield them, but in the early days the necessity for such precautions was not understood. The rays are now kept under control, and their power of affecting animal tissue is used to cure instead of being harmful. In certain diseased conditions, local application of Röntgen rays has been used with marked success, and the field of their utility will certainly extend as improvements are effected in their technique. Radium has proved to be a valuable agent for the removal of certain ulcers and small cancerous growths, but neither it nor X-rays can at present be looked upon as a cure for cancerous growths of large size. In many cases, radium emanation is more convenient to use than its parent; for it can be inhaled, and when dissolved can be injected into the body tissues, or swallowed. We are only just beginning to learn something of the biological significance of the new rays; and no one can yet predict with confidence the beneficial action which the next generation will discover in them.

CHAPTER XII

TOWARDS INFINITY

Go, speed the stars of thought
On to their shining goals.   Emerson.

God has placed no limit to the exercise of the intellect He
has given us on this side of the grave.   Francis Bacon.

The heavens are calling you, and wheel around you,
Displaying to you their eternal beauties,
And still your eye is looking on the ground.   Dante.

A thorough advocate in a just cause, a penetrating mathe-
matician facing the starry heavens, both alike bear the
semblance of divinity.   Goethe.

Trees in their blooming,
Tides in their flowing,
Stars in their circling
Tremble with song.
God on His throne is
Eldest of poets:
Unto His measures
Moveth the whole.   W. Watson.

WHEN the stars sparkle upon the azure canopy of
heaven, the human mind seeks silence and solitude to
contemplate them. It is upon such an occasion that
man realises he is face to face with infinity; and, his
soul is uplifted, a sense of helplessness fills him, and
the spirit of David makes him ask of his Creator,
"What is man, that thou art mindful of him? and the
son of man, that thou visitest him?"

If these devout thoughts inspired the Psalmist when he considered the heavens, what words are now adequate to express the feelings to which increased knowledge of the universe should give rise? Less than three thousand stars can be seen when a watcher, unaided by optical power, looks upward on the finest night; but even a small telescope or field-glass will show many times this number. With the great lenses which are directed heavenward in these days, it is possible to see one hundred million stars in the whole celestial sphere, instead of the few thousand visible to the naked eye.

Carry your mind back to pre-telescopic times, and consider what was then conceived to be the content and extent of the universe visible to man. Nothing could be known of the stars and other celestial objects beyond the range of unaided vision, and not the boldest of the speculative philosophers imagined that there were millions of celestial bodies in addition to those which were within their bounds of knowledge. What they saw seemed to be the beginning and end of things celestial, and there was no thought of anything beyond it.

Astronomy, more perhaps than any other science, teaches the imperfection of human understanding, and hesitates to set limits to the planes which may be attained in the future. Celestial things are rarely what they seem. A brilliant sky at night gives the impression of infinite calm and peace, and we speak of the "fixed" stars, whereas not a single one is at rest, and many are moving through space with velocities greatly in excess of any express train on the Earth. It is difficult also for anyone unacquainted with astronomy to believe that the Earth, and other members of the Solar system, in addition to their movement of revolution around the Sun, are being carried by the Sun into unknown regions of space at the rate of nearly a million miles a day, yet that is certainly the case.

Through every year, every hour, every minute of human history from the first appearance of man on the earth, from the era of the builders of the Pyramids, through the times of Caesar and Hannibal, through the period of every event that history records, not merely our earth, but the sun and the whole solar system with it, have been speeding their way towards the star Vega, on a journey of which we know neither the beginning nor the end. During every clock-beat through which humanity has existed, it has moved on this journey by an amount which we cannot specify more exactly than to say that it is probably between five and nine miles per second. We are at this moment thousands of miles nearer to Vega than we were a few minutes ago; and through every future moment, for untold thousands of years to come, the earth and all there is on it will be nearer to that star, or nearer to the place where the star now is, by hundreds of miles for every minute of time come and gone. When shall we get there? Probably in less than a million years; perhaps in half a million. We cannot tell exactly; but get there we must if the laws of Nature and the laws of motion continue as they are. To attain to the stars was the seemingly vain wish of the philosopher; but the whole human race is, in a certain sense, realising this wish as rapidly as a speed of six or eight miles a second can bring it about. *Prof. Simon Newcomb.*

The Sun itself deceives us by its appearance; for what we see of it is relatively small in comparison with the vast sheets and rays of luminous matter that surround the brightly visible disc, and are revealed only during a total eclipse. If the Sun could be seen from a point outside the Earth's atmosphere, it would appear more blue than the yellow tint with which we are familiar. Surrounding this bluish ball would be seen a brilliant scarlet layer like a sea of flame, from five thousand to ten thousand miles deep, out of which enormous masses of incandescent gas would be tossed from time to time to heights of tens or hundreds of thousands of miles. The manifestation of such tremendous energy would produce fear rather than the calm assurance which at present exists as to the constancy of the Sun's condition.

Because the total amount of heat received annually from the Sun has not varied appreciably for the past two thousand years or so, we are accustomed to assume that this uniformity will be maintained. But as almost nothing is definitely known as to the source of the Sun's heat, this belief in a continuity of the present conditions is purely a matter of faith that the future will be as the past. Atomic, or other changes may occur at any time which would raise or lower the Sun's temperature sufficiently to have a profound influence upon the Earth. Any large variation of this kind would completely change the face of the world; and a decrease of ten per cent. in the amount of solar heat received would convert the temperate regions into frozen wastes.

Observations made in recent years have shown that at times the Sun does radiate more heat than at others, the amount fluctuating by about ten per cent. during irregular periods of from five to ten days' duration. These changes are possibly due to local differences of temperature on the Sun, but they may become general and progressive in one direction or another. In fact, though theoretical considerations suggest that the Sun's heat will remain practically constant for millions of years, no one can state decisively that it will do so for a hundred years.

Astronomy thus gives no support to the mind that uses the knowledge existing at any epoch as if it were a complete inventory of the universe. We can reason about things known to exist, but we must remember that beyond the phenomena which have so far been brought within the range of our senses there may be many others awaiting to be revealed by more potent or refined means of observation, or new methods of inquiry. During the past few years, for example, the conviction has been forced upon astronomers that there are probably more dark stars than bright; and that completely blank regions here and there in the sky represent immense clouds of non-luminous cosmic dust which blot out the light of stars behind them.

Masses of material have been revealed by photography which are beyond the visual reach of the largest telescopes; many bright stars have been found to possess acolytes ponderous enough to influence their movements but without intrinsic luminosity; and the millions of meteoric particles which enter the earth's atmosphere daily, producing the appearance of shooting stars or meteors, show that space should not be regarded as a void, but rather as a plenum of dead matter.

It is easy to understand that as the power of seeing is enlarged by the improvement of instruments or the development of methods of inquiry, new spheres are brought within the range of human knowledge. Our eyes have in truth been opened by the lenses of giant telescopes, and we have come to know that greatness is not to be measured by visibility. For not only are the stars revealed by telescopes vastly more numerous than those bright enough to be seen by the naked eye, but they also contribute more to the total quantity of starlight received by the earth than the brilliant objects which make a view of the midnight sky an impressive sight. As it is estimated that three-quarters of the total starlight that reaches this world of ours is from stars beyond the grasp of unaided vision, it is not difficult to understand that what we see is only a limited view of the universe.

The astronomical evidence for the existence of invisible bodies in the universe is not a matter of assertion, but of interpretation of results based upon scientific inquiries. Effects are measured and are referred to physical causes which account for them in every detail, though the exact mechanism of the action may not be understood. Galileo discovered the laws of motion of falling bodies, and Newton showed that the law of gravitation is sufficient to prescribe the movements of the moon or a planet as precisely as it does for the fall of a pebble to the earth, yet the nature of gravitational attraction remains a mystery still.

From such a familiar case of relationship between fact and inference as is afforded by a falling stone, it is easy to pass to larger effects of gravitational action. For those who have little faith in intangible evidence, the discovery of the planet Neptune may be put in as a plea for confidence in conclusions based upon it. The observation of this planet in 1846 close to the position which mathematics based on the law of gravitation had assigned to it, afforded a striking instance of the ability of the law to respond to any demands which could be made upon it in the solar system.

The planet Neptune happened to be an object bright enough to be seen with telescopic aid, though it is quite invisible to the naked eye. If no telescope had existed when this new member of our system was discovered, the actual test of the validity of the mathematical results could not have been made—the processes of the intricate mathematical argument would have touched the planet and followed its movements, but, in the absence of ocular demonstration, the conclusion that a massive object existed beyond Uranus would have been regarded as an interesting statement which remained to be proved.

Another case in which the existence of an unknown mass was suspected before the body itself was seen is that of the Dog Star, Sirius. This star—the brightest in the heavens—is moving through space, as, indeed, all stars are, but its change of position is not uniformly in one direction. The difference is very slight, and requires good instrumental means to detect it, but it could not be disregarded when once it had been established, and an explanation had to be found for it. This was given by Bessel in 1844, who suggested that a dark body near Sirius was exerting an influence upon its movements. Referring to the matter in a letter to Sir John Herschel, he wrote, "Light is no real property of mass. The existence of numberless visible stars can have nothing against the existence of numberless invisible stars," and upon this idea he based the opinion that Sirius was a double star consisting of an invisible body as well as the visible one, the two forming a couple united by the bonds of gravitation. At that time it seemed scarcely credible that there were stars which could not be seen as well as those revealed by the telescope, but Bessel's belief has since received ample justification. Twenty years after he had given expression to it a faint star was discovered near Sirius, and it proved to be the body which causes the bright star to swerve from a straight path.

Stars with bright companions were discovered by Sir William Herschel towards the end of the eighteenth century, and their majestic march around one another was recorded. Many of these twin suns are nearly equal in brightness, but in most cases the two stars are badly matched in regard to visual appearance, a brilliant star often being joined by the force of mutual

attraction to one several degrees fainter. In the star
Sirius this difference is accentuated to a noteworthy
amount; for while it is the brightest object in the stellar
universe, its companion is so faint that it can be seen
only by using telescopes of great light - grasping
power.

There is really nothing strange in this disparity when
the matter is logically considered. Why should we
measure mass in the universe by what we are able to
detect with our limited optical sense? To a blind man,
or to an eye capable of seeing everything, the brilliant
star Sirius would not seem so overpoweringly great by
the side of the dark heavy body to which it is united;
and if mortals possessed a sense capable of being
affected in proportion to substance, as the sense of
sight is by luminosity, the dark body would have been
noticed as soon as man turned his face towards the
skies. For though the faint star now seen to accompany Sirius would need to have its brightness increased
twelve thousand times to equal the brilliancy of that
gem of the sky, it is nearly half as heavy when measured by the standard of mass.

There are other cases in which the companions of
bright stars are very faint, but heavy out of all proportion to their brightness. As with Sirius, the astronomer Bessel expressed the conviction that Procyon,
which rises about half an hour before it, had a dark
companion, disturbing its movements. Half a century
later, in 1896, this companion was detected by Prof.
Schaeberle, so we have here another example of a body
known to exist long before it was seen.

The difference between mass and luminosity accounts
for the interval that elapsed between prediction and
discovery of each of the cases mentioned. The companion of Procyon has a mass more than half as great

as that of our sun, and is, therefore, capable of exerting appreciable gravitational influence upon a body near
it. But though it is such a ponderous globe, its light
is much less than that which the sun would give if
placed in the same position among the stellar host. It
is therefore not surprising that the gravitational influence was detected before the faint glimmer of the
rays from the star was seen and understood.

Three instances have now been mentioned in which
invisible celestial bodies were found by indirect evidence before they were looked for with telescopic aid
—we refer to the planet Neptune, and the companions
of Sirius and Procyon. Predictions fulfilled in this
way should encourage confidence in conclusions based
upon similar premises. That is to say, if observations
show that a star is not moving through space in a
straight line, they afford presumptive evidence of the
existence of one or more bodies near it. The problem
thus resolves itself into one of studying stellar motions.

A comparison of the exact positions of stars year by
year shows that every one has a motion of its own
across the blue background of infinity. The amount
of movement as seen from the earth is very minute,
and can only be detected by accurate determinations
of position, but it is none the less real, and has to be
taken into account in precise astronomy. Every movement has a cause, and when deviations from a direct
course are found, it is certain that the star showing
them is being disturbed by a massive body which may
or may not be visible.

But what of stars which are moving straight towards
the earth or away from it? Such movements cannot
produce any change of position upon the background
upon which they are projected. This is true enough,
but they can be detected by other effects. To an as-

tronomer with a spectroscope, the light of a star is a gamut of colour crossed by dark or light rays comparable with musical notes. Just as the pitch of a note can be raised or lowered by rapid motion of the sounding body towards or away from the listener, so the positions of rays in the light-scale are affected by similar movements of approach or recession. If the distance between the moving star and the earth is decreasing, the rays analysed by the spectroscope are increased in colour pitch, and if the distance is increasing the rays are moved towards the lower end of the gamut of light, or, expressed in the terms of music, their notes are flat. So perfect a means does the spectroscope provide of measuring the movement, back or forth, that the velocity of a star can be determined within a quarter of a mile a second, though the star itself may be at an immeasurable distance from us. Here, then, we are provided with another means of studying stellar motions, and to it we owe the proof of the existence of many dark stars.

That such dark stars existed was first suggested by John Goodricke, who, though deaf and dumb from birth, used his sight to such good effect that his name is renowned among astronomers. He died at the early age of twenty-two, yet his observations, made in a small observatory at York, obtained for him in 1783 the Copley Medal of the Royal Society, the highest honour which the Society can confer. Goodricke was the first to make a systematic study of the variations in brightness of the star Algol—a name derived from the Persian word signifying the "demon." This star shines steadily with a brightness equal to that of the Pole Star for nearly two and a half days, and then suddenly its light is reduced. In about four and a half hours the star's brightness is diminished by about two-

VIII. Apotheosis of the Sciences.
Ceiling painting by Paul Albert Besnard (1849- . . .),
Salon des Sciences, Hôtel de Ville, Paris.

thirds, and three and a half hours later it has regained
the former intensity, which continues unaltered for
another fifty-nine hours. These variations succeed
one another with clock-like regularity, so that the time
when the brightness of Algol will fade can be tabulated
years in advance, as they are in astronomical calendars
and similar publications. So accurately are these times
known, that an astronomer with such a table at hand
might correct his chronometer by observing when the
star dims in brightness, and comparing the tabulated
time of this occurrence with the moment shown by his
timepiece.

To explain the sudden reduction in light of Algol,
Goodricke suggested that a dark body is revolving
around the star, and periodically comes between us and
it, thus causing a partial eclipse in each revolution.
As a star can never be seen as anything but a point of
light, whatever telescopic means are employed, it is
impossible to distinguish any outlines of a dark body
upon a luminous disc, such as is seen, for instance,
during a partial eclipse of the sun by the moon, but
Goodricke's explanation was accepted, because it
accounted for the observed variations. The proof of
the hypothesis was not forthcoming for more than a
century after Goodricke suggested it; and then it was
reached by indirect methods. Assuming that Algol has
a dark companion, the two bodies must swing round
their common balancing point, or centre of gravity.
When the dark body is moving towards us before passing in front of the bright globe, the latter must be
swinging back; and when the dark companion is reced-
ing after the eclipse, the bright star must be approach-
ing. Algol must, therefore, alternately recede and
approach in a period which coincides with that of its

changes of brightness, if Goodricke's explanation of the cause of variability is correct.

The spectroscope has proved that these periodic back and forth movements of Algol do occur. By means of this instrument, the velocity of approach or recession of a star, with reference to the earth, can be determined within a fraction of a mile a second; and in the year 1888 Prof. H. C. Vogel, of the Potsdam Observatory, showed that Algol recedes from the earth with a velocity of about twenty-four miles a second before its light dims, and approaches us at the rate of about twenty-eight miles a second, after having been thus partially eclipsed. Taking the average velocity as 26½ miles a second, the number of miles traversed around the balancing point in the whole period can be easily calculated, and thus the diameter of the orbit can be obtained. Knowing these dimensions, and the period of revolution, Kepler's third law (see p. 142) enables the mass of Algol and its companion to be determined in comparison with that of the sun. The conclusion arrived at by this reasoning is that the dark companion of Algol has about the same diameter as the sun, while the star itself is somewhat larger.

The dark companion has never been seen, and probably never will be, yet there is not the slightest doubt of its existence among astronomers, nor can there be in any mind that has considered the testimony given by the spectroscope. About twenty stars are known to fluctuate in light in the same manner as Algol, and each of them is regarded as having a dark satellite which periodically comes between us and the luminous star.

The condition of things represented by Algol and other stars of the same type must, however, be exceptional. It happens that stars of this type have their

light partially obliterated by the interposition of dark
bodies between us and their luminous surfaces at regular intervals; but if these dead worlds passed a little
above or below the line of sight from the earth to the
bright star there would be no periodic eclipse, and,
therefore, no visible indication which would lead us to
suspect the existence of dark globes near the stars we
see. Dark stars may revolve around bright stars in
orbits inclined at any angle to the level in which the
earth travels around the sun, but only in those cases
in which they are near this level when they pass between us and their luminous companions can a variation of light caused by them be noticed.

It may seem, therefore, that the score or so stars
which are periodically dimmed by eclipse are the only
objects which are known to possess dark partners; but
this is not the case. If two globes—a bright one and
a dark one—are really a united couple, each influences
the movements of the other, no matter what the direction may be in which they revolve around their common balancing point. The spectroscope shows that
Algol is swung back and forth by the invisible mass
near it. By what may almost be termed a fortunate
accident, this dark body passes in front of the bright
star every three days, and causes a sudden loss of light,
but even if it did not come directly between us and the
luminous surface the spectroscope would still detect a
periodic increase and decrease of pitch in the light
rays. The spectroscopic evidence of the movements
of stars towards the earth or away from it is, in fact,
independent of variations of light. If upon analysing
determinations of movements of approach or recession,
it is found that a star has its velocity increased and
decreased in a definite period, we are justified in concluding that there is an invisible body in the neigh-

bourhood swaying the bright one round an orbit by the controlling influence of gravitation.

A new field of study has thus been opened, and it promises to add very greatly to our knowledge of the universe. Measurements of the movements of stars towards or away from the earth have been made for a third of a century, but it is only in recent years that the method employed has been brought to sufficient perfection to enable the observations to be made to a high degree of accuracy. Now, however, that the rate of approach or recession can be determined accurately, the exact analysis of the motions has assumed a completely new aspect. Hitherto it has been of little importance to know whether a star was increasing or decreasing its distance from the earth, but now, by examining the details of the movements, we find in many cases secondary impulses backward or forward, and these are unmistakable signs of bodies to be considered in addition to those of which we have ocular proof.

The star Spica is an example of a bright body which has a dark partner like that belonging to Algol, but does not undergo a periodic loss of light by eclipse. Spectroscope observations show that the bright star alternately swings toward the earth and away from it in a period of four days, and they can be completely explained by assuming that Spica has a companion that cannot be seen, but is massive enough to make the visible star move in an orbit. This attendant may be a dark globe or a faint one so close to the star Spica that the most perfect telescope available is powerless to show the two bodies separately. But, whether lucid or obscure, the evidence of the spectroscope has shown that a star which passed for a single body until a few years ago has really a partner which insists upon making its presence known.

The North Star—Polaris—also shows by its movements that it is under the influence of one or more bodies near it. In a period of about four days the star is found to swing back and forth, doubtless as the result of movement in an orbit. Moreover, there are indications that Polaris and its satellite are in revolution together around a third body, so that the system must be regarded as a triple one. The movements of the moon and earth with reference to the sun provides us with a similar case, though on a much smaller scale; for the moon revolves around our globe once a month, while the earth itself is traversing its annual path around the sun.

The few cases of dark stars already mentioned represent only the first fruits of the inquiry into the invisible worlds in space. It is estimated that one star in every three or four thus far investigated has near it a partner which can never be seen. New methods of inquiry may reveal many bodies beyond the power of the telescope to show to human eyes, but even as the evidence stands at present, we are assured of the existence of a vast universe of invisible stars. The astronomy of the future will be concerned as much with the study of these dark masses as with those from which luminous radiations are received.

The spectroscope has demonstrated the reality of dark stars, but there are other means by which evidence of the existence of invisible matter in space has been obtained. The telescope and photographic camera have shown that what seems to be blank regions of the sky in many cases are crowded with sparkling points and realms of celestial light of so refined a

nature as to be imperceptible to unaided vision. Looking into the background of infinity, the chemical retina
of the photographic plate may record nothing at first
sight; but let it remain with steadfast gaze for an
hour or so, and the accumulated impressions produced
by faint rays acting continuously upon it will often
show that there is indeed light in the darkness of space.
Stars and sheets of luminous material have thus been
depicted which no human eye has yet been permitted to
see directly.

It may be assumed that new worlds will continue to
be brought into light as new methods and new instruments are used in the study of the heavens. There are
reasons for believing, however, that the thousand million stars which can be seen with our largest telescopes,
or registered upon photographic films, represent practically all that are shining in our universe.

Photographs of the streams and sheets of luminous
haze that exist in many parts of the heavens lead to the
conclusion that the starry universe visible from the
earth is limited in extent. Beyond a certain limit,
long exposures of sensitive plates to celestial light do
not reveal additional stars or nebulous realms; and
the evidence suggests that, so far as number and extent are concerned, the visible stellar universe has been
completely surveyed.

But though the stars can be numbered, no sounding-line has yet been imagined which will fathom the
depths of infinite space. The human intellect may, in
the course of ages, comprehend the whole of our universe, but infinity is beyond its grasp; and in boundless
space there may be many universes like that around us.
Measured with our finite minds, the distances of the
stars are too great for us to have an adequate concep-

tion of them; yet, immense as are these distances, there is endless space beyond. The light which we now receive from many of the faint stars has probably taken hundreds of years to reach us, though it has travelled through space at the rate of 186,000 miles per second. There are other stars so far away that their rays, which touch the earth to-night, left them long before the commencement of our era. May it not be possible, therefore, that beyond the whole of this starry universe which we know, there are unknown universes even surpassing our own in glory, but the light of which has not yet come to us?

As to the existence of invisible universes beyond the stars, we can only speculate; but there is much dark material within the boundary of our own universe, and it has only been made manifest in recent years. "Evidence of things unseen" has been and is being accumulated, and we now know that there are in stellar space vast clouds of cosmic dust, and many dark globes which can never be seen or photographed. The parts of a nebula visible to the eye or a camera are, in all probability, only the luminous gases proceeding from concentrated portions of a mass of dark particles— cosmic dust—occupying a much greater region of space.

What is seen or photographed is thus only a small fraction of the whole bulk of a nebula. In the course of aeons the irregular group of cosmic fragments is whirled into shape, and as the mass contracts, portions are detached which form stars, and these, in turn, are the parents of worlds like the earth and other planets. First, a congeries of cosmic dust; then the faintly luminous gleam of a nebula, arising from gases evolved and illuminated by heat or electricity; then a star in which the heat is so intense that all known substances are driven into vapour; then a ball like the earth, with a thin, solid crust covering a nucleus of rock hot enough to be fluid; and finally, a globe like the moon rolling through space as a frozen world—this apparently represents the course of evolution in the heavens.

But we only see these things "through a glass darkly"; we grope in unfathomable space, and try to understand the structure of a universe which may be only one among many. Though a position may be gained from which the whole of our universe may be grasped, there will still be the boundary over which man cannot look to see whether there are other universes beyond. Yet, with unceasing desire for new knowledge, the man of science pursues his ascent to exalted planes. Conscious that he can know only in part, he still seeks to read the signs and wonders of the heavens, and to find the interpretation thereof. He takes the visible universe in his mental grasp, and sees worlds in all stages of growth, from formless mist to the finished star, which, though fervidly shining now, must finally end and be numbered among the dark and decaying systems in space.

The human intellect can comprehend these things because they have a beginning and an end, but imagination shrinks before the prospect of an infinite number of universes, each perhaps more glorious than the one we are permitted to explore. The heart that weeps and trembles cannot face infinitude, which even in a vision is awful in its majesty. In Jean Paul Richter's beautiful dream, a man was called up into the vestibule of heaven and carried to universe upon universe in endless space, until his mind reeled before the transcendental distances which were still before him.

Then the man sighed and stopped, shuddered and wept.
His overladen heart uttered itself in tears, and he said,
"Angel, I will go no further; for the spirit of man acheth
with his infinity. Insufferable is the Glory of God. Let me
lie down in the grave and hide me from the persecution of the
Infinite, for end I see there is none . . ." Then the Angel
lifted up his glorious hands to the heaven of heavens, saying,
"End is there none to the universe of God. Lo! also, is there
no beginning!"

BIOGRAPHICAL INDEX

SUBJECT INDEX